WHITE GOLD

WHITE GOLD

The story of Alcoa of Australia

Geoffrey Blainey

ALLEN & UNWIN

First published in 1997 by
Allen & Unwin
9 Atchison Street
St Leonards NSW 2065
Australia
Phone: (61 2) 9901 4088
Fax: (61 2) 9906 2218
E-mail: frontdesk@allen-unwin.com.au
URL: http://allen-unwin.com.au

National Library of Australia
Cataloguing-in-Publication entry:

Blainey, Geoffrey, 1930– .
    White gold: the story of Alcoa of Australia.

    Includes index.
    ISBN 1 86448 355 5.

    1. Alcoa of Australia—History. 2. Aluminium industry and
    trade—Australia. I. Title.

338.2749260994

Set in 11/13pt Goudy by DOCUPRO, Sydney
Printed by KHL Printing Company (Pte) Ltd, Singapore

10 9 8 7 6 5 4 3 2 1

Contents

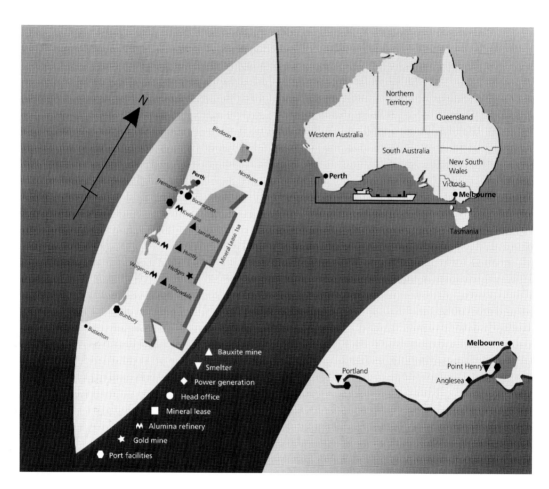

Alcoa of Australia's operating locations

Preface

Alcoa of Australia was born, without a name, in 1957. It was the frail child of an Australian company which mined gold, mostly at Kalgoorlie, when gold faced a clouded future. Lindesay Clark, a Melbourne mining engineer, had the first vision of an aluminium empire but even he had not the faintest idea of how large it would become. Mainly through his initiative his company and two Broken Hill allies explored the shunned deposits of bauxite that were spread along the crests and flanks of the Darling Range, not far from Perth.

In the face of high obstacles the small venture advanced. In 1961 an alliance was formed between the three Australian companies and the huge Aluminum Company of America, the global giant of the industry. With American technology the new Alcoa of Australia opened bauxite mines and an alumina refinery near Perth and a power station and aluminium smelter near Geelong, on the opposite side of the continent.

This is the story of a venture which, after ups and downs extending for a quarter of a century, had remarkable success. By the early 1990s it was producing nearly one sixth of the world's alumina, and its two smelters in Victoria were major producers of aluminium. In the long history of Australian mining, probably no other company had ever produced such a large share of one of the world's major minerals.

Alcoa was unusual in some of its policies. Mining in a watershed close to a big city, it faced environmental problems which were accentuated by the spread of a virulent fungus in the surrounding jarrah forest. A legitimate target of the green movement, it responded in a distinctive, constructive way. It also led unprecedented changes in the world's

White Gold

aluminium industry, facilitating the rise of independent smelters in many lands.

I should mention several potential points of confusion. In North America the word *aluminum* is always used to describe the metal referred to in Australia as aluminium. Throughout the book I have used the word Alcoa to describe Alcoa of Australia, while the Pittsburgh company (which is known in the USA as Alcoa) is referred to by its formal name of the Aluminum Co. of America. Another source of confusion is the word 'refinery'. Whereas in most branches of metal mining the refining is the final process, in aluminium the refinery performs the first process: refining comes before smelting.

I express thanks to those in Australia and the USA who have read and commented in some detail on the final drafts of chapters. I especially thank Sir Arvi Parbo, Phil Spry-Bailey and Gilbert Ralph. The final point of view and the errors that remain are mine.

Geoffrey Blainey
October 1996

PART ONE

◆ 1 ◆

The Range

The Darling Range follows the coast of part of Western Australia like a chain of low timbered lookouts. Sailors coming into the ports of Fremantle and Bunbury notice the hills, sitting low on the horizon. Aircraft about to land in Perth cross the range during the last minutes of their flight from the cities far to the east.

In places the range rises steeply from the narrow coastal plain, but it reaches no great height. The loftiest hill is Mount William, and its height above sea level is not much more than 500 metres. Too humble to be called mountains, they were, at one time, called the Darling Hills and later the Darling Range: General Ralph Darling was the governor in distant Sydney at the time when Perth was founded by the British.

Perth was founded by free immigrants from the British Isles in 1829, and in the following year the nearby hills were explored. Soon, a few settlers drove their livestock to the more park-like sections of the Darling Range and grazed them there. A few farmers came and enclosed paddocks with post-and-rail fences. The charcoal-burners came and set up camp, woodcutters plied their trade in the ranges nearest Perth, and a timber-milling industry arose. Jarrah was the favoured tree with its dark grey stringy bark and its red hardwood, and increasingly it was shipped to Britain where it slowly became the best known of all the commercial Australian woods. Ideal for jetties, bridges, railway sleepers and piles for wharves, the jarrah liked the wetter spots in the Darling Range. Its roots even penetrated into the softish mineral which lay unrecognised just below the ground. For decades the range was sparsely settled, and the only towns were villages clustered around the bigger sawmills.

Western Australia became famous for gold in the 1890s. Rich

Coolgardie was found in 1892 and the infinitely larger and deeper lodes of Kalgoorlie a year later. By the end of the decade Western Australia had replaced Victoria as the great producer of gold, and Kalgoorlie-Boulder formed one of the dozen important cities of the continent. So far, no gold worth talking about had been found within 300 kilometres of Perth but prospectors still diligently went along the range, eager for the sight of a speck of gold.

For decades the Darling Range's main connection with goldmining was to dam the water which, day and night, was pumped by a chain of wood-burning powerhouses along a pipeline to remote Kalgoorlie. The day would come when the Darling Range would surpass Kalgoorlie as a producer of minerals.

Along the range the most visible rock was bauxite. It was easily noticed because its colours were strong. Locally it was called simply 'gravel' but its scientific name was laterite. In places it was rich in alumina—the raw material of aluminium—and laterite that is rich in alumina is commonly known as bauxite. Bauxite, however, was not worth touching in the nineteenth century. It was not until 1861 that it was even called bauxite, the name coming from the earthy, clayish deposits at the village of Les Baux, near Arles in the south of France. By 1900 the bauxite mines were busy at Les Baux, serving a small but rising market for aluminium. The metal's unusual combination of strength and lightness was already making a name. In the opinion of many it was the metal of the future—if only its price could be lowered.

In the Darling Range the farmers, timber-workers and roadmakers could not help noticing the bauxite. Mostly red or brown or yellow-earthy or a striking white, its colour usually called for attention. For a long time, however, no resident of the range knew that this was the raw material of aluminium. Even the word aluminium was probably unfamiliar to them because in 1900 not one of the cottages or huts scattered along the range possessed even one item made of this material.

At times the more inquisitive residents must have collected specimens of bauxite, passing them from hand to hand with the query, 'what is it?' Hardly anybody knew the answer. Those who had come from the British Isles and had some curiosity about minerals did not know what the mineral was: the British Isles held virtually no bauxite. Those who had once lived on the Victorian goldfield, the hub of mineral activity, could only express puzzlement when shown the strange rock.

A few specimens of bauxite were sent from the range to the government's geological collection, set up in Perth in 1897. One specimen came from the Wongan Hills and, upon being assayed, was found to contain about 45 per cent of alumina. Another, from Smith's Hill, was similar. Both specimens, however, also contained more than 10 per cent of iron oxide. At that time it was believed that iron oxide in bauxite was rather like pepper in a fruit cake—too much iron, people thought, robbed the bauxite of all value.

In the town of Perth the only permanent resident who was an expert on minerals was Edward S. Simpson, the young government mineralogist, who had recently graduated from Sydney University. Aged about thirty, he did not have deep experience of any mineral but gold, but at least he knew, from his textbooks, that any bauxite carrying more than 3 per cent of iron was useless. In short, the bauxite so far discovered in the Darling Range was probably worth nothing. Nonetheless Simpson published his sparse information on bauxite in a small paperback, published in Perth in 1905 and entitled *Minerals of Economic Value*. The booklet must have helped to make Western Australians more observant: there was an increase in the number of reports of bauxite.

Simpson guessed that bauxite might someday prove important to Western Australia. He now knew that it was distributed widely near the southwest coast. In the Darling Range he noticed that the capping of bauxite could be as deep as two metres: in fact it was much deeper and of course much wider.

One advantage of this interesting rock was that it lay right on the surface and was easily quarried. Here and there it was mined and the bigger blocks and boulders were arranged in dry-stone walls, some of which still stand. The rock and gravel were also being quarried as roadmaking material and carted downhill by horse and dray to Perth. Many roads and footpaths in Perth's suburbs were built with the colourful bauxite.

To use the material for making roads suggested that it held little value. On this question Simpson kept an open mind. While much of the bauxite was too permeated with iron to be capable of producing aluminium at a reasonable price, some patches were relatively free from this impurity. In shallow quarries and gravel pits he tested the humble bauxite. To his pleasure very little iron was present. In 1907 he announced that 'workable deposits' of bauxite did exist, but the news was of little economic importance. Nobody then had the least incentive to mine bauxite in Western Australia or, for that matter, anywhere in Australia. The world's only markets for bauxite were the few aluminium smelters that existed. They lay on the other side of the equator, and the cost of shipping bauxite from Australia to the smelters would have eaten any profit.

More specimens of local bauxite arrived at Simpson's small museum in Perth. High-grade lumps of bauxite came from Greenbushes, the centre of tin mining towards the south end of the ranges. Another specimen came from near the Mundaring Weir which stored the water that was pumped up the long pipeline to the Kalgoorlie goldfield. These further finds aroused no excitement: if they had been gold, unpayable gold, a rush would have set in. Gold was all-important in Western Australia, which was then one of the world's main gold producers. Before the First World War the only other visible minerals that attracted local prospectors were coal, tin, and lead.

In Europe and North America the aluminium was used for a widening variety of purposes. While each year the quantity of aluminium produced was still small compared with that of major minerals such as copper and lead, the new metal was finding markets. In wealthier countries it was used in saucepans and pots, replacing the iron kettles and the copper and enamelled pots. In cooking vessels the aluminium was revolutionary, for the old pots and kettles were heavy for the housewife to handle. Furthermore, a cast-iron boiling pan was brittle, but an aluminium pot could hit the kitchen floor and bounce; and whereas the cheap tin plate often used in kitchens could easily rust, aluminium did not rust or wear out.

A sheet of aluminium was only one-third the weight of a similar-sized sheet made of copper, but it was just as strong. Its lightness promised many potential uses, none more exciting than in the building of flying machines, a dramatic development in the early 1900s. In North America, Wilbur and Orville Wright flew for 38 minutes during a flight in October 1905, and in France three years later Wilbur Wright remained in the air for more than two hours. In July 1909 an aircraft flown from Calais by Louis Blériot crossed the English Channel. Two years later the first aircraft was seen aloft in Western Australia. Nothing did more than the development of aircraft to point to the future significance of aluminium. It was to be the metal of the aviation era.

Aluminium was increasingly used for the parts of motor cars and torpedo boats. It was used for making scientific instruments, field glasses and other portable equipment in which lightness was a virtue. In the 1920s it was used for high-grade packaging. Cigarettes, for example, were wrapped in shiny aluminium foil.

When a little copper was added as an alloy to form aluminium-bronze, new uses for aluminium arose. The alloy was used for casting in foundries; it replaced silver in surgical items. Not long before the First World War, numerous experiments in mixing metals led to the discovery of duralumin. A wonderful alloy, it combined the lightness of aluminium with some of the strength of steel. Duralumin consisted largely of aluminium with small amounts of copper and, usually, 1 per cent or less of magnesium, manganese and silicon.

One of the metallurgists whose work led to that discovery was the Melbourne-educated Walter Rosenhain, who was then living in London.

He had actually emigrated from Prussia to Australia in 1880 as a five-year-old child because his parents feared that eventually he would be forced to do military service. He could not avoid, however, becoming entangled with new armaments. The alloy he helped to discover was a boon in the First World War. It was used in the manufacture of the Zeppelin airships at a time when the airship rather than the aircraft was hailed as the fast arrow of aviation. The new air-cooled engines for aircraft used aluminium but the widespread use of aluminium for the bodies and wings of aircraft came later.

Attracted by its strength and lightness, the builders of racing yachts turned to aluminium, though a mast made of aluminium would not come till later. An aluminium propeller was an early innovation; not only was it light, but it also resisted corrosion. In sports, where lightness was sought, aluminium was a windfall. On the racecourses an aluminium shoe was tested on horses.

Each kilogram of aluminium was expensive, and that restricted its use. Whereas today a tonne of copper is much dearer than a tonne of aluminium, in the decade 1901–10 copper was often half the price of aluminium. But as aluminium became cheaper, it began to challenge copper as the wire for conveying electricity. As an additive or reagent in metallurgical processes, whether the casting of steel or brass, it improved quality and purity. The little blowholes inside the metal were not likely to appear if a smidgeon of aluminium were added.

At that time the world was not short of bauxite. The demand was small, and a few minor deposits were sufficient to supply the world's needs. In 1910 'the most important beds' of bauxite lay in the south of France, in county Antrim in the north of Ireland, and in the southern states of the United States, especially Alabama, Arkansas and Georgia. The best specimen of bauxite displayed in the Perth museum came from Georgia.

It was soon discovered that huge deposits of bauxite lay in the tropics. Some of these deposits, especially those near the southern shores of the Caribbean, had an economic advantage over any bauxite in Australia: they were much closer to the North Atlantic nations which turned the bauxite into aluminium, and so the shipping costs were low. British and Dutch Guiana produced more and more bauxite in the inter-war years. The 1920s were a boon for aluminium and especially its alloys which became the main consumers of the metal. Foundries cast the metal into parts of motor cars and aircraft, and aluminium cables challenged the old copper cables as transmitters of electricity. Between 1911 and 1925 the world's annual output of aluminium leaped from about 45 000 to 200 000 tonnes.

White Gold

Australia was not seen as a potential producer of aluminium. A large flow of cheap electricity was needed by refineries and smelters, and North America and Western Europe with their hydro-electric stations could supply that electricity. Even if rich bauxite had been found in Australia in 1920 it would probably have been worthless—unless by chance it was found near the cheap water power of Tasmania. The economics of the aluminium-smelting industry still favoured the northern hemisphere where fast rivers fed by melting ice could be harnessed for hydro-electricity.

In the 1930s the Aluminum Company of Canada (known as Alcan) explored the Australian market. Alcan and British Aluminium and an Australian mining group even set up a company in 1938 in the hope of producing aluminium metal. Their Australian Aluminium Co. even planned a tiny smelter alongside the big zinc refinery on the banks of the Derwent estuary in Hobart. Tasmania's cheap hydro-electricity was the seduction. But for the outbreak of the Second World War a Hobart aluminium smelter, with an annual capacity of 2000 tonnes of ingot, would almost certainly have been built. But the Australian syndicate led by Alcan did build an aluminium rolling mill at Granville near Sydney's harbour. Using aluminium ingot imported from Canada, it supplied essential metal for Australian factories which made fighters and bombers for the war against Japan. By the end of the war Australia had three rolling mills: one at Granville, the mill of G.E. Crane & Sons at nearby Concord, and a new mill at the Victorian inland town of Wangaratta. Canadian engineers and raw materials were foremost in creating this wartime industry. If an expert in 1945 had been asked to predict who would shape the new aluminium industry in Australia and snap up any major discovery of bauxite, the Canadian giant Alcan would probably have been nominated.

In 1944, late in the war, the Commonwealth and Tasmanian governments began to plan a small self-contained aluminium industry. Bell Bay, on deep water not far from Launceston, was selected as the site for the refinery and smelter. Cheap hydro-electricity was to come from a power station planned at nearby Trevallyn. By 1950 the builders were busy at Bell Bay but progress was not fast. The smelter was initially designed to produce 10 000 tonnes of aluminium ingots each year, or five times as much as the planned output of the smelter that had almost been built at Hobart just before the war—an indication of Australia's rapidly increasing appetite for aluminium.

Only a small supply of high-grade bauxite was needed at Bell Bay. Which Australian region would supply it? A search in the late 1940s established that the reserves of the bauxite were plentiful. Whether they were in the right place—whether transport costs would devour all the potential profits—was not yet clear. Harold Raggatt, who had been head of the Bureau of Mineral Resources and was now secretary of the Department for National Development, set down what was currently known about Australian bauxite in the first chapter of his massive book, the *Geology of Australian Ore Deposits*, which was published for the benefit of mining men who were visiting Australia for the Empire Mining and Metallurgical Congress in March 1953. Throughout the whole book, references to bauxite were few, and the Darling Range rated only a passing mention.

In Raggatt's view the largest proven deposits lay in the high country of New England in northern New South Wales. He also mentioned the smaller deposits around Bundanoon, not far from Canberra, near Tamborine Mountain in southeast Queensland, near Mirboo North in eastern Victoria, and at the Ouse in southeastern Tasmania. The sum total of bauxite in these deposits was about 20 million tonnes. Significantly, to this day, none of those deposits has been mined on more than a token scale.

Raggatt must have almost completed writing his chapter when news of a major deposit on the northern, or tropical, coast of Australia came to light. On the Wessel Islands a big relatively high-grade deposit, two and a half square kilometres in area, was found. Even that deposit, however, has not been worked on a large scale.

The Bell Bay smelter produced its first ingots of aluminium in July 1955. The raw material came from Malaya! At that stage Malayan bauxite was considered more predictable in its metallurgical qualities. The operators of Bell Bay, the Aluminium Production Commission, had possession of two main sources of bauxite inside Australia—those at Wessel Islands and New England—and it was widely assumed that eventually those places would provide the raw material for Australia's infant aluminium industry.

No sooner was the first aluminium smelter at work than further discoveries of bauxite were made on opposite sides of the continent. Dramatic finds, they hinted that Australia might become more important in producing the raw materials for aluminium than in smelting aluminium itself.

One of the 'discoveries' was the Darling Range. For fifty years the existence of its bauxite had been known but ignored. Now its day was coming.

◆ 2 ◆

'It Can't Be Any Good'

Lindesay Clark did as much as anybody to crack open the wealth of the Darling Range. In his early sixties, he was relatively old to be a mining entrepreneur. Indeed in Australian history he was one of the oldest men to launch a great mining enterprise. In appearance he was more like a reserved scholar, which in one sense he was, than a mover of mountains. His speech was quiet and slow and his words were selected with care and precision. He could write the most persuasive letter, and in his persuasiveness the gifts of courtesy and clarity were prominent. His interests were scholarly as well as commercial. Not many successful businessmen in the English-speaking world could match his knowledge of books, especially the classics of history.

At first sight Lindesay Clark did not seem dynamic but sometimes he was. He had imagination and a knack of seeing far ahead. He had an ability to make tough decisions. Almost shy in manner, he sometimes gave the impression that he might be trampled on, but he could be determined and tough. He was infinitely courteous but occasionally his deep reservoir of patience would dry up and he would be inoffensively obstinate. In build he was thin and tall, his face was lean, his hair was white and thinning. Very fit, he loved golf and tennis, and liked a game of billiards after dinner before he buried himself in a book.

Clark's career had been mainly in mining. He had spent his child-hood on mining fields, first at the cold, windy copper town of Gormanston in Tasmania, his father being the manager of the big open cut at Mount Lyell. The father, also named Lindesay Clark, moved to the tinfields in the northeast of Tasmania and was general manager of the Anchor, and later the Briseis, mine. The son Lindesay studied at home with the family governess until the age of twelve when he went to the grammar school in Launceston, the nearest large town. When he completed his science degree at the University of Tasmania at the end of 1915, the First World War was in its second year. He enlisted, went to France as a sapper, and served in the 2nd Field Co. of the Australian Engineers. Commissioned as an officer on the battlefield at Ypres, he won the Military Cross a year later: he was then twenty-two. A photo of him in his khaki uniform shows an innocent, almost babyish, face below the peaked officer's cap.

Returning to Australia, he studied mining engineering at the University of Melbourne. After completing his course in 1920 he worked for the Sulphide Corporation which, at Cockle Creek near Newcastle, treated lead concentrates from Broken Hill. He became assistant metallurgist: forty years later he was to astonish and sometimes provoke heads of America's biggest aluminium company with his refusal to accept that their metallurgical methods were the best.

Mines and smelters were in the doldrums in Australia in 1923, and so Clark was fortunate to win a post as lecturer in mining at Melbourne University. So that he could do outside work, he was permitted to crowd five weeks of lectures into two and then hurry away as a consultant for a short visit to a remote mining field. When a consulting job came his way he snapped it up.

'I was sent', he recalled in old age, 'by a local syndicate to Western Australia to review the potential of the Darling Range as a source of minerals.' Whether he actually saw bauxite is not clear. At that time it was considered too low-grade to be worth more than a glance. Even if it were high-grade it would not have aroused much interest. To set up an aluminium industry a volume of cheap electricity was considered more important than rich bauxite; and Western Australia then had no hope of providing cheap electricity.

At last, when gold was beginning to boom during the world depression of the early 1930s, Lindesay Clark—now in his mid thirties—found work as exploration adviser to a new gold-exploring and finance company, Gold Mines of Australia. Backed by South African gold interests, it explored throughout Australia. Indeed in 1932 Clark went to The Granites, a new rush in one of the most isolated parts of the Northern Territory. There his small party seemed to come under noisy attack from Aborigines—until he realised that they were simply calling for tins of 'bully beef'.

At first Clark was the part-time adviser to Sir Colin Fraser, the company's chairman. The company grew and soon Clark became its chief executive with the title of 'manager' and with, from 1935, a seat on the board. The company's head office was in Collins House in Collins Street,

White Gold

Melbourne, the home of most of the big Broken Hill mines and their myriad investments.

Gold Mines of Australia investigated a host of new and old finds and fields. It had early success in floating Mount Coolon Gold Mines in north Queensland and Morning Star Mines, which revived old Woods Point in Victoria. Dredging for gold in Victorian river valleys was another success but the attempt to revive the famous goldfield of Bendigo on a big scale was a failure. Bendigo, some observers say, almost ended Clark's mining career, for the venture was a financial disaster.

The company's interests in Western Australia were floated in March 1933 into a separate company, Western Mining Corporation. It became a middle-sized player on the Golden Mile, where it operated as Gold Mines of Kalgoorlie, and a key player on smaller goldfields including nearby Norseman. Clark, now called the 'technical managing director', carried out bold experiments. His company bought two De Havilland aircraft, capable of flying at a speed of about 150 kilometres an hour, to make a photographic survey of large areas in the hope of detecting geological anomalies that were not clearly visible on the ground.

This gold group had one hallmark: it was incessantly exploring. On the surface or far underground, the clues that might lead to further finds were constantly assessed. Clark's company began with an emphasis on employing fine geologists recruited in the Americas. In the late 1930s the Western Mining group probably employed a greater wealth of geological talent than the hundreds of other mining companies in Australia combined. Some employees who returned to the United States became famous there.

By 1939 the company had so many mines and prospecting camps in and around Kalgoorlie that when Clark had to inspect them, his tour of inspection—from the time he reached Kalgoorlie on the transcontinental train—took about two weeks. He and a few colleagues travelled in a car, sleeping, and often eating, beside the dusty roads. Clark recalled that in the car they kept their butter, meat and drink cool with the aid of blocks of ice packed into wooden kerosene cases. Always there were new shafts or trenches to inspect. In the first 25 years his Western Mining group and its associated companies investigated some 2400 untested discoveries around Australia. Only 22 of those finds became producing mines.

In 1942, after Japan entered the war, Australia urgently needed to produce minerals which it had previously imported. A directorate of minerals production was set up with the power to control and operate mines. Clark became deputy controller of mineral production under J. Malcolm 'Ginger' Newman, with the task of finding or opening mineral deposits urgently needed by factories making munitions or urgent civilian equipment. Tungsten, tin, copper, aluminium, mica, antimony, asbestos and tantalite were among the minerals sought.

During the war Clark joined the board of two major mineral companies, Broken Hill South and Broken Hill Associated Smelters. With the directors he made an annual visit to the South mine and mill at Broken Hill and the lead smelters at Port Pirie, the world's biggest. Gold remained his first love, and the Western Mining group was his main interest in the early years after the war. When its head office was transferred from London to Melbourne, Clark became absorbed in the company's financial, as well as its mining, problems.

He became Western Mining's chairman in 1952, succeeding Sir Walter Massy-Greene. Its cluster of gold companies was earning modest profits but, some critics said, could not hope for a very long life. Costs of mining were rising much faster than the price of gold. Of all the major metals, gold was the only one whose price fell in real terms between 1935 and 1955. Clark, a gold man through and through, believed that ultimately gold would again become a central part of the monetary system, as in the 1920s, and that its price would be lifted in order that the world's output of gold would keep pace with what he saw as the world's monetary needs. His hopes were thwarted year after year. He was to be an old man before gold really leaped in price.

From the gold industry Clark experienced many jolts, the hardest coming from Great Western Consolidated N.L. Formed in July 1948, with Western Mining as its general manager, Great Western developed a large low-grade goldmine at Bullfinch, north of Southern Cross in Western Australia. In 1950 an issue of shares raised more capital, L.C. Brodie-Hall became the company's general superintendent and a steady output of gold began in 1952. The early 1950s, when the Korean War was being fought, were inflationary; and the inflation cuffed gold more than any other commodity because the international price of gold was fixed. Moreover, Great Western chanced to begin production near the apex of the inflation. Its costs were hopelessly beyond predictions. To make matters worse, its ore was not as valuable as the preliminary tests had predicted. About one-fifth of the gold estimated to be in the average tonne was simply not there. In a low-grade mine that margin of error could not be compensated for.

In 1956 Great Western tried to retrieve its fortunes by buying a goldmine at Nevoria, to the southeast of Southern Cross. Again a vanishing trick took place almost before the company's eyes. The gold in the ore was not as rich as careful tests suggested. Great Western paid no dividend. Instead the debts accumulated, and they had passed 2 million pounds when the company was wound up in 1970.

Such a defeat, which had long seemed likely, did not humiliate Clark.

White Gold

He knew that mineral exploration was like a guerrilla war. A proportion of defeats was inevitable. Fortunately there were two successes stories in the 1950s: Kalgoorlie, which remained a moderate profit earner; and Central Norseman, which was a bonanza. Part of the profit from these mines went into the search for other mines. In 1953 Clark, as chairman, announced that his company would widen its searches and cease to concentrate solely on gold. In the four years to March 1958 it diverted 47 000 pounds into exploring for uranium, 8000 pounds into copper, 5000 into nickel, 3000 into bauxite and smaller sums into the search for oil and nickel. The sums seem small today but they represented hard-earned savings. In addition, another 58 000 pounds went into the search for new goldmines. Clark's imagination was fired by the hope of finding, far underground, a southern extension of the Golden Mile. It was not found by the deep holes drilled.

In searching for mines Western Mining had an asset that was probably more important than money: it had a vigorous geological team. More than almost any other Australian mining leader, Clark believed in geologists. From 1945 the chief geologist at Western Mining was Don Campbell, and he was to turn the company's eyes to the Darling Range.

Campbell had studied mining at the University of Melbourne where he had his first taste of geology, a minor part of the mining engineering course. H.S. 'Doc' Summers, a fine teacher with a love of geology and a sense of fun, impressed Campbell. Another influential teacher was the lecturer in mining, Lindesay Clark, who was about to leave the university to become the chief technical officer with the infant Western Mining group. So Campbell, on graduating in the depression year of 1933, went to work with Clark's company. Hired as an assistant geologist on the small goldfield of Norseman near Kalgoorlie, Campbell boarded in the 'derelict ruin' of a pub and became immersed in the fortunes of that smallish goldfield.

There he fell increasingly under the spell of geology and one of its most charming advocates, the North American Terence Conolly. A mixture of loquacity and moody silence, Conolly brought all his intelligence to geology. He believed in the new Harvard prospecting formula— that careful mapping of the geology of an ore body and its vicinity should enable him to see the relationship between the ore and the surrounding structure and so to drill in areas where that structure seemed most favourable for further ore bodies. At Norseman he met setbacks, but his formula sowed the seeds of wonderful success.

This formula was carried further by Haddon King, a Canadian geologist, and even further by Don Campbell, who had turned from mining engineering to geology. Campbell began to find rich hidden ore bodies at Norseman. It so happened that the gold output of Norseman soared from 1953, just when Western Mining needed more revenue to compensate for the troubles in its Great Western mine at Bullfinch. Most of the gold at Norseman came from concealed ore bodies which were found largely through an ability to mount reasoned hypotheses and to drill on the basis of those hypotheses. An intellectual success story, Norseman's success owed much to Campbell. Its gold helped to keep Western Mining afloat in a difficult decade. Moreover, it was a testing ground in which Campbell developed some of the skills that proved valuable in re-examining the long-neglected bauxite of the Darling Range.

As chief geologist of Western Mining, Campbell was stationed at Kalgoorlie. While gold dominated his work, he was interested in all minerals. When the company decided it could no longer concentrate solely on gold he was the key man in other investigations. What turned him towards bauxite was not a discovery in Western Australia, his company's special territory, but a discovery in the corner of the continent most remote from Kalgoorlie. In 1955 rich bauxite was found at Weipa in far north Queensland, almost opposite Papua.

The finder of Weipa was Harry Evans, an oil geologist. While prospecting for oil in Queensland he had been urged to keep one eye open for bauxite and phosphate. Hearing that a discovery of bauxite had been made on the western side of the Cape York Peninsula back in 1902, he decided to investigate it. To his surprise the bauxite stretched along a vast strip area of tropical coastline. Of the six samples he sent to Bell Bay for testing in July 1955, several were of good grade.

Returning to the region, he landed in a small aircraft at the tiny town of Coen—the region was almost devoid of towns. He managed to hire a landrover and a portable dinghy with an outboard motor, and motoring along bush tracks, he reached the eastern shore of the Gulf of Carpentaria. Together with an Aborigine, he went exploring by boat, hugging the low-lying tropical coast. To his surprise he saw cliffs that were red with bauxite. Without even having to dig a shaft he made with pencil and paper a rough estimate that at least 250 million tonnes of payable bauxite were present. His estimate turned out to be conservative indeed.

Harry Evans' employer was Consolidated Zinc, the biggest of the mining companies at Broken Hill. As the chief executive of the company, Maurice Mawby, had urged Evans to be alert for bauxite, the discovery was instantly appreciated at head office in Melbourne. Mawby instinctively knew that a bauxite deposit of that magnitude was potentially valuable. He began to think of building an alumina refinery at the remote mine or at a more accessible port in Queensland. In December 1956 his new company, Commonwealth Aluminium Corporation, was formed: it

White Gold

is commonly known as Comalco. Exploration continued, proving that Weipa was one of the world's major deposits of bauxite. Consolidated Zinc needed a partner to provide expertise and part of the huge sum needed to develop an industry. In January 1958 it was to join with British Aluminium on a 50–50 basis.

Soon after Clark heard of these discoveries of bauxite in northern Australia he sent Reg Clappison, one of his geologists, to look around. Much of the promising ground had presumably been taken up by then. Clappison found nothing to excite him but on his return to Melbourne did suggest that the bauxite in the Darling Range might be worth examining. It seems that his opinion was not followed up. Nonetheless the Darling Range was tentatively in Clark's mind as one of those prospects that might some day be investigated.

Clark was now interested in bauxite, especially if it was in the tropics. As Western Mining probably knew more than other companies about the geology of Western Australia, and as Clark had smooth relations with the Western Australian government, he thought any bauxite in the tropical zone of that state would be worthy of investigation. High-grade bauxite had been found near Admiralty Gulf, in the Kimberley, but it had not been pegged out. At first glance this was more attractive than the Darling Range could ever be. A region not yet systematically prospected

Lindesay Clark inspecting a drill rig used for exploring the bauxite deposit in the Darling Range.

was more likely to yield a valuable deposit. Moreover, by now what was known of the world's major bauxite deposits was sufficient to support the axiom that the best bauxite was to be found in the tropics.

In the autumn of 1957, Clark raised the question of bauxite with Don Campbell, his chief geologist, and with Frank Espie, who was in charge of the company's Western Australian operations. In casual discussion in the Kalgoorlie offices he talked of the promise of Weipa and the possibility that similar deposits might be found in tropical Australia. At this stage Campbell made a crucial contribution. He turned attention away from the tropics. He mentioned the bauxite that was known to lie, untested, in the Darling Range.

Most geologists would have argued differently. After all, the Darling Range tested credulity. Many of its hills and valleys were close to Perth, and thousands of people must have seen the exposures of bauxite. Therefore it was reasonable—but not foolproof logic—to argue that if the bauxite was valuable, it would have been pegged by now and already investigated by other mining companies. There was another tentative argument against the Darling Range: it lay in the temperate zone and yet most of the world's major deposits of bauxite lay in the tropics. Indeed there were valid geological arguments why most bauxite deposits were likely to be in the tropics. On the other hand one fact could not be taken away: the first bauxite deposit ever found in the world was in France and that was well and truly in a temperate zone.

Campbell had long known of the Darling Range and its signs of bauxite. He had been casually told of the bauxite by an old geologist, Henry W.B. Talbot, who had inspected the range on behalf of the Zinc Corporation back in 1940. Talbot, then in his late sixties, was a walking filing cabinet of mineral knowledge about the state; he had mapped much of it. He had even found iron ore at Mount Newman in the Pilbara, some forty years before it was rediscovered. Talbot did not tell Campbell anything worthwhile about the bauxite, but Campbell added it to his general knowledge of where certain minerals could be found in Western Australia.

So in the office of Western Mining at Kalgoorlie, Campbell mentioned the bauxite in the Darling Range. Perhaps it was worth a simple investigation before any remote region, requiring days of travelling and heavy costs of exploration, was inspected. 'Fortunately', he recalls, 'my suggestion was adopted.' We now know, in the light of subsequent exploration, that if the Western Mining Corporation had concentrated on the Kimberley it would have earned only a headache.

Campbell had to set aside time to inspect the bauxite in the Darling Range, for it was the best part of a day's drive from Kalgoorlie. Meanwhile he asked his young assistant, Roy Woodall who, a decade later, would discover a major nickel field at Kambalda, to gather what background information was available. Woodall came across a pamphlet published by the Bureau of Mineral Resources three years previously. Its geologist, H.B. Owen, had surveyed the bauxite finds so far made in Australia. While Owen possessed, to use his own words, 'little first-hand knowledge' of the bauxite in the Darling Range, he made one simple observation that may have eluded other prospectors and geologists who had seen and dismissed the bauxite. He challenged, without making a fuss about it, the idea that the high content of silica in the Darling Range bauxite was necessarily an impediment.

As soon as Woodall began to read the Owen pamphlet he saw the implications clearly. In short, the bauxite or laterite in the Darling Range was more attractive than anybody had so far realised. Its high component of silica, which had discouraged other prospectors and geologists, was in the form of quartz which, being unreactive, would cause no harm in the treatment process. In contrast, if the silica had been present in clay minerals rather than in the quartz, it would have reacted in a harmful and costly way in the treatment plant. Woodall even thought that the silica present in the quartz might actually help in the filtering process. This advice he passed on to Campbell.

Right from the start, then, Western Mining had a ready answer to those pessimists who might be tempted to retort that this bauxite 'can't be any good—otherwise it would have been pegged out long ago'. It was not pegged partly because its composition had been misunderstood.

Owen's brief comment on the Darling Range, available in every geological library, was ignored in the mid 1950s when the mining industry for the first time was afflicted with bauxite fever. Even the government which employed Owen took no notice of his words. Following the publication of his report, the Commonwealth and Tasmanian governments which owned the aluminium smelter and refinery, by now almost completed at Bell Bay, did not even bother to investigate the Darling Range. Instead they imported their bauxite from Malaya.

Admittedly, Owen had not spelled out the economic implications of the grains of quartz that were present in the bauxite; his whole report was low-key. It was Roy Woodall who realised that the Darling Range bauxite was probably more amenable to cheap treatment. 'He had a better knowledge than I on matters mineralogical and chemical', Campbell generously recalled.

In July 1957 Campbell set out to inspect the neglected bauxite in the Darling Range. With his draughtsman, Wilf Keddy, he drove a car along the bush roads in the higher parts of the timbered ranges. Learning from Roy Woodall that the payable bauxite was likely to lie in the granite country at least 250 metres above sea level he took an excellent aneroid barometer so that he could save time by skipping the ground just below that altitude. He also carried military maps which showed the contours. So equipped, he concentrated on the higher ground. Often the bauxite was visible, sometimes on the ground, sometimes in road cuttings, sometimes on eroded slopes. It was there in immense quantities. Campbell recalled that his method was crude:

> I drove the car at some speed and Wilf sat beside me taking notes. I called 'laterite' or 'no laterite' as we went by and Wilf recorded the reading of the car's odometer and the height above sea level from the aneroid barometer. At infrequent intervals we stopped to collect samples for assay, usually from road cuttings.

In the course of 'four hectic days', Campbell and Keddy drove nearly 2000 kilometres. They went as far as the port of Albany where Campbell saw that the far southern ranges 'showed no promise'. As bauxite near a major port was more likely to be profitable, for cartage would be cheap, he looked closely at the bauxite visible not far from the ports of Fremantle and Bunbury. He even drove almost as far north as the old monastery of New Norcia. While travelling he sensed the vastness of the deposits, but there was still much to learn. Whether they could compete with Weipa in Australia and with other big deposits in South America and west Africa was still an open question.

The abundance of silica found in this Western Australian bauxite continued to feed Campbell with a nagging doubt. He knew that most bauxite consumed in the world's refineries carried only a small amount of silica. In North America, the hub of the industry, a content of 8 per cent of silica was about as much as could be profitably leached away by the Bayer process, the best known method of treatment. In Europe the refineries did not tolerate that much silica in the bauxite. Indeed the original bauxite which came from the village of Les Baux in France contained virtually no silica. A low proportion of silica was almost a characteristic of the bauxite mined for the ever-expanding aluminium industry in Europe. In contrast, Western Australian bauxite carried a deadweight of silica which European refineries would have promptly shunned. Only wartime America, where the demand for aluminium was avid and the supply of good bauxite was poor and precarious, had relaxed the rule of thumb which denounced excessive silica. Using a special process, some American refineries had managed to treat bauxite containing as much as 13 per cent silica. The Darling Range bauxite, it seemed, was much higher in silica.

The well-known Canadian analyst of aluminium, Wilfred K. Grummer, insisted that too much silica in bauxite was virtually a disqualification. That was the current wisdom in the late 1950s. Readers of his long article on 'Bauxite' in the latest edition of the *Encyclopaedia Britannica* were warned that too much silica was a poison. Grummer listed the amount of silica—presumably the reactive silica—in the bauxite mined in the main producing regions:

Jamaica	0.5–4.0 per cent
West Africa	1.0–5.0 per cent
North and South America	1.0–8.0 per cent
Mediterranean	2.0–14.0 per cent
Southeast Asia	3.0–8.0 per cent

By these standards the Darling Range was not in the contest.

Normally, in a refinery, an excess of the silica could be removed only by adding large quantities of expensive caustic soda. The cost of the additional caustic soda—needed to remove the excess silica—could make a mining venture unprofitable. Campbell's quick tour of the Darling Range confirmed the impression he had gained from Roy Woodall and from Owen's published report: that much of the silica was friendly rather than hostile. Being present in the form of grains of quartz, it would not react with the caustic soda and impede the process. Instead it would pass out with residue.

Don Campbell calculated that a big tonnage of bauxite must lie just below the surface of the range. Two and a half square kilometres of bauxite, even if only two metres in thickness, was capacious enough to contain about 10 million tonnes. Much more of the bauxite had a depth of more than two metres, and so, by any quick estimate, a total of at least hundreds of million of tonnes must be waiting to be mined. Quantity was never a problem. The crucial question was whether each tonne of bauxite was rich enough to be worth mining in a highly competitive market which many nations supplied. On the earth's surface, bauxite was actually the most common of the well-known mineral materials. The crucial question was, therefore, whether this Western Australian bauxite was sufficiently enriched to be worth mining.

It was too early to know whether a payable mine would emerge. Metallurgists first had to test the bauxite for quality. Accordingly, samples of bauxite, all taken from the surface, were collected and placed in bags. Eight small samples of the bauxite were sent as air freight to Launceston and then by road to the new aluminium plant at Bell Bay. Only the richer material was sent. On 11 December 1957, Campbell took up his fountain pen and plain sheets of notepaper and gave his cautious views to Frank Espie who was in charge of Western Mining's operations in the west: 'A curly one at the moment is that the tests being done by the Bell Bay people may show there is no chance of the bauxite being of economic value.'

The tests proved favourable though not decisive. The best three samples yielded more than 40 per cent of soda-soluble alumina. In theory that was not very high grade. As for the poorer samples, Bell Bay reported that they 'could probably be of doubtful economic value except under very favourable circumstances'. On hearing of the results, Campbell evaluated them in a brief confidential report written in Kalgoorlie on 26 March 1958. He envisaged that the Darling Range, on the basis of the present sparse evidence, held 'very large tonnages of bauxite of possible economic importance'. He was right to be cautious. Not one hole had been drilled below the surface. He estimated that several years of drilling might be needed to test whether sufficient bauxite was present. And then bigger samples, hundreds of tons rather than hundreds of pounds, would have to be treated in a refinery on a large scale to give a more reliable test. So much was still unknown about the bauxite.

In the investigations carried out so far, Western Mining was all alone. Nobody in the company had direct experience of the mineral. Nor could the company safely bring in an expert from another company—unless it was a very friendly company—because that company might become too interested in the possibilities of the region. The first outsider came by chance. Chester Guest was a director both of Western Mining and North Broken Hill, and he chanced to hear that North Broken Hill employed a young geologist, Peter Howard, who had explored for bauxite outside Australia for the Reynolds company. Guest told Clark, and it was arranged for 'young Howard' to fly to Perth where Campbell met him. Howard visited part of the Darling Range and said nothing that contradicted Campbell's hopeful but cautious views. Howard's only fear, and it was not pressed emphatically, was that the high proportion of quartz or silica in the bauxite could pose metallurgical or economic problems.

One heartening fact was that the bauxite covered a huge area. It is doubtful whether any mineral field that had previously been discovered in Australia could match the Darling Range in sheer vastness. Celebrated fields like Ballarat, Bendigo, Mount Morgan, Charters Towers, Mount Isa, Mount Lyell, Moonta, Iron Knob and Kalgoorlie were relatively compact. A walk of six kilometres in one direction was long enough to embrace most of these fields at their longest stretch. In contrast, the bauxite of the Darling Range stretched for several hundred kilometres.

There were few short cuts in looking for surface traces of bauxite. In contrast, in the traditional Australian minerals, all kinds of useful observations had been made or gathered about the conditions that seemed to give rise to the presence of minerals. Thus the presence of a certain rock might indicate that payable gold was nearby, or the juxtaposition of two rock types might indicate a chance of copper nearby. In the Darling Range, however, the prospectors had to begin from scratch.

White Gold

The pit near Dwellingup where bauxite was mined by Western Mining in mid 1960, in preparation for the first trial shipment.

Little was known about the vital question: what are the signs indicating that payable bauxite might lie below?

The area to be prospected was bigger than most English counties. To scour the hilly surface was a mammoth task. And then, having found a few of the more promising deposits, prospectors had to explore them according to a regular pattern. Campbell concluded that even the scout drilling—the initial phase of drilling—could take many years.

Bauxite tended to be on the higher ground. Height above the sea level was one clue to the presence of bauxite. Campbell believed from the outset that hills that stood a certain distance above sea level were more promising. Still, the areas at that altitude were vast, and the magnitude of the task of exploring was not drastically reduced by that observation. Of course it was easy to measure the presence of alumina by taking samples of the rock and clay in the cuttings made by the few bush roads that cut through the range. Here and there the bauxite was easily seen in the cuttings or in boulders that had been pushed aside in the roadmaking. Some observers said that a high plateau was more likely to yield bauxite, and that richer material would be found on the western side of the ranges than on the eastern.

By the start of 1958 prompt action was needed if Western Mining was to acquire rights to prospect, and ultimately to claim, the hills where bauxite could be seen. The company at first feared that the freehold land already held in the hills would create obstacles: it was not always easy in Western Australia for prospectors to gain access to freehold land. It was soon clear that most of the freehold land was in the more fertile valleys whereas the bauxite lay on the rougher hilltops and slopes, and they were still in the government's possession. The premier of Western Australia was A.R.G. Hawke, whose nephew was to become prime minister of Australia a quarter of a century later. Hawke was sympathetic to mineral development and when approached by Clark, he agreed to grant to Western Mining a temporary reservation of 6250 square miles

(16,200 square kilometres). The land formed a corridor running about 325 kilometres from north to south, with Bridgetown at one end and Toodyay at the other. The corridor, about fifty kilometres wide, covered nearly all parts of the Darling Range. Western Mining now had time to identify which areas might contain bauxite.

Western Mining was able to secure such a huge area, so close to Perth, because no other company was yet interested in such low-grade bauxite. After all, much richer deposits could probably be located in tropical Australia. Furthermore, Weipa in all its richness still captured the imagination of the mining industry. Indeed the idea of searching for bauxite close to Perth was considered to be so impractical or so unglamorous that Western Mining was able to do its searching and assessing with the secrecy it needed. Nobody else was interested.

Clark's faith in the value of the discovery was increasing but some who heard the rumours about his find were sceptical. Clark was slightly peeved when that celebrated leader of Australian mining, Essington Lewis, then in his late seventies, expressed doubt about the find. Lewis and Clark had chanced to meet in the street on their separate ways to lunch at the Australian Club in Melbourne, and out of the blue Lewis offered the casual remark: 'I hear you have pegged the whole of the Darling Range'. Lewis, not one for small talk, expressed his doubts in his tone of voice more than in his words. Clark inferred that, in Lewis's opinion, 'we had bitten off more than we could chew'.

Most of the bauxite was in the form of the mineral called gibbsite. The mineral had been named after Colonel Gibbs, an American soldier who was an ardent collector of minerals and the father of a famous Harvard professor of chemistry, Wolcott Gibbs, who died in 1908. Some geologists who were working along the range and making a map of what lay on the surface, felt certain that they could identify the mineral gibbsite in the laterite and even the areas where the bauxite was richest. Campbell, however, was not so sure. On one point, however, he felt fairly confident. The bauxite near the top of the deposits was usually richer than that near the bottom.

From the start Campbell had a fair understanding of how the bauxite, in the course of hundreds of millions of years, had been created. The original country rock had been granite, formed maybe 2.5 billion years ago, during the Pre-Cambrian epoch. Over the ages, rain and every kind of weathering had turned the granite into laterite. As Campbell explained in an early report: 'Laterite is similar in origin to soil', being the result of the weathering of rock under special conditions. The special conditions in that part of Western Australia included flat terrain, and an enormously long period—Tertiary and Pleistocene—in which the climate was wetter and warmer than it is today. In the process of weathering many of the minerals on higher ground had been leached away, leaving a remnant of laterite that in places was rich in gibbsite—namely hydrated aluminium oxide. Other weathered places were rich in iron and quartz and the clay mineral known as kaolin, but the valuable parts were those rich in gibbsite.

Much of the capping of laterite had not survived the drawn-out process of weathering. Part had been eroded away by streams and found its way towards the plains and the sea. What survived was the target. As further knowledge accumulated, it seemed that the alumina was rarely rich on the crests of the surviving hills of the Darling Range and never rich in the valleys. The slopes had the valuable concentrations of the bauxite, which was normally found in small pockets covering 10 to 25 hectares. Rarely did the bauxite descend for more than five metres; it was simply a topping concentrated on scattered parts of the ancient weathered granite rocks.

The task for Campbell was to find these richer 'puddings' of bauxite. He found them with increasing skill. In the weathered laterite that capped much of the Darling Range, the top parts of the bauxite puddings tended to be the richest. The unwanted reactive silica was stronger at the bottom of the pudding. At a small depth the bauxite usually gave way to what was later described as 'the pallid clay zone'. In essence the prized material was at the top, but the bottom was also worth mining, though more expensive to treat. Naturally part of this knowledge was not available at the end of the 1950s when the deposits were first explored.

Neither Campbell nor Clark was able to give the bauxite his top priority. Both had other tasks of importance. Gold was their main occupation. Moreover, they knew that even if the bauxite passed all tests they would have to find a huge sum of capital to turn the bauxite into aluminium. Their company did not possess that huge sum. Even if they invested a huge sum of money on mine and treatment plants they knew that market conditions might alter and that their venture might not turn out to be profitable.

◆ 3 ◆

The Man with the Magic Carpet

While Campbell was planning the exploring of the Darling Range, Clark was thinking about money. Even the search for the richer puddings of bauxite—just the first of many steps— called for more money than Western Mining could spare. For advice Clark turned to Denny Marris, a financier in the City of London.

Denny Marris was a partner in the well-known firm of Lazard Bros & Co., merchant bankers, who gave financial advice to some of the world's major companies. At the Lazard head office at 11 Old Broad Street, London, Marris was usually to be found submerged by business papers, with piles of folders that seemed about to topple, papers resting on the floor, a heap of letters on his desk and a Persian carpet or two rolled up in a corner of his room. On carpets he was an expert and could quickly identify their 'make' just as some people identified the year of a vintage car. Marris himself could be slightly dishevelled in appearance though, as one of his old friends hastens to observe, 'not outrageously so'.

Now about fifty years of age, Denny Marris had been a student at Winchester College and Trinity College, Oxford, before joining Lazards. His mind was tidier than his office, and held compact stores of knowledge. His experience was wide, his powers of criticism most noticeable and his judgment balanced. He could work through the night with little loss of concentration. When he set down his views on paper he set them down with patient care, as if he was fearful that otherwise the document might haunt him in years to come. When sitting down with colleagues to draft a document which had to be completed with speed, he was like a dog worrying a bone. He inspected every second word for hidden

25

meanings or flaws. He spelled out every matter that might give rise to dispute. At the memorial service held for him in London in July 1983 it was heard, with restrained humour, how he once sent from Australia to Lazards a telex that was eight and a half metres long when finally printed out.

Marris had a penetrating eye for what was happening in finance in London. He sat for long periods on the boards of the Commercial Union, Barclay's Bank, the shipping giant P & O, and the E.S. & A. Bank which, based in London, was strong in Australian mining. He was to sit on the committee that reshaped the Oxford University Press in the 1960s. International affairs he also watched closely. At the conference which devised the Marshall Plan after the Second World War, he was deputy leader of the British delegation.

Clark and Marris must have known one another for at least ten years before the bauxite brought them even closer together. After the war Lazards had taken part in the negotiations which enabled Western Mining to buy out Boulder Perseverance and several other London companies which owned ground on the Golden Mile. Marris came to Australia occasionally and in March 1948 he was at the Menzies Hotel in Melbourne and about to undertake a trip arranged by Clark. Marris flew to Perth and so on to the goldfields where he was first shown the Central Norseman mine by Don Campbell and the Golden Mile by Frank Espie, the Western Australian manager for Western Mining. He then flew with Campbell in a tiny aircraft to Southern Cross, from where they drove out to the rising Great Western mine, the hope of the firm, at Bullfinch. Marris was impressed and he carried back to London favourable impressions of Clark's small gold empire.

The friendship with Clark probably dated from that tour. Clark sent Marris bottles of Australian wine—then a novelty in London. Clark's daughter, who was working in England, spent a weekend at Marris's large country house with its fine library. Marris offered to ferret out scarce books for Clark who loved reading history. Soon a secondhand copy of Helen Waddell's book *The Wandering Scholars* was in the post for Clark with a promise that Henri Pirenne's *History of Europe*, also out of print, was on order from an Oxford antiquarian shop.

First names were exchanged. The 'Dear Marris' of 1949 became 'Dear Denny' a year later, while Gordon Lindesay Clark became the half-familiar 'My Dear Gordon' and then 'Dear Lindsay': the correct spelling of Lindesay soon followed. Matters were discussed in airmail letters. Even in those last years of the slower propeller aircraft, an airmail letter often reached Australia as speedily as it arrives today.

It was late in 1957, in an airmail letter marked 'confidential', that Marris first learned of the bauxite in the Darling Range. To the question 'how could the money be raised for exploring the shallow deposits?', Marris gave patient thought. He happened to be familiar with the world's aluminium industry and the intense rivalry between the handful of companies which controlled the world's markets. 'Aluminium was a very big time game,' said Marris. He knew that several of these whales might be eager to swallow a newborn Australian sardine, once they heard of its existence. It would be wise, Marris advised Clark late in 1957, to keep tight lips at least for the time being about the Darling Range.

Clark initially had hoped to raise exploration money, at least 350 000 pounds, by floating the bauxite deposits into a public company. Marris said such a scheme would instantly attract the whales. Instead Western Mining must borrow money privately and quietly in order to continue its exploring. The hitch in that plan was that its main banker, the English Scottish & Australian Bank, had already lent heavily—on the security of Western Mining's assets—to support the struggling Great Western gold mine. The bank's general manager, Harold Ensten, advised Clark to be wary of new investments while that debt hung heavily.

Clark had to look elsewhere. On the advice of Marris, he approached a bank with which he rarely did business: the Commonwealth Trading Bank. In Sydney the bank's general manager, A.N. Armstrong, felt sympathy for Clark's argument that the bauxite deposit should, if at all possible, remain in Australian ownership. In March 1958 Armstrong verbally promised to lend money though he knew that the loan was slightly risky. Equally important, he promised to keep the matter secret for a short time. Western Mining had climbed its first hurdle. The Commonwealth Bank eventually lent 75 000 pounds. How long could Clark keep the bauxite a secret? It was soon likely to leak out. Clark knew that his old-time business friends would be vexed if they heard the news by rumour rather than from his own mouth. On the advice of Denny Marris, Clark decided to inform L.B. Robinson, the chairman of Consolidated Zinc, which controlled the new-found deposit of bauxite at Weipa in Queensland. Robinson usually visited Australia every year and so he might chance to find out about the rival discovery in the Darling Range.

For personal and commercial reasons, Robinson had to be let into the secret, but not admitted too far. On 25 June 1958 Clark addressed an airmail letter to him at 37 Dover Street, London. Clark said his team had found bauxite and 'the quantities could be great'. He added that he was not in a hurry to explore it systematically because the price of aluminium was low and, furthermore, gold was still the company's main interest. Clark was foxy about the precise whereabouts of the bauxite, noting that it lay in the 'Darling Ranges . . . which, as you know, are about 150 to 100 miles from the coast'. In fact most of the bauxite lay much closer to the coast.

Campbell was about to begin the systematic exploring for bauxite. In September 1958 he set out to make a map of the bauxite visible on the surface of one of the promising areas. Using forestry maps and military maps, a few geologists followed the roads and bush tracks, and in the favourable areas they jumped from the car and looked for samples of bauxite, collecting each sample at distances ranging from about 100 to 350 metres apart. The exact places from which samples of bauxite were collected were marked on a map, the mileage register on the dashboard of the car serving as a measuring tape. Most of the samples were chipped with a geological hammer from boulders of bauxite that had been dislodged by roadmakers, from places where the bauxite out-cropped and from cuttings in the roadsides. This survey was done with speed and a fair degree of accuracy.

As more and more samples were being taken from the ranges, the company needed its own laboratory for assaying them. Frank Espie, who from his office in Kalgoorlie superintended all activities in Western Australia, set out to find a building. In Kalamunda, now almost a suburb of Perth, he found a large disused building that had been an iceworks and a cold store for apples and other rural produce. It became the bauxite

Kalamunda laboratory, 1961, showing the bomb room. The heating and rotating mechanism is on the left and vacuum cooltration is on the right.

laboratory—indeed it was the only building devoted to the aluminium project. Colin Kleeman, metallurgist at the goldmines at Kalgoorlie, supervised the laboratory from afar and sent Keith Bower from Kalgoorlie to manage it.

The son of a gold prospector, Bower had worked at the Wiluna goldfield just before and just after the war. Becoming an assayer, he improved his qualifications by studying metallurgy at the School of Mines in Kalgoorlie at night while he worked in treatment plants during the day. In 1958 he and W.S. Symons were sent to the aluminium plant at Bell Bay to learn the laboratory procedures used in analysing bauxite and to decide which equipment should be bought for the laboratory being set up in the West. Bower recalls that there was almost a military-type security at Bell Bay. Not once during his two months there was he allowed to enter the alumina refinery. He and Symons were permitted just one tour of the smelter, at 'whistle-stop' pace. Even when they went to the canteen at lunch time they were escorted to and from the assay office.

Bower quickly realised that the aluminium industry was far removed from gold. Gold companies were not competitors in one sense simply because they could sell, at a fixed price, all the gold they produced. There was no advertising, no struggle for market share. Moreover companies, both big and small, were usually happy to exchange the latest information. In contrast, in the aluminium industry each company was a giant fighting for its share of the market; secrecy was normal. Any technical advance that enabled it to outstrip its rivals was guarded fiercely. Bell Bay, then linked to British Aluminium, was actually being generous—by the standards of the aluminium industry—towards these interlopers from the West. Later Bower guessed that one reason why permission was granted was that 'very few people ever expected an economic plant could be sustained' on the basis on the hungry-looking bauxite from the Darling Range.

By August 1958 the old cool store and iceworks in the foothills near Perth were stripped of their benches and fittings and fully equipped as a laboratory. Some equipment was scavenged from old assay offices in the Western Mining goldmines and some of the sophisticated equipment was hurriedly brought from overseas. Bower set to work to assay thousands of samples of bauxite sent from the ranges nearby. In one week he did more assays of bauxite than had been done in the fifty or sixty years since the first lumps of bauxite were taken to the geological museum in Perth for inspection and analysis. More staff came to Kalamunda to drill the deposits and to do experiments. Ernest Gaspar, a talented Hungarian immigrant who had driven a milk delivery cart in Perth, came to do analytical work. He was already a specialist, and he brought new eyes and a sense of humour to the task.

The assays made in the laboratory enabled Campbell and his team to mark on the maps the particular slopes where the bauxite seemed to be of higher grade. But were these surface tests, based on 'surface knapping', an indication of what lay below? Western Mining began drilling shallow holes. By December 1958 the only scout drill was busy, moving quickly from hole to hole. Each day seventy or eighty samples were taken from below and sent to the laboratory for assaying. As Campbell emphasised on 12 December 1958: 'At this stage the drilling should not aim at outlining ore bodies.'

Early in the new year the picture was clearer. Many drill holes showed that some of the deposits were five or six metres in thickness; occasionally the promising bauxite went down almost ten metres. Campbell began to conclude that the tops and slopes of hills were the most promising areas. Especially promising were the more prominent ridges standing 'in terrain of generally low relief'. Aerial photographs enabled his staff to select those ridges. The drillers with their mobile drill rig went to that higher ground and, amongst the trees, they began to drill. As a rule they drilled three shallow holes on the top and one on each side. Assays revealed that much ore was close to 'world standards'.

More money was needed to continue the exploring. The cost was already stretching Western Mining's cheque book. Clark therefore enlisted as partners the two oldest Broken Hill mining companies. Of the non-ferrous mining companies in Australia, they had been for many years two of the five most profitable. One was Broken Hill South, of which he himself had recently become chairman; the other was North Broken Hill, of which he was a director. These two companies had the oldest working mines on the line of lode, being producers of silver, lead and zinc, and they also possessed more assets and outside investments than Western Mining. South and North and Western Mining belonged to the loose mining alliance called the Collins House group, the name of the office building they shared at 360 Collins Street, Melbourne. As they generally worked as friends, the new aluminium partnership was a logical step.

Already the three Collins House companies had formed their own Western Aluminium company. Melbourne was its head office and the directors came from the three Collins House companies, which took up all the shares, none being allocated to the public. That the full name of the company was Western Aluminium No Liability was a clue to its humble scope. No Liability was a category of company peculiar to the speculative end of Australian mining. A Victorian invention of the 1870s it enabled small companies to raise capital on the time-payment principle. Instead of shareholders contributing all the money at the outset, they paid in stages or calls, retaining the right to end all association with the company by simply refusing to pay any further call.

The partners of Western Aluminium first met in Collins House on Tuesday 19 August 1958. For an unknown reason an office of North Broken Hill was selected for the meeting, and no high official of the three companies was present. The first item on the agenda was to set up the new company with the token capital of 1000 shares, each of one pound. The first call or contribution demanded was one shilling on each share and that provided a working capital of less than forty pounds. At a second meeting, held at 4 p.m. on the following Thursday, it was announced that the Western Aluminium company had been formally registered as a No Liability company. It was merely the skeleton of a company; its first members of staff, not yet full-time, were supplied by the Western Mining group, with Fred Morgan acting as secretary.

More decisions were formally made on 16 September when John Webb, representing North Broken Hill, and Gerald Fewster, a solicitor representing Broken Hill South, met as directors of Western Aluminium. At about 12.30 p.m. they formally resolved to increase the nominal capital of the company from 1000 to 5 million shares. The meeting lasted less than five minutes, and in the same room at 12.35 p.m. the shareholders formally held their general meeting. The two shareholders' representatives already in the room were joined by a third, J.H. Waite, representing Western Mining. That meeting, having agreed with the board's resolution to increase the company's capital, was succeeded at 12.40 p.m. by a special meeting of directors. Now was the time to allot the new shares, and Fred Morgan as the company's secretary read out the names of the applicants:

Commonwealth Bank	749 000
Western Mining Corporation	250 750
North Broken Hill	249 750
Broken Hill South	249 750
Total	1 499 250

On each share, nominally of one pound, the shareholders each paid one penny, thus raising a tiny sum for working capital. Those first pence found their way to the office of the company's bankers, the Commonwealth Trading Bank in Melbourne and the E.S. &. A. Bank in Perth and Kalgoorlie. In November 1958 a first call of eleven pence a share was made. Early in the new year another sixpence was collected on each share. As more money was needed, further calls were made. By 31 March 1959 a total of 106 216 pounds had been collected—just over one-third of the money thought to be needed for exploring. This was merely the first in the long series of steps to raise money for exploring the bauxite.

Once everything was in sound legal order, the standby directors gave way to new directors. At the meeting of the board on 27 October 1958, Lindesay Clark took his seat as chairman. Two other directors, Frank Espie and Bill Morgan, represented Western Mining, while Chester Guest and Wilfred Brookes represented North and South. The Commonwealth Bank demanded no seat on the board; it merely sent a representative to sit at each board meeting. Its intention was to help finance the early stage of exploration and then withdraw completely from the company after its loan and interest and commission were repaid. In February 1960 it decided to pay no further calls, though it remained briefly a shareholder.

Western Aluminium N.L., to give it its formal title, was still a shadow. Its shares were not traded on the stock exchange. It possessed the mining leases and prospecting rights recently acquired by Western Mining, but it had only a few employees, some of whom were part-time. These staff came mostly from Western Mining Corporation which agreed to act as general manager and consultant for a period of up to ten years. In the field the company's 'Officer In Charge of Operations' was James N. Langford, a versatile New Zealander who had worked as a mining engineer at Kalgoorlie. The company borrowed money to buy him a house in the Perth suburb of Mount Lawley, and for a time the house was one of its few saleable assets.

By March 1959 the exploring was well under way with the aid of simple equipment. The company owned a one-ton truck, a quarter-ton jeep and a landrover, largely for the use of the small prospecting teams and for the carrying of samples back to the laboratory. The company also owned a caravan where men could camp out in the bush while prospecting. A Holden utility completed the mobile equipment. By the end of the winter the company owned two Gemco drills, which put down shallow holes to test the richness and depth of the bauxite. The drills, however, worked only during the day shift.

So large were the areas to be examined that short cuts had to be sought. A small Perth company, which owned a small plane, took photographs of the most favoured area, embracing some 2195 square kilometres. The photographs facilitated the drawing of contour plans covering the more attractive areas. Not a word of the results was breathed to the press. The tradition of secrecy and silence—strong in the international aluminium industries—was at work in Australia.

The testing laboratory in the big wooden shed at Kalamunda became busier. More and more equipment was added. Next door an office was established. When the first cold days of winter arrived, three single-bar radiators were installed. When summer came, two electric fans were set in place in the hope of bringing a little coolness to the workplace. The purchase of a Remington increased the speed at which letters were typed.

In the head office of Western Mining in distant Melbourne and in the mine offices at Kalgoorlie nobody could yet tell whether any of the bauxite would be mined in the course of the twentieth century. The world seemed to be overflowing with bauxite, following the major discoveries in western Africa and northern Australia. Clark feared that if the big deposit at Weipa—now known as the Comalco mine—was developed quickly, there would perhaps be faint interest in the Darling Range, at least in the short term. The future of his mine seemed to be overshadowed by that of a richer deposit which was itself uncertain.

Clark and his partners went on drilling in order to determine the value of their bauxite. The huge area to be tested—hill after hill, slope after slope—meant that information was gathered only slowly. The bauxite was scattered over some 13 000 square kilometres, and the task was to find the higher grade areas. The results, Clark said privately just before his Christmas break in 1958, were 'quite good'. It was not altogether a resounding verdict. The future of the Darling Range was still in the clouds.

◆ 4 ◆

A Tossing Ship

Western Mining was like a ship carrying a hidden cargo that was far more valuable than the ship itself. The cargo was not insured. The danger was that someone would quickly buy the ship and gain the cargo for almost nothing.

Significantly, a far bigger company, British Aluminium, was about to be seized by a foreign raider. Owning smelters in Norway and Canada, and a partner in the deposit at Weipa, it was important in the world's aluminium industry. If British Aluminium was an easy target, then Western Mining along with its bauxite interests was an easier one. It could be taken over in a week if its individual shareholders were made an offer by a bigger company.

It so happened that in London at the end of 1958, Denny Marris, on behalf of Lazards, was trying to advise British Aluminium how to avert being captured. He decided to advise Lindesay Clark that his company in Australia might also be captured. On 12 December he wrote privately that in his opinion Western Mining Corporation was in danger of being taken over 'lock stock and barrel'. It now held bauxite deposits which potentially were worth far more than its goldmines. A raider successfully buying Western Mining at a little above its market price could win the bauxite for nothing. Both Clark and Marris agreed that the pleasing assay reports now coming from the makeshift laboratory at Kalamunda simply made Western Mining Corporation the more vulnerable.

Clark desperately needed a big overseas partner with experience in the aluminium industry. And yet to invite such a partner was to risk being gobbled up, sooner or later, by the partner. Denny Marris was turned to for confidential advice. In February 1959 in London he was

34

called upon by Clark's deputy, Frank Espie. During the discussions Marris explained that Western Mining could not risk approaching any one of the world's aluminium giants and offering to sell it a controlling interest in the bauxite project. As a first step the giant might buy say 60 per cent of the bauxite project and then resolve to buy the other 40 per cent, leaving Western Mining with nothing.

Marris suggested another solution: Western Mining should seek the protection of a friendly but strong mining company that was essentially a stranger to the aluminium industry. He suggested the old English mining company, Rio Tinto, whose fortune was based on a copper mine in Spain. Rio Tinto was already interested in exploring for base metals in Australia. It might prove to be a friend, providing financial help to Western Mining but not threatening its independence. Rio Tinto could be trusted, said Marris, not to exploit a close relationship as ultimately a way of buying out Western Mining. Marris added that its chiefs, Val Duncan and Mark Turner, worked 'by agreement and not by force'. They would guard Western Mining against a hostile takeover. Their disadvantage was that their company lacked one vital quality—it had no experience in aluminium.

In Melbourne the directors of Western Mining Corporation chewed over the advice from Marris. To Clark's dismay one director—he was not named in Clark's correspondence—said the bauxite deposits should be sold for cash as soon as possible. A cheque for two million pounds, he said, would boost Western Mining.

Clark for his part was appalled at the idea that Western Mining should sell out the bauxite prize, let alone for that small sum. At the very least Clark hoped that Western Mining and its two Broken Hill partners might retain say one-third of an interest in the bauxite project, while selling, at a good price, the majority interest to a company which had the expertise to make and sell aluminium. At the end of the discussion his colleagues—with perhaps one director abstaining—agreed that there was no point in forming a relationship with Rio Tinto, for that company lacked the expertise needed in aluminium. The matter was dropped. The problem remained.

Western Mining did join with Rio Tinto in searching for copper in the Kimberley where Don Campbell had reported on promising outcrops. First found at Tarraji in the early 1900s, the copper lay about 100 kilometres northeast of the port of Derby, in difficult terrain that was isolated by creeks that were flooded in the wet season. The diamond drills revealed that the copper was low grade. It has not been mined to this day.

For the bauxite Clark hoped to find a partner, not a devourer. In March 1959 Denny Marris offered him hope. He confided that the

White Gold

Aluminum Company of America was the giant most likely to be interested. The largest aluminium company in the world, operating from a head office in Pittsburgh, it was, according to Marris, 'by far the most gentlemanly and straightforward'. The Pittsburgh giant could offer another advantage. Having not the least interest in gold, it presumably would, if it became a partner, concentrate on the bauxite in the Darling Range and allow Western Mining to continue as an independent company, mining gold on its own, as in the past. Under that arrangement, Western Mining would remain a goldminer but it might not be permitted to hold any interest in the bauxite.

In Marris's view, the Pittsburgh company would demand control of any aluminium venture it entered. 'I think they would want to buy you out,' wrote Marris in March 1959. Clark did not like the sound of that sentence. To him it was tantamount to a sentence of death. Accordingly he made up his own mind to make no approach, not even a sideways approach, to the Aluminum Company of America. He was determined to be a major partner in the aluminium project, when it eventuated. He had no wish to be totally devoured and left only with cash.

Marris chewed over the question of what else Clark should do. At that moment he saw more obstacles than rewards in front of Clark. He felt certain that the bargaining position would be improved if Clark could find out more about the extent of his bauxite deposits. Were they ordinary or extraordinary? His small syndicate, Western Aluminium NL, had to do far more exploring. A reserve of at least 150 million tonnes of bauxite running at 42 to 45 per cent had to be located by drilling. It must be said that, to this day, it is doubtful whether so much high-grade bauxite exists in the whole Darling Range. The typical ore was poorer than Marris had hoped.

Far from proving the existence of 150 million tonnes, the company at the end of 1959 had proved a mere 0.5 million tonnes. Don Campbell the geologist saw 'broad indications' of another 10 million tonnes and prospects of many more but such a total was still small. The task of testing the ground was formidable. Campbell regretted that if the whole area was to be tested at the present slow rate, another thirty years of work would be needed. The pace of exploration was slow, partly because the area to be explored was vast, and partly because his exploration budget was low.

The attitude of the Western Australian government was also unknown, though it was presumed to be sympathetic. Even if Clark's team eventually succeeded in discovering the required tonnage of ore, they had to persuade the government to give them a permanent lease instead of the present temporary permit. And yet the government might not grant a lease unless there was a promise to build an alumina refinery near Perth to remove much of the barren matter from the bauxite. Naturally the government would try to insist that the bauxite discovery give rise to as many jobs as possible within Western Australia, and most jobs would be created if a local refinery converted the bauxite into alumina. But if the alumina was produced near Perth, which nation would buy it? The world's aluminium industry was run by powerful giants which tried to control every step in the operation. What hope was there for a Western Australian independent?

Marris doubted whether an Australian dwarf would survive on its own. To set up an industry, including mine and refinery and smelter, might require well over 100 million English pounds. The three Australian mining companies that held the bauxite had no chance of raising that large sum.

Everything pointed to Clark having to find a major foreign partner, but that partner would probably insist on taking total control of the bauxite deposit. In England in the late spring of 1959, Clark met Marris and heard about the trap he was in. Marris said that Clark simply had to keep on exploring. Then, when he did approach one of the giants, he would at least be in a better bargaining position. It was probably on this visit to London that Lord Brand, the head of Lazards, gave Clark a gloomy opinion. About a quarter of a century later Clark recorded, with some amusement, the actual advice: 'Young man, you will have to wait a long time before you get this off the ground'.

When Clark returned to Melbourne he got wind that an American giant, the Reynolds Metal Co., could be interested in the Darling Range. Reynolds was definitely interested in Australia. In the previous year it had taken over British Aluminium which had a stake in Weipa, and in September 1959 it was said to be searching for more bauxite in Western Australia and Victoria.

Clark began to think that Reynolds might be eager to tie up Australia and its bauxite supplies. A bid on the stock exchange for Western Mining, which controlled Western Aluminium, would give Reynolds command of the Darling Range as well as its stake in Weipa. Western Mining shares were cheap and therefore vulnerable to takeover. On 4 September, Clark wrote to Marris: 'How then should we proceed?'

The Australians certainly did not 'wish to be exposed to a takeover bid'. Eleven days later Marris replied that in his opinion Reynolds might make a bid. If so, what should Clark do? 'Do nothing' was Marris's advice. Clark should thank his lucky stars and accept the bid. He could take, as the purchase price, shares in Reynolds or the new company. He might also ask for a royalty on every ton of bauxite mined. It wasn't the ideal solution but Clark's chance of retaining control of the bauxite was small.

The days of anxiety slipped by. Reynolds made no bid. Perhaps it decided that in Australia and other parts of the world it had enough bauxite to last for centuries. Moreover, other deposits of bauxite were being developed: the Volta River Scheme in West Africa seemed full of promise.

Just at this time a Pittsburgh man called at the Lazards office in the City of London and happened to mention that 'bauxite was running out of everybody's ears'. Marris must have sounded him out, casually inquiring whether his Aluminum Co. of America was interested in Australia. The answer was 'no'. Why should his giant be interested in the Darling Range when the world was possibly on the eve of a glut of bauxite? Clark heard this gloomy comment direct from Marris. It must have represented rock bottom for his aluminium project.

Another question continued to puzzle Clark. His bauxite was definitely unusual. Could it be treated effectively in a refinery? Bell Bay, in northern Tasmania, operated by the Tasmanian and Commonwealth governments, was Australia's only alumina refinery. Its smelter, using alumina from the refinery next door, supplied about half of the 25 000 tonnes of aluminium ingot consumed in Australia. Bell Bay was not only willing to cooperate with Clark—in the aluminium industry cooperation was abnormal—but also likely to consider buying bauxite from the Darling Range on a regular basis if the tests proved favourable. Bell Bay itself did not own a bauxite mine.

The head of Bell Bay, Noel Brodribb, gave Clark every help. He agreed to buy 7300 tons (7500 tonnes) of bauxite, running at 42 to 43 per cent of recoverable alumina. In December 1959 the *River Murrumbidgee* arrived at Bell Bay from Fremantle and unloaded the rock. For Western Aluminium the cost of shipping the bauxite was expensive, being equal to the cost of six months of drilling at the mine.

The cargo of bauxite aroused more publicity than the company wanted. Western Mining had to inform its shareholders in a half whisper what was happening in the Darling Range. Understandably, Consolidated Zinc, the company which owned half of the big rival Weipa deposit, pricked up its ears and tried to find out as much as possible about the quality of the Western Australian bauxite. Surprisingly, no reporter from the business pages found his way to the Darling Range to see what was there.

Early in January 1960 the bauxite was crushed and fed into the refinery at Bell Bay. No trouble was envisaged by the local metallurgists but, on the other side of the continent, Don Campbell was less confident. When the rock had been being mined in the Darling Range and mechanically shovelled into the tip trucks, he noticed that it carried a lot of vegetable matter or 'detritus'; soil, leaves, tree roots, twigs and clay were all mixed with the bauxite. As the bauxite had lain so close to the surface, the detritus had to be mined. Even at some depth twigs and tree roots could be seen in the deep vertical cracks in the bauxite rock. Campbell wondered whether this organic material should be screened and washed before being shipped but he knew that process would inflate the costs. Anything that added to the costs, in an operation where every penny counted, was to be avoided.

Colin Kleeman, a Western Mining metallurgist, came from Kalgoorlie to observe the process of refining the Darling Range bauxite at Bell Bay. All seemed to go well, and he returned to the mainland with a feeling of confidence. On Friday 12 February 1960, he was in his company's head office in Collins Street, Melbourne, when he received a call from Bill Leane, the alumina superintendent at Bell Bay. Leane conveyed bad news. Two days after the last bauxite was fed into the refinery, he had noticed a darkening in the large volume of circulating liquor which was chemically treating the bauxite. His phrase was 'liquor poisoning'. He believed that the organic material, the detritus, that came with the bauxite was the culprit. Kleeman was astonished. If the organic material was the culprit, why did it wait some thirteen days before poisoning the liquor stream? The liquor should have been dark within 24 hours.

Lindesay Clark (chairman), followed by Jim Langford (mining manager) and Al Kaltwasser (Kwinana project manager), inspecting bauxite deposits in the Darling Range in 1961.

The poison meant that the precipitation of alumina would be retarded. It was still too early to determine what the economic penalty would be. Even the exact cause of the poisoning was in dispute. Western Aluminium thought the cause was the big tree roots mixed with the bauxite; Bell Bay thought it was some humus material within the bauxite as well as deficiencies in the design of their own plant. The CSIRO, invited to investigate, found a resin material in one of the 31 samples analysed, but the Australian Mineral Development Laboratories in Adelaide could find no such resin. The problem of the detritus would persist.

Clark and his staff found the poison an acute embarrassment. Just when they were trying for the first time to sell their bauxite—and Bell Bay was a potential customer—the bauxite was found to be impure. Moreover negotiations with overseas buyers were beginning. What would they conclude if, on visiting Bell Bay to inspect the first alumina produced from the Darling Range, they heard of the poisoned liquor and all it implied? An explanation—not fully convincing—was prepared should the overseas buyers ask awkward questions. The official answer was that the tests were incomplete.

The more likely buyers of the Western Australian bauxite were the big Japanese companies. Japan, a dynamic producer of aluminium, mined no bauxite and therefore had to import increasing quantities from east Asia. Back in 1954 the United States and Canada produced two-thirds of the world's aluminium, and Japan ranked only eighth; but now Japan was surpassing Italy and Norway to become sixth in the world. Japan continued to climb the ladder. Between 1954 and 1965 Japan's annual production of aluminium was multiplied by four. Here was an attractive market for Australian bauxite—if only Clark and his syndicate could enter it.

Three Japanese aluminium companies, which bought bauxite mainly from the Malay peninsula, sensed that Australia was possibly a cheaper source. In 1960 the Mitsui Co., which had a branch office in Melbourne, asked to inspect samples of Western Australian bauxite. For some reason Clark was not willing to release samples at this stage, perhaps because of the doubts raised by the treatment tests at Bell Bay. A little later Hamilton Sleigh, an Australian shipowner who was a close friend of the Western Mining director Wilfred Brookes, mentioned that Mitsubishi Chemical Industries was interested in starting a fourth aluminium refinery and smelter in Japan. It was even possible that Mitsubishi would provide finance for plant and equipment in Western Australia in return for the first call on bauxite for its smelters in Japan. The Japanese market was a ray of light. Here was an opportunity for Clark to develop his mine by slow stages, and then perhaps build a refinery in Western

Australia, without becoming dependent on the existing giants of the international aluminium industry.

Bill Morgan, general manager of Western Mining, flew to Japan in February 1960. His mission was to try to sell bauxite but he was also interested in selling iron ore, large quantities of which were being found in Western Australia. A fine mining engineer, he was a patient and courteous negotiator, and he also had a talent for learning foreign languages. He spoke German and was even willing to begin learning Japanese. At this time few Australians spoke Japanese and no secondary schools taught it; few Australian businessmen saw any purpose in visiting Japan. Morgan soon acquired a knowledge of the delicacies of doing business in Japan though he was in the dark on several occasions, not knowing exactly what Japanese ritual required. He later confided to Clark that the Asiatic style of bargaining was 'like a cross between trout fishing and chess'. At the same time he sang the virtues of sumo wrestling even to Australian women thinking of visiting Japan with their husbands.

Morgan learned the rules for the giving of presents and the exchange of courtesies during these first visits to Japan. When eventually Mr Takagachi, chairman of Mitsubishi Chemical Industries, accepted an invitation to visit Melbourne, a day of golf was specially staged in his honour at what he called in his letter of thanks 'your world-wide known Royal Melbourne Golf Club'. When Takagachi in return posted to Lindesay Clark the first volume of the lavish book Art Treasures of Japan, Clark laid on his thanks with a silver trowel, saying 'you would not have found another present which would give me more pleasure'. When Clark later made his first tour of Japan, he carried, on Morgan's advice, a list of dos and don'ts as well as presents ranging from golden kangaroo medallions, bought at Gaunt's the jewellers for fifteen pounds apiece, all the way down to opal tiepins, wool and mohair scarves and earthenware ashtrays decorated with Aboriginal motifs.

Staying at the Imperial Hotel in Tokyo, Morgan met the potential buyers. Nippon Light Metals, he reported, might buy 300 000 tonnes of bauxite each year, enough to provide a useful profit of say 150 000 pounds a year. This was the best news Clark had heard for more than a year. In the end the Mitsubishi Chemical Industries proved the most eager to finalise the drawn-out discussions with Morgan. It even proposed to build bulk ore ships each of which would load 20 000 to 30 000 tonnes of bauxite at Fremantle. To Morgan's surprise, Fremantle was classed by the Japanese as a capacious port compared to some of the bauxite ports in tropical Asia. With specially designed ships the cost of carting bauxite to Japan might be cheaper from Fremantle than from the closer Indonesian and Malay ports. Mitsubishi Chemical Industries finally resolved to test the Western Australian bauxite on a large scale. The inaugural shipment, made in July 1960 from Fremantle, was 9891 tons (10 089 tonnes) of bauxite, half of which came from Jarrahdale and half from Dwellingup.

This shipment was crucial for the Australian company. If the bauxite proved to be of sound quality and the price was right, the Australians could remain independent. Likely profits from the sale of bauxite would help finance the next stage—the building of a refinery near Perth—or persuade other financiers to lend money. At this stage Morgan in his optimism thought that shipments to Japan would soon be on what, in his view, was a large scale, running at 500 000 tonnes a year.

The first bauxite shipped to Japan was astonishingly rich, by today's standards. That mined at Dwellingup carried 46 per cent of available alumina, with a minimum of 44 per cent. That mined at Jarrahdale was expected to average 47.5 per cent. The contract set out bonuses to be paid if the bauxite was slightly richer than predicted and penalties to be extracted if the bauxite was rather poorer than predicted. It was all measured in shillings a long ton, with the Australians to receive 46 shillings and 6 pence—less than five Australian dollars—if the bauxite was true to the specifications.

Unlike the material that is mined today, the first loads of bauxite were rich. Where, observers now ask, did they find such material? Moreover it was surprisingly low in silica; the bauxite from Dwellingup reportedly contained a mere 1.5 per cent of silica. Presumably the first bauxite came from very rich but untypical patches near the surface.

Morgan soon sensed that, since Japan had no new hydro-electric schemes and no other source of cheap power, it was not suited for the aluminium industry. He realised that eventually his own company might sell the treated alumina instead of the raw bauxite to Japan. Marris, however, was not a supporter of such reliance on Japan. In his eyes the alternative to reliance on Japan was to form an alliance with an American company, preferably the Aluminum Company of America, which was the largest in the world.

The Western Australian government supported Clark's idea of Australian independence, so long as most of the activity took place in its own territory. It hoped that the bauxite would lead to the creation of numerous new jobs near Perth. At the very least there should be a Perth refinery to upgrade the ore. If possible there should later be a Perth smelter to produce pure aluminium. And even more, there should be local fabricating plants to turn the ingots into wire, sheet and other products. Sales of untreated bauxite to Japan were welcome but they must be only part of the story.

To envisage a local and integrated aluminium empire close to Perth was to assume that somehow or other vast volumes of cheap electricity could be generated nearby. That in turn required an efficient mine producing coal of quality. Western Mining set out to search for such a mine. The coal town of Collie offered hope, for it lay at the southern end of the Darling Range, not far from the most southerly bauxite. Not many regions in the world had coal and bauxite so close together. The question was whether the coal was of sufficient tonnage and quality to provide cheap power. The first black coal in the region had been found, reportedly by a shepherd, on the edge of a water pool in the dryish bed of the Collie River in 1883. When, fifteen years later, the railway reached Collie, coalmining began with some vigour. The coal easily captured part of the Western Australian market, including the railways, because the cost of importing coal by sea from eastern Australia was high. Collie coal, however, was not of high quality. Admittedly it was low in ash and sulphur, but it was high in moisture and it decomposed rather quickly when exposed to the atmosphere. In an average year in the 1950s less than 1 million tonnes was being mined, and over 1000 men were employed.

Western Aluminium was tempted to use Collie coal to generate electricity. In December 1958 there was a possibility of buying the Griffin Company's mine—one of the three main mines at Collie—but no deal was made. Perhaps there was suitable coal in other parts of the Collie district. The Wilga basin, south of Collie, was explored but the coal was deep and the seams were not thick. In December 1959 a 'suspected coal basin' was investigated northeast of Collie. Prospects of coal at Lake Muir and Manjimup were also examined by the company. Coal was found here and there, but would it produce cheap electricity?

At first Clark had no thought of setting up a smelter in any other state than Western Australia. The advantages of Victoria slowly became visible. Victoria was more than 3000 kilometres by sea from Perth, but it could provide cheap and reliable power. Victoria had huge deposits of brown coal, admittedly low in heat and high in moisture, but they were close to the surface and were mined cheaply in big open cuts and converted to electricity in huge power stations, mainly using techniques developed on the brown coalfields of Germany. There was another advantage in building an aluminium smelter in Victoria—if the time ever came when a smelter would be economic and affordable. The molten aluminium, fresh from the smelter, could be fabricated for local Victorian customers, who were far more numerous than Western Australian ones.

The attraction of Victoria was increased by the news that it had a large deposit of brown coal that might be for sale. While the Victorian government, and its reputable State Electricity Commission, owned all the brown coal in eastern Victoria, one coalfield in western Victoria lay outside its leases. It was one of Clark's colleagues on the board, Sir

Wilfred Brookes, who first realised that the Victorian brown coal might be married to the Western Australian bauxite. Brookes, like Clark, was a director of two of the three mining companies which controlled Western Aluminium. A grandson of Alfred Deakin, who was three times prime minister of Australia, Brookes was an early aviator. He recalls that the rotary engine of his early Avro bi-plane used a vegetable oil as a lubricant: 'you felt you were sniffing castor oil when flying.' During the first perilous months of the war against Japan, Brookes was commanding officer of a pilot wing in Rabaul in the territory of New Guinea. Later he became chairman of the Associated Pulp and Paper Mills Limited, which operated a big paper mill at Burnie in Tasmania. The company also owned a smaller paper factory at Ballarat, where it burned brown coal delivered in yellow Ford Thames trucks from a coalmine at Anglesea, on the coast. Brookes knew the Roche brothers who owned the coalmine, and that was to prove an important link.

The Roche brothers had worked hard to develop the only brown coal deposits that competed with the Victorian government's massive deposits. Beginning at Wensleydale, near Winchelsea, they moved their equipment and portable buildings across the bush to Anglesea where they opened another open cut for brown coal. Their main market was the small powerhouse at North Geelong to which they trucked the coal. They hoped ultimately to attract coal-using industries to Anglesea: perhaps a petrochemical plant or a chlorine plant using Geelong salt and Anglesea coal. Meanwhile a German company was also interested in using Anglesea coal as an ingredient for making carbide: four tonnes of coal were needed to produce every five tonnes of carbide. The main virtue of Anglesea coal was that it had twice the calorific value of the Gippsland coal though it was not to be compared to good black coal. Anglesea was also close to a deep sea port.

Jim and Victor Roche brought their coalmine to the attention of Wilfred Brookes in the second half of 1959. They approached him indirectly, also sending him a clipping from the Melbourne *Sun News Pictorial* which described their coal deposits. As a result Brookes and Lindesay Clark motored to Anglesea and inspected the brown coal, which they guessed was more promising than the black coal so far inspected in Western Australia. Brookes then wrote to Jim Roche at Dynon Road, South Kensington, saying that he liked the coal's 'great power and steam generating potential'. Everything was falling into place.

Bill Morgan was also friendly with Jim Roche—in letters he is sometimes referred to as 'your cobber Roche'. Morgan was also invited to visit Anglesea and see the coal for himself. Estimating the costs of generating power from Anglesea coal, he realised that, if worked on a certain scale, it would provide cheaper electricity than Sydney's existing black-coal powerhouses. There was one hitch: the cheap electricity in Victoria might not be enough to compensate for the high price of shipping the alumina to Victoria. The cost of coastal shipping was high, and when Marris heard of the possible plan to ship alumina from Western Australia to Victoria he blinked a little.

At first the Roche brothers wished to sell coal, but not their coalmine. They saw the mine as a wonderful asset. Whereas the State Electricity Commission controlled the huge deposits of brown coal in the Latrobe valley to the east of Melbourne, the Roche family held the only payable deposit close to Geelong and Melbourne. Moreover, Willis Connolly, the head of the State Electricity Commission, was not a monopolist. He did not object when the Roches said they were thinking of building a large power station at Anglesea. He said he was even willing to buy their surplus electricity.

Western Aluminium became more attracted to Anglesea coal. Bill Morgan had talks with Jim Roche and learned much about the coal. He did not yet indicate that his company was firmly interested. On 4 May 1960 Morgan wrote to Clark, who was visiting gold mines in Kalgoorlie, outlining a tentative plan. The main partners in Western Aluminium would themselves buy the brown coal mine, expand it, spend 15 million pounds on building a 200 megawatt powerhouse at the mine, and initially sell the power to industrial companies and the State Electricity Commission. When the time came to erect an aluminium smelter, and perhaps even a refinery, near Geelong, most of the power would then be used for making aluminium.

While the Roche brothers did not want to sell they were experiencing the same problems as Western Aluminium. Operating only a family firm, they needed more capital than they could raise. In May 1960, Morgan and Clark heard privately that Roche Bros was financially extended and that their bank wished to reduce the overdraft. Western Mining, it was suggested, should put in 200 000 pounds to clear the overdraft and repay creditors, and that sum would give it control of the mine. It was not a high price for a potentially valuable property. Apparently 30 million tonnes of coal was already proved to exist but Western Mining had to be certain of 200 million tonnes to justify the high cost of building a large powerhouse near the mine.

An option to buy the mine was arranged. Western Mining could not afford the option fee, so Clark went to Broken Hill South, of which he was chairman, and persuaded that company to pay the fee. If in the end the aluminium venture did not go ahead, the coalmine could probably be sold for a similar price to the State Electricity Commission of Victoria. Don Campbell travelled from Kalgoorlie to offer an answer to the crucial question: how much mineable brown coal really lay beneath the windswept scrub at Anglesea? On the basis of the drilling that had been done, by no means systematically, by the Department of Mines, he was able to make estimates of the coal available. By the end of the year he calculated that the coal reserves could be close to 200 million tonnes: many times as much as has been mined, in total, at the time of writing (1996). The ash content of the coal was pleasingly low. Moreover, no huge tonnage of overburden had to be removed to give access to the coal below.

A scheme was falling into place. Whether it would succeed, nobody knew with certainty. It was still just a scheme, a roll of rough plans. The company had found big deposits of bauxite, but whether they were big enough and of sufficient grade was not clear. The bauxite was amenable to treatment but the liquor poison remained a worry. There was also a prospect, not yet finalised, of shipping this bauxite or alumina to Japan and thereby earning a major supplementary income. In the long term, if a big sum could be borrowed, the brown coal could supply electricity to a new aluminium smelter built not far away. The overall plan remained a secret. To announce it would increase the risk of a foreign aluminium company taking over Western Mining, which controlled the new venture.

What Clark, Morgan, Campbell and others had achieved was far short of the plans they had in mind. The tiny scale of their venture can

An early pit at the Anglesea coal mine in 1961.

be seen in the report of Western Aluminium No Liability for the year ending 31 March 1961. In the last three years the company had raised a mere 300 000 pounds, in successive calls of sixpence a share. In the last twelve months the company had spent 119 256 pounds of this sum in the exploring and developing of the property. The laboratory in the former cold-storage shed at Kalamunda had been busy, testing a total of 21 000 samples for alumina. In the East Wilga basin, near Collie, a deep hole had been drilled in search of coal. On Anglesea virtually nothing had been spent so far, according to the report. Everything had been done on the smell of an oil rag. The auditors did their work for 147 pounds and the directors did their work for nothing.

5

The First Hurdle

Charles Martin Hall was one of those young Americans who were forever experimenting in their spare time, The son of a Congregational missionary, and himself an opponent of tobacco and strong drink, he was single-minded at an early age. After studying chemistry at Oberlin College in his own Ohio hometown of Oberlin, he began to experiment in the backyard woodshed which served as his laboratory. In 1886 he found a new way of turning bauxite, which was incredibly common, into aluminium, a metal which was incredibly rare. His electrolytic method, still used in essence, soon became the basis of a patent which for seventeen years protected his venture from serious competition within the United States. By coincidence a young Frenchman, Paul Héroult, invented a similar process almost at the same time, thus giving France an early start in the same industry.

Hall found capital to develop his process in Pittsburgh, which was then about the size of Melbourne and the great iron and steel city of the United States. Steel executives provided much of the money for his Pittsburgh Reduction Co. which was formed in 1888, and the banking house of T. Mellon & Sons provided more. Work began slowly: the economics of the new industry had to be worked out. Much of the first bauxite and alumina was bought from others. Eventually the company mined its own bauxite in Arkansas, sent it on its own railway and river barges to East St Louis where a large refinery was opened in 1902. As electricity generated by coal was too dear, hydro-electricity was vital for the smelting process, and the company set up its aluminium smelter by Niagara Falls. A plant to fabricate the aluminium into other products was set up at New Kensington in Pennsylvania. It was thus a scattered industry stretching all the way from Arkansas to the Canadian border.

49

The First Hurdle

Not many aluminium products were manufactured in the 1880s because aluminium was too dear. The new invention by the young American and Frenchman eventually made aluminium far cheaper. In 1854 one pound weight of aluminium had cost $US 550. When the little Pittsburgh Reduction Co. began work a pound of aluminium cost

Aluminium Price History

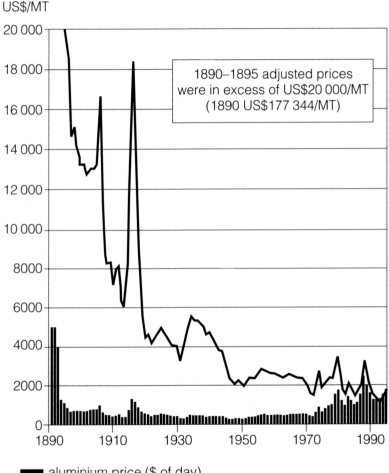

Aluminium was once an expensive metal but following the discovery of the Hall–Heroult smelting process the price fell dramatically and the usage of aluminium increased from a few tonnes a year to over 20 million tonnes today.

$US 5, and by the end of the century it was a mere 30 cents. While much dearer than copper and lead and tin, aluminium was beginning to multiply in usefulness. It was light and yet strong. And so Hall's company, making and selling this wonder metal, became a rising giant in the American mining industry.

In 1907 the Pittsburgh company changed its name, adopting the grander and more specific name of the Aluminum Co. of America. The name of the company, it must be emphasised, was not *Aluminium*. It is strange that such a major metal, known throughout the world, should retain a different spelling and different pronunciation in North America. Aluminum, however, was the original name given to the metal by the English scientist Humphry Davy in 1807.

The Aluminum Co. of America, known as Alcoa in modern times, was shaped and chiselled by legal actions and threats of legal actions. Under the American anti-trust laws it was seen as all-pervading and all-powerful. The United States dominated the world aluminium industry, and that industry in America was dominated by The Aluminum Co. of America. Of all the major American industries this was closest to being a monopoly. Its business activities had been first investigated by the US Justice Department in 1911. During the First World War it was prevented, by law, from buying control of its sole competitor in the business of sheet rolling, the Cleveland Metals Co.

The Pittsburgh company was a target of anti-trust investigators for another reason. It was closely identified with the Mellon family of Pittsburgh; and Andrew Mellon was one of the most powerful men in the United States when he was Secretary to the Treasury during the Republican presidency of Herbert Hoover. Mellon was said by the Left to run America: it was an easy step to say he ran the Aluminum Co. of America, which in fact he didn't.

In the 1920s and 1930s the company was the centre of a long anti-trust case. The evidence collected ran to 58 000 pages. It was therefore almost an anticlimax when in March 1942 the US District Court found the company not guilty on each of more than 130 charges that had been investigated at length. The federal government appealed. It was alleged that the company had violated the Sherman Act; and in March 1945 Judge Learned Hand, celebrated for his legal insights as much as for his apt first name, delivered what became one of the more influential judgments in American commercial law. The company, he decreed, was a monopoly. To become or remain a monopoly even by legal means and by sound business methods, he added, was no defence.

Judge Learned Hand found no evidence that the company violated the anti-trust laws and only once did the evidence possibly indicate that the company had used its monopoly unfairly—in the 1920s when its aggressive pricing of aluminium sheet products was possibly unfair. Over-ruling the legal interpretation applied since 1911, he decreed that there was no such thing as a good monopoly. He said the monopoly should be broken up.

At this juncture the United States government itself had an opportunity to break the monopoly. It so happened that the Aluminum Co. of America had built and operated many wartime plants for the government, including eight smelters. By 1944 just over 52 per cent of the American production of aluminium ingots was produced by the company in government-owned plants, and another 44 per cent in the company's own plants. The remaining 4 per cent was produced by Reynolds Metals in new smelters.

Perhaps the government, once the war was over, could sell its plants to other firms in order to fracture the Pittsburgh company's monopoly. At the end of the war it did just that. Reynolds was permitted to buy three smelters and three fabricating plants at bargain prices. Henry Kaiser, who had become wealthy by building ships and making steel, was allowed to buy other plants. On the other hand the Aluminum Co. of America was permitted to buy only a fraction of the plants offered at the bargain sale. Its dominance was drastically reduced, and many of its staff went to work in Reynolds and Kaiser plants. The Aluminum Co. was still the leader but its margin was narrower.

In 1950 another blow came from the courts. The big shareholders in the Aluminum Co. of America were told that they could not hold shares both in their own company and in the big Canadian company known as Alcan. They were allowed ten years in which to sell either their American or their Canadian aluminium interests. 'It was the first time in history,' wrote Professor George David Smith of New York University, 'that American investors were ordered to relinquish their control of a foreign company.'

The leaders of the company in Pittsburgh were slightly nervous of the future. While producing more ingots for an expanding market, their dominance was weakening. By 1958 their share of America's total output of ingots was down to 38 per cent, compared with Reynolds' 27 and Kaiser's 24 and the 11 per cent held by three small but jostling new-comers. Moreover, many of the Pittsburgh company's plants had been built before the war and were therefore less efficient. The modern wartime plants largely belonged to the competitors.

While the incentive to remain big was diminished by an official edict that bigness could be illegal, there were signs in the late 1950s that the Aluminum Co. of America was reviving. It retained at least one big advantage. Unlike its rivals, it was not shouldering heavy debts. It was also stronger in research and innovation because it employed about three times as many technical staff as its combined rivals. It was skilled, too, in finding new uses for aluminium. It was therefore in a better position to expand—if it could find places where it could legally expand.

To expand overseas was a possibility, so long as the company did not again become so dominant as to excite the lawyers entrusted with enforcing the American anti-monopoly laws. Deprived of its main overseas offshoot in Canada, it had been wary of overseas adventures for some years. Some directors, especially Frank Magee and I.W. 'Chief' Wilson, favoured overseas expansion and some eschewed it. A chance to enter west Africa was lost through this internal rift in the company. The expansionists, however, had minor victories. In the late 1950s they persuaded the company to investigate bauxite deposits in Latin America, including Panama and Costa Rica.

The company's main overseas operation was in nearby Suriname—the Dutch Guiana—where it mined a valuable deposit of bauxite used by several refineries in the United States. In 1957, with new confidence, the company began to turn Suriname into a major venture with its own smelter and hydro-electric plant. A year later it took a one-third interest in the aluminium-fabricating plant of the Furukawa Electric Company in Japan. This venture had been initiated by the American firm, Lockheed, which assembled aircraft in Japan but was not satisfied with the hard-alloy sheet initially supplied by Furukawa.

In 1958 Pittsburgh ventured into riskier territory. Across the Atlantic it was persuaded by Lord Portal, chairman of British Aluminium, to take a minor interest in his company, which was weak in money but strong in assets in Britain, Norway and Canada. The Aluminum Co. of America did not retain its minor shareholding in British Aluminium for many months. Its American rival, Reynolds, had its eyes on British Aluminium. Towards the end of 1958 the takeover battle developed, and British Aluminium decided that, if it was to be controlled from abroad, it preferred to be controlled by Pittsburgh rather than by Reynolds. Eventually, Reynolds won a dashing victory over its slow-moving, cautious rival from Pittsburgh. Reynolds now held half of the shares in British Aluminium. Curiously, if Pittsburgh had won the battle, it would have gained a big interest in the major Weipa deposit. With such an attractive deposit in its control, Pittsburgh would probably have shown no interest whatsoever in the rival bauxite deposit which Clark was trying to promote at the opposite corner of the continent. At that time Weipa was viewed as superior to the Darling Range. Furthermore, in those early days for a foreign company to gain access to one major deposit in Australia seemed enough. In any case, Pittsburgh's interest in Australia was lukewarm.

The First Hurdle

Marris now aroused Pittsburgh to the possibilities of Australian bauxite. Having, as an adviser, indirectly supported Pittsburgh during the thwarted takeover battle with Reynolds, he was, some observers said later, eager to offer compensation by giving it first offer of the Darling Range bauxite. That story was only part, if any, of the truth. Marris was also an adviser to Clark, who urgently needed a big aluminium company as partner.

Clark felt a sense of urgency because the world now had a glut of aluminium. Moreover, the world's known reserves were increasing at an almost astronomical rate. With so much bauxite being found, Clark was worried. What if west Africa should really interest the big international metal companies, promising them cheap bauxite for shipment to the east coast of America and to Europe? Clark later recalled that west Africa became 'the over-riding factor in my mind'. Its bauxite was perhaps of higher grade, its labour and construction costs were low and its closeness to the markets in the northern hemisphere meant that its shipping costs would be low. At that time Pittsburgh was certainly interested in west African bauxite.

It was during this short period of over-supply early in 1960 that John Mitchell, who was in charge of the international activities of the Aluminum Co. of America, visited Melbourne. Interested in promoting the sales of aluminium in Australia, he went for discussions to the head office of the Imperial Chemical Industries of Australia and New Zealand. The big shareholder in this company was Imperial Chemical Industries in England, which had long been in non-ferrous metals in Birmingham, and it was in the process of selling its interest in its British fabricating plants to the Aluminum Co. of America. Indeed Denny Marris had fathered this sale, and so it is possible that he suggested that Mitchell, while visiting Melbourne, should also informally meet Clark and those who, with him, now controlled the Darling Range bauxite. Mitchell for his part had his own reasons for finding out as much as possible about the emerging aluminium industry in Australia.

On a high floor of the ICI House, an office in the new glasshouse style, a small luncheon was arranged by the heads, Ken Begg and Archie Glenn, for 'Doc' Mitchell. There he met Lindesay Clark and Wilfred Brookes, directors of Western Mining and also Western Aluminium. They discussed bauxite, and Clark spoke a little about the deposits and his plans for a refinery and smelter in Australia. Mitchell asked whether, after producing alumina, they would be permitted by the Australian government to sell part of it to Japan. Clark, who was on good terms with R.G. Menzies, the prime minister, was confident that alumina could be exported to Japanese smelters. That assurance did much to arouse Mitchell's interest. He realised that a complete stranger might be about to enter the world's alumina industry. Moreover if this stranger sold alumina to the expanding Japanese or other overseas markets it would be competing indirectly with his company.

The luncheon with Mitchell proved to be a landmark, being the first time a head of the Pittsburgh company had met the heads of the Melbourne company. Largely as a result of this meeting, the Aluminum Co. of America decided that an Australian who was knowledgeable about the bauxite in Western Australia should be invited to visit Pittsburgh.

Don Campbell was the first member of the Australian syndicate to visit Pittsburgh. It was the practice for Western Mining to send senior employees to see the world, and Don Campbell and his wife Ruth set out from Australia in a ship bound for Vancouver. After inspecting the Sullivan lead-zinc mine in British Columbia he was staying in Spokane, Oregon, when he received a Melbourne cable advising him to make a detour to Pittsburgh while going across North America.

The Campbells flew first to Salt Lake City in an 'all-time record heat wave' and after inspecting more mines went south to Pittsburgh, arriving late on Saturday 13 August 1960. Expecting a grimy steel city he found it 'a pleasant surprise'. He was disappointed, however, with the set of plans which his own company had mailed in advance. They were of many shapes, and 'scrabbled together with little thought' of how they might be used in an effective presentation to the potential bidders for a share in the mine.

At the weekend Campbell attended informal meetings with the company heads, and it was arranged that he would meet them again on Monday. The head office of the company was the aluminium showplace of the world, a lean skyscraper erected in 1952 and using—everywhere from the elevators to the blinds—more aluminium than any previous tall building. The head office, despite its glamour, was deficient in meeting rooms. To Campbell's dismay the only suitable conference room had been booked by a lesser group. In a smaller room allocated for his meeting he had to do his best to display his inadequate plans on a table that was not large enough. Years later he recalled how the 'plans flopped all over the place' and could hardly be seen by the circle of people from a distance of more than one metre.

If the Americans already knew a lot about the Australian project they gave little indication of it. Much that Campbell told his listeners must have pleased them, but being excellent businessmen they did not show too eagerly what they were thinking. Campbell, as a geologist, was particularly alert to the reactions of the two geologists in the gathering of senior staff. He was pleased to see that Lawrence Litchfield Jr, the president of the company, 'caught on quickly'. While McBride, more junior, said little, he too saw the potential.

Occasionally they commented on the information Campbell gave them. They wished that the bauxite in the Darling Range was not in such a 'scatter of deposits' but the low grade did not worry them. A description of the brown coal at Anglesea seemed to win their instant approval, but the report compiled from the American side showed that they were not quite so enthusiastic in private, calling the quality of the brown coal 'rather low'. They wished that the coal lay in Western Australia rather than Victoria, which was too far away. As for Bell Bay's difficulty when treating the consignment of Western Australian bauxite that was mixed with organic matter, they seemed just a 'little concerned'.

For the Aluminum Co. of America a new project not only had to be sound but also had to be superior to other sound projects. The surviving evidence suggests that Pittsburgh was not yet convinced about the Darling Range. In an internal Alcoa document of 15 August appears the following, containing in effect a large if: 'Should Alcoa become interested . . .'

In Australia, Lindesay Clark was anxiously awaiting the result of Campbell's visit. Twice he had written letters to Pittsburgh, before Campbell arrived, to urge him to set down his 'impressions' of the conferences as soon as possible. On the Tuesday afternoon at about 4 p.m., Campbell sat down to write to Clark. Filling seven sheets of ordinary quarto paper with observations, he came to his optimistic conclusion: 'I feel that we are past the first hurdle in that their interest is keenly aroused'. After folding the letter tightly so that it could be squeezed into a small envelope, he decided also to send a cable to Melbourne. It read simply: DISCUSSIONS VERY SATISFACTORY STOP PROJECT APPEALS TO OUR FRIENDS

Clark was delighted to hear the news. But the game was far from over. Clark promptly wrote to Campbell, who had left Pittsburgh and was resuming his travels to his chosen mining fields, urging him not to tell anyone that he had visited Pittsburgh on the company's business. Campbell and his wife continued their slow roundabout trip through Canada, England, Southern Rhodesia and Johannesburg. Naturally, gold geology was even more exciting to him than bauxite, for the deep hole to the south of Kalgoorlie was being drilled.

Campbell's visit to Pittsburgh was only the beginning. The American company preferred the opinion of one of its own experts. Curiously the Australians were willing to pay the fee of 5000 dollars and the travelling and living expenses of the expert and his wife, if she wished to visit Australia too. Presumably they paid because they wished to have full use of the report if by chance it led to no favourable response from Pittsburgh.

White Gold

Ralph Derr, the expert, was one of the old guard from Pittsburgh. While never one of its top leaders, he was respected for his soundness and shrewdness. Aged 65, he had just retired, and was eager to take on new assignments. Born at Milton, Pennsylvania, a graduate in chemical engineering from Bucknell University, he had worked from 1917 to 1926 with the General Chemical Company in New York State, specialising in insecticides during his last two years. With the Aluminum Co. of America he spent twelve years in research before moving to chemical sales, bauxite mining and alumina refining, where he was chief chemical engineer of the company's refining division just before he retired. Derr had actually been contacted by Lindesay Clark before Don Campbell reached Pittsburgh. 'It seems to me,' wrote Clark, 'we have the necessary raw material for an aluminium industry. We require advice . . .' Derr's task was to estimate the cost of establishing and running an industry in Australia.

Derr and his wife, Sarah, arrived in Australia before Campbell returned. Staying in hotels in Melbourne and Perth for nearly three months, they learned much about Australia and its economic conditions while Derr himself investigated every detail of the aluminium project. People trying to read his mind found him friendly but not loquacious: he was content with few words. He did not give away many clues to his thinking but his final report was optimistic. Clark and his fellow directors must have been jubilant when they read his simple verdict: 'an attractive commercial venture'. He envisaged a refinery in Western Australia, a smelter in Victoria with an initial capacity of 40 000 tonnes of aluminium ingots a year, and a low rate of profit followed by a high return of 15 per cent a year in the 1970s.

The bauxite deposits, the basis of the whole enterprise, impressed Derr. The typical ore in the bottom half of the deposits had been considered unpayable and not worth drilling. Derr, however, thought otherwise. His intimate knowledge of the refining process made him see that bauxite carrying only 28 to 30 per cent of available alumina, while worth nothing in a typical mine, was actually valuable in the Darling Range. The so-called poor bauxite was 'really high grade ore diluted with quartz'. Being inert, the quartz could be cheaply eliminated in the refinery. Derr was able, with Campbell, to recalculate all the ore reserves so far delineated. His conclusion was that massive reserves of payable bauxite were available for mining.

In the Pittsburgh discussions there were doubts whether enough ore existed to justify a huge investment. Derr removed those doubts. In August, on the basis of the evidence Campbell produced, about 12 million tonnes of payable bauxite had been proved. Four months later there were 93 million tonnes by one definition and 122 million tonnes by another. Campbell now estimated that in the stretch of range between

The First Hurdle

Perth and a point about twenty kilometres south of the timber-milling town of Dwellingup, 'it is easy to see a potential of 300 to 500 million tons'. Derr was inclined to agree with this cheerful picture.

Nearly all of the doubts in Derr's mind were resolved. On a slip of paper Derr privately put down a few of his thoughts about the refinery and smelter that were likely to be based on Comalco's rich Weipa bauxite deposit in north Queensland. The paper in his handwriting survives. It ponders that crucial question: will Clark's venture be able to outsell Comalco in the Australian market for aluminium? He was optimistic, perhaps unduly so. He was satisfied that Weipa—the deposit Reynolds had bought into by way of British Aluminium—was in the weaker position. Possibly relying on the American grapevine, he argued that Reynolds was wise in recently changing its mind and walking out of the Weipa project and that the new partner, Kaiser, would eventually walk out. Derr thought that for Comalco to enlist Kaiser, a relative newcomer to aluminium, was 'a desperation effort'.

Ultimately both Comalco and Alcoa would depend far more on the world markets for alumina and aluminium than on the small Australian market, but it was almost impossible to predict this in the Australian summer of 1960–61. For the Australian leaders of Western Aluminium and presumably of Comalco, Australia was a crucial market in which perhaps there could only be one winner.

On 26 January 1961, Australia Day, Derr was sitting in Collins House, Melbourne, ready to leave next day for Manila, Hong Kong and Tokyo. In a short note, signed 'Ralph', he informed John Mitchell in Pittsburgh that probably the total tonnage of the bauxite 'greatly exceeds anything known except Africa and Surinam'. It would be valuable for producing aluminium in Australia and as a source of alumina for Washington state where the Aluminum Co. of America owned a big smelter. Mitchell, knowing how cautious Derr was, must have been heartened to read these words: 'Giving you my own opinion, for what little it is worth, I believe this whole proposition is very good'.

On the strength of Derr's optimism it now seemed likely that the Aluminum Co. of America would bid for a share of the Australian project. The question was, when? Clark, however, remained cautious: he had too often been thwarted in the past to feel that victory was clearly in sight. As a safeguard, his staff continued to work hard to enlist Japan as a buyer of bauxite or alumina. If the American deal fell through, Japan would probably underwrite a humbler venture.

At the start of 1961, Bill Morgan, accompanied by the company's secretary, Fred Morgan, returned to Japan for a series of conferences, afternoon after afternoon. They learned with pleasure that the Mitsubishi Chemical Co. was now interested in buying alumina rather than bauxite.

Japan's interest was quickened by Morgan's news, passed on in confidence, that his Australian company would build the alumina refinery in association with a prominent American company, though Morgan refused to release the name of the American company. When the Japanese negotiators asked whether the new Western Australian refinery would be punctual in shipping the alumina, Bill Morgan suggested that the unnamed American partner would, if necessary, ship its own alumina to Japan in order to meet any shortfall. On 12 January 1961 in the Imperial Hotel, Morgan wrote to Clark in light green ink, expressing optimism that a big Japanese order for alumina was likely.

In these prolonged negotiations the sunshine was often followed by cloud. A fortnight later Morgan heard that another Australian deputation was about to visit Tokyo in the hope of selling bauxite from the rival deposit at Weipa in Queensland. What if the Weipa bauxite was deemed superior to that of the Darling Range? The three potential Japanese buyers might be deterred from actually signing the contract because the Darling Range bauxite held large amounts of 'reactive silica'.

Pittsburgh, hearing news or rumours of Morgan's negotiations with Japan, felt the need to make its own decision, and make it quickly. One fear was that the Japanese might indirectly acquire an interest in the proposed Australian alumina refinery. The main Japanese producers of aluminium might turn from Indonesia and Malaya to Western Australia for their raw materials and, with the aid of cheaper alumina, might thereby compete more fiercely on world markets with American companies. By March 1961, Morgan was talking privately of the possibility of selling 114 000 tonnes of alumina a year to Japan—more alumina than would be consumed in the planned smelter in Australia.

Even if negotiations with Pittsburgh should break down, Clark's company—thanks to its links with Japan—now had a chance of entering the industry in three easy steps. Opening a mine and building a refinery near Perth was the first step. Selling the alumina to Japan was the second step. And then the likely profits from Japan and the increased power of borrowing would be the springboard for the third and most expensive step, the smelter in Victoria. Such a scheme might allow Clark to retain complete control of the venture.

Meantime, Ralph Derr's confident report on the Australian project was arousing firm interest in Pittsburgh. The high officials of the Aluminum Co. of America did not wish to see the project fall into the hands of a North American rival or pass to an Australian–Japanese partnership. Action was needed: they invited Lindesay Clark to visit Pittsburgh.

6

Wedding Year

In April 1961, Clark and his wife Jane prepared to set out for
Pittsburgh on what was to be the most important mission of his
business career. Flying in one of the new commercial jets, they halted
for a few days' rest in Honolulu, as the custom was. They halted again
in San Francisco: it was the head office for the American gold company
Homestake, where Clark met old business friends. Flying east to Pittsburgh the Clarks were met at the airport and escorted to the new Hilton
Hotel, near the junction of the rivers.

Negotiations began on Thursday 20 April in a long room near the
top of the spectacular Alcoa building. The 'all-aluminium' head office,
completed nine years earlier, it had aluminium elevators, aluminium
windows and waterpipes and an outer skin of aluminium. Wherever the
lightweight metal could be used, it was emphasised. In this city of steel,
the home of US Steel, this skyscraper was a proclamation that aluminium
was challenging steel on every front.

All the grand men of the company and their assistants, perhaps
twenty in all, assembled on one side of the long table. On the other side
sat Clark, Denny Marris, who had come from London as adviser, and a
young Australian mining engineer named Arvi Parbo who knew the
technical details about the bauxite project. After everyone had taken a
seat, there was initial laughter at the incongruity of the scene—the large
American group confronting two Australians and an Englishman.

The massed ranks of the Americans reflected the new business
culture introduced after the war by the company's head, Chief Wilson.
It was once observed that the company was now conducted like 'a family
debating society' and here was the proof of it. 'Ours is the exact opposite

of military organisation,' said Chief Wilson in 1955. From the crowded side of the table Frank Magee led the Americans. No decision would be made unless the company's best mining engineers, refiners, smeltermen, powerhouse operators, salesmen, lawyers were all present.

Nearly all the Americans were friends who dined at each other's houses. They were utterly loyal to the company and conscious that it was their lifelong career. So there they sat in their business suits, looking at chairman Magee, 'an out-going straight-shooter', and feeling surprised when he announced at the start of proceedings that his company would not demand a majority interest in the project. Normally the company wanted to control everything. That was its tradition.

For six days the discussions went on, in groups large and small. Every fact gathered from Australia was closely examined—the grade of the bauxite, the relations with the Western Australian government, the attitudes of the trade unions, the quality of brown coal at Anglesea, the likely cost of making one tonne of aluminium ingot and the effect of Australian and American taxation laws on profits that might be earned.

There was earnest talk about the potential disadvantage of the mine, refinery, smelter and power station being on four separated sites. The Americans at first were wary of the idea of shipping alumina more than 3000 kilometres around the coast to the smelter. While the distance was not large by world standards the alumina would have to be carried in Australian ships which usually were over-manned and inefficient. It could be that 3000 kilometres in Australian ships along the Australian coast would cost as much as 15 000 in foreign ships elsewhere. In other words, it might be cheaper to import alumina from overseas to a smelter sited near the Victorian coalfields than to import alumina from Western Australia.

Clark presented the Australian case with all his courtesy and patience. The informal debating atmosphere suited him, for that was how he ran his own board meetings in Melbourne. Some 22 years later Marris recalled in a private letter:

> I don't think that I have ever admired any presentation more than that given by Lindesay. It was chaotic, it followed no strict rule of logic, but his conviction and faith in the project shone throughout all the meetings and cross-examination, not always satisfying the 'experts', but completely winning the support of the senior management with whom the decision lay. It was a marvellous performance.

The Americans did not immediately make up their mind. They perceived that the Darling Range held one of the world's larger sources of bauxite. It was remarkably close to a port and large city, thus giving a chance of low mining and refining costs, but a long way from a smelting site. It was in a country with political stability and relatively favourable taxation laws. But there were imponderables. If the project was to serve largely the protected Australian market, producing aluminium for local users, then the big test was not how it would fare against world competition but against the other potential Australian competitor, the project based on new-found Weipa. The vital question was cost: would the new venture produce cheaper metal than the rival venture based on Weipa, more than 3000 kilometres across the continent? The question was not easily answered.

The Darling Range could also serve overseas smelters. At this stage, however, the world had plenty of bauxite and alumina. On the other hand, Perth was relatively close to Japan and its rising aluminium industry. Of all the major known deposits of bauxite, the Darling Range and Weipa were much the closest to Japan. The Americans probably sensed that if they did not take up its bauxite the Japanese might well finance it, buying much of the alumina and thereby producing cheaper aluminium at its smelters than hitherto. If the Japanese did not move in, one of the North American competitors might come to control it.

Clark hoped at first to retain half or more of the shares in the bauxite project and to sell the remainder to the Aluminum Co. of America. In the initial bargaining, a 50–50 deal was tentatively accepted. But if the Australian side had to finance part of the venture, could it raise the huge sum required? Clark had already gained promises of finance, partly from a machinery firm, but far from enough. Again, the capital required would be much less if their smelter bought its electricity from the State Electricity Commission of Victoria, but such electricity would probably be dearer than if they generated their own. Expensive electricity in turn could defeat the whole scheme. Then again Clark thought of separating the powerhouse from the aluminium project, floating the Anglesea powerhouse as a separate company and buying electricity from that company.

Anything Clark could do to limit the capital required by the aluminium project would give him more chance of controlling the new enterprise. Being so short of capital, his bargaining position was risky. To possess the bauxite and the coal was not as important as possessing, as the Americans did, the capacity to raise the huge sums needed to turn bauxite into aluminium and the capacity to sell alumina and aluminium and aluminium products.

A realistic solution was for the Aluminum Co. of America to raise the finance in the initial years. It had such a financial reputation and such powers of borrowing that it could easily raise the money on favourable terms, in effect underwriting the loans. There was a price for that concession. If the big company was to be the financier it wanted control. That meant it would receive 51 per cent of the shares. In the end Clark agreed, though deep was his disappointment that Australians could not control the new project. He saw no alternative. His own Western Mining Corporation was tiny by American standards. Its powers of borrowing, even in Australia, were limited, and its credit rating was further reduced by the fact that its last big venture, the Great Western goldmine at Bullfinch, was a financial failure.

There was one other option for Clark. He could enlist big Australian partners who together would provide half of the capital, leaving America to provide its half. But big Australian banks and life insurance houses were not yet interested in this kind of resource project; the Commonwealth Bank had already withdrawn as an early financier. Another option was to invite the biggest Australian mining company, Broken Hill Proprietary. But such an invitation would have meant that Clark and his company ceased to be the leader of the Australian syndicate. Clark saw the bauxite as a prize for his company, a consolation for past losses.

Each afternoon, after returning to the Hilton Hotel, Clark informed his Australian colleagues of the state of the negotiations. Normally he wrote a brief letter, giving it to Arvi Parbo who converted it into Bentley's code so that it could retain confidentiality when it was sent as a telegram to Melbourne that evening. Next morning, or late that night, Parbo opened the incoming telegram from Melbourne, and decoded it, again using his Bentley's code book. The telegrams were often long, and he might spend an hour and a half in decoding them into simple English. As the Australians were usually entertained each evening at a private house or company dinner, Parbo began to curse the codebook: 'I wished that our hosts had been a little less hospitable'.

When the first stage of the negotiations was over, Clark and Marris flew to London, while Parbo went to Texas to inspect a refinery and aluminium smelter at Point Comfort before flying back to Melbourne. The deal was not yet clinched. A hundred details and several points of principle had to be sorted out. On 12 May Clark was back in Pittsburgh with his advisers and two of his fellow directors of Western Aluminium, Chester Guest and Ralph Burt.

During the discussions around the long table in room 2924 in Pittsburgh it was clear to the Americans that the Japanese were intensely interested in the Western Australian bauxite. Indeed there was a suspicion that Clark and Morgan were close to signing an agreement to build a refinery, come what may, and supply alumina at bargain prices to Mitsubishi Chemical Industries. Moreover, Mitsubishi might buy 20 per cent of the shares in the venture if the Americans did not take up their interest. This deal with Japan was closer to the stage of signing than Clark was willing to admit. W.H. Krome George, a rising executive, admitted in a confidential letter on 4 May 1961: 'it is obvious that we are starting from way behind the goal line'.

It was decided that the potential Japanese buyers of Western Australian alumina should be invited to Pittsburgh in May to join in discussions. If the Aluminum Co. of America endorsed the Australian project, a long-term contract by Japanese firms to buy a proportion of the local alumina would improve the economic prospects of the venture. As Magee learned more about the advanced negotiations in Japan, he realised how independent Clark and Morgan were in spirit. He realised that the Australians might even be willing to launch a project on a humbler scale without any American support. Perhaps the Australians would begin with a mine and refinery in Western Australia, later raising the capital for a power station and smelter in Victoria.

As a tactician Clark was patient. He was willing to concede a procession of minor points while his eye was fixed on winning major points. There was something 'statesmanlike'—Americans said—about his ways. On his best days he seemed to be much older and wiser than any man of almost the same age on the opposite side of the table. He created a favourable impression at the long table. He gained esteem for other reasons: he had not hawked his project from one big company to another so that he could in effect auction his asset; he did not call for an early decision with the accompanying threat that he would take his business elsewhere if the deadline was not met. He acted as if time were on his side.

In the end the Americans said they wanted 51 per cent and effective control. In return they would raise most of the big sum of capital needed for the venture. Clark was disappointed but he had no reason to be. That his syndicate would hold 49 per cent of the shares, and that America with its 51 per cent would finance most of the early construction of refinery and smelter, was a wise solution. In some ways Clark was fortunate to receive 49 rather than 40 per cent, but when he left Pittsburgh, he still hoped for 50. Perhaps he did not know that some officials on the other side of the table still hoped to push his share down to 45 per cent.

A team of Americans set out to inspect the sites in Western Australia and Victoria and to check information. Everything remained confidential, and no news appeared in the press. It so happened that several of the heads of Kaiser—the partner in the new Comalco venture—were also visiting Melbourne to discuss the future of the Weipa deposit in north Queensland. Several Kaiser men had been colleagues of the Pittsburgh visitors during the war and would easily recognise their competitors and perhaps guess that they were in Melbourne to buy up the Darling Range deposits. Each evening, from the Menzies Hotel, the Pittsburgh men were taken out to dine at slightly inferior restaurants or hotels for fear that they would meet the rivals if they went to the best dining rooms in a city which then had few chefs of distinction.

Krome George, a member of the party visiting Australia, was worried that somebody might intercept his messages to head office in Pittsburgh. 'It was a precarious situation,' he recalled. He decided that it was safest to communicate with his parents in Florida who would then forward the message to Pittsburgh. For double safety he communicated in a code centred on the Polish surname of a Pittsburgh baseball star, Bill Mazeroski.

The precariousness of the situation made Magee, in Pittsburgh, resolve to sign the deal as quickly as possible. He had already moved away from his earlier proposition that Pittsburgh and Melbourne should share in the new project in the proportion of 50–50. He wanted certainty. Pittsburgh must have 51 per cent of the shares, he insisted, otherwise the Australian company could not use the valuable Pittsburgh names and advertising slogans. Clark agreed to this ruling but in his own mind he never fully accepted it. He still hoped, somehow and someday, to reverse the 49 and the 51.

The Aluminum Co. of America. defeated by Reynolds in the celebrated takeover battle for British Aluminium in London less than three years previously, did not wish to be defeated in what was becoming another takeover bid. Secrecy was vital if it was to win. An outside company, suspecting or knowing that a deal was about to be clinched, could have wrecked it by making a public takeover bid for the shares in the Western Mining Corporation. A strong bidder could easily acquire them in a sudden raid. Western Mining Corporation now held, by virtue of its option on the Commonwealth Bank's shares, some 78 per cent of the shares in the bauxite project. As the share market valued Western Mining shares primarily for their tax-free gold dividends, and placed virtually no value on their bauxite interest, an outside bidder could in effect buy the bauxite for a song.

In Pittsburgh, Frank Magee wondered about the chance of another company backstabbing him by making a successful takeover of Western Mining. No option, no contract, was yet signed; his own company therefore had no rights over the Australian bauxite. On 22 May Magee glimpsed a temporary solution. Perhaps the proposed agreement between Melbourne and Pittsburgh should contain a let-out clause, abandoning the aluminium venture if in the near future the Western Mining Corporation were to be bought out by 'hostile parties'.

In any case an agreement must be signed quickly, even though important points were unresolved. The price Pittsburgh would pay for any alumina imported to northwest America was not yet fixed, and the thorny question of whether Pittsburgh could take out bauxite leases in its own name in the Darling Range was not yet decided upon. Vital negotiations with the governments of Western Australia and Victoria had not been finalised. These and other points were left hanging. Signatures were more urgent than full agreement on all the details. Ralph Burt, a leading Melbourne solicitor and member of the Western Aluminium board, did much of the legal work. By the second week of June the lawyers on both sides decided that the agreement was virtually ready for signing.

It later transpired that each side, as a result of the hasty discussions, placed its own interpretation on those crucial parts of the agreement that were not spelled out. Moreover, any agreement depends on the way it is executed, and neither side realised how its partner normally did business. Pittsburgh was highly centralised: it wanted a hand in everything. The Australians did not realise what this would mean when the business was under way. So at this stage the two parties agreed, not knowing how much they would disagree.

On 14 June 1961 the deal was announced. Frank Magee issued his special press release in Pittsburgh announcing that his company was venturing to Australia, that 'island continent'. A map of Australia was issued showing how the enterprise would be based in two opposite corners of the continent, 2700 kilometres apart by sea.

In Australia it was announced, simultaneously, that an unlisted company called Alcoa of Australia Pty Ltd would be formed to run the aluminium project. In that company the Aluminum Co. of America would take up 51 per cent of the shares and have the right to nominate more than half of the directors but not the right to nominate the chairman who initially would be Lindesay Clark. The American company would act as technical manager and appoint the managing director. It would also provide the knowledge and, just as important, raise the fixed-interest loans that would provide two-thirds of the 45 million Australian pounds needed to construct the project. The remainder of the sum, being 14 375 000 pounds, would be subscribed by the shareholders, with just over half coming from the Aluminum Co. of America and the rest coming from the Australian companies which were shareholders. The announcement caused a stir. It was possibly the biggest mining venture ever launched in Australia.

On the afternoon of the announcement, the directors of the new Alcoa of Australia held their first board meeting at 120 William Street in Melbourne. Lindesay Clark and Frank Espie came as directors in their own right, John M. Baillieu represented Chester Guest on behalf of North Broken Hill, and three Melbourne men—John Burt, Ian D. Mackinnon and Beamish Brett—sat as alternate directors on behalf of the Aluminum Co. of America. Brett acted as secretary of the board for the first seven months, being replaced by Fred Morgan. By the end of the year there were four Australian and five American directors, though the Americans usually were represented by their Australian alternates at meetings of the board.

At first Alcoa was barely the shell of a company. The board held the briefest of meetings and concerned itself mostly with legal formalities and the formal recording of decisions agreed upon elsewhere. The company's first financial year was to end on the last day of 1961 but the preparing of annual accounts and an annual report were deemed of little importance. The first annual report was not to be written and signed until almost fifteen months after the end of the inaugural financial year.

With the formation of the new aluminium company, Western Mining could breathe easily. It was no longer in peril of a takeover: indeed its powerful American ally might protect it if called upon. More important, Western Mining was moving away from dependence on gold and its clouded prospects.

The bauxite dwarfed a variety of other interests, acquired in the last few years. Western Mining also owned a profitable little talc mine at Three Springs, Western Australia, with a 'Heath Robinson outfit' of machinery. It held a deposit of iron ore at Koolanooka Hills, Western Australia, which would be the basis of the first Australian purchase contract signed by the Japanese steelworks in the iron ore boom of the 1960s. It retained its goldmines which for the next few years—so long as inflation did not surge—would yield some dividends to shareholders. Above all, it held a large share in the aluminium venture which was now certain to go ahead. The aluminium would prove to be far and away the most important of these ventures but it would have to pass through dangerous straits.

To clinch his side of the deal, Clark formally approached the other mining companies that formed Western Aluminium No Liability. Being chairman of Broken Hill South, he easily enlisted it. North Broken Hill, of which he was also a director, also agreed to remain in the alliance. On the other hand Clark was disappointed that no capital was subscribed by Electrolytic Zinc, which was one of the world's biggest zinc companies and that made its living by treating zinc mined at Broken Hill and the Tasmanian town of Rosebery. A small parcel of 100 000 shares, being 0.4 per cent, was allocated to the Cushion Trust Co. representing Lazards and Morgan Grenfell & Co.

Western Mining had held 77.8 per cent of the shares before the Americans arrived. As the Australian shareholding in total had to be reduced to 49 per cent, to accommodate the American share, Western Mining became the chief loser. It now held only a 20 per cent interest in the project. It could have acquired more but that would have called for its own subscriptions in cash, a commodity not plentiful.

Wedding Year

In the new Alcoa of Australia were two kinds of one-pound shares, some being free and fully paid and others being bought for cash. Of all the shareholders Western Mining received the largest proportion of its shares in the form of free shares. More than two of every three shares it received were free. The Aluminum Co. of America received half of its shares free but it had to pay for the other half. In contrast the two Broken Hill companies between them paid for about six of every seven shares they received. At the time it was hoped that the three Australian shareholders could sell all or part of their shares to the general public and that the company would be listed on the Australian stock exchanges but the company to this day is not listed, and no shares are held directly by individual investors.

The shares in Alcoa of Australia were initially allocated thus:

	Free-shares Fully-paid	Cash Shares To be paid for	Total Shares	Percentage
Aluminum Co. of America	6 250 000	6 500 000	12 750 000	51
Western Mining	3 402 778	1 597 222	5 000 000	20
Broken Hill South	486 111	3 663 889	4 150 000	16.6
North Broken Hill	486 111	2 513 889	3 000 000	12
Cushion Trust	100 000		100 000	0.4

The free shares were fully paid up and in effect represented payment for earlier or future services given to the infant company. The Aluminum Co. of America was deemed to be making the major contribution—in short it had agreed to sell its latest technology. Western Mining had made the next major contribution—it had played the chief part in the finding and testing of the bauxite and brown coal and the arranging of the major contracts. The two Broken Hill companies, it was agreed, had contributed rather less but they had the right to buy substantial holdings on the time payment principle.

The cash payments were to come more from the combined Australian companies than from the big American. The American was to provide 6.5 million pounds in cash and, in addition, a loan that would extend to about 28 750 000 pounds, or twice the total cash to be contributed by the American and Australian companies. It was agreed that when each company paid the instalments on its shares, the Aluminum Co. of America would provide loans equal to twice that amount. The total cost of the project was estimated at 45 million pounds, and in loans and cash the Americans would provide just over 35 million pounds. They were the financier of this expensive project and were to supply or arrange about four-fifths of the capital needed.

While an American partner had now been signed up to take 51 per cent of the shares, the signing up of the Western Australian government was just as important, because it owned the bauxite. An agreement had been signed on 7 June, just seven days before Pittsburgh and Melbourne shook hands, but that agreement had to be ratified by an act of parliament—the Alumina Refinery Agreement Bill, the details of which were debated in September.

At the state election of March 1959 the Liberals led by David Brand had replaced the Labor government. The new minister for industrial development, Charles Court, was to do more for mining in Australia than probably any other politician of the post-war years. His bill authorising the mining leases and the alumina refinery was one of the first mining projects under his care. Court announced that his government would dredge a shipping channel to the wharf that was to be built at the refinery, provide some 80 hectares of land as a waste dump for the red mud discarded in the course of the refining process and extend its railway by 26 kilometres to reach the first bauxite mine. Guiding the bill through the lower house, he said the venture was a landmark 'in the industrial history of Western Australia'. He privately wished it was even more of a landmark. His hope had been for the smelting as well as the refining process to take place in his state, but the local price of electricity was too high. The mines department warned that the Muja coal deposit developed by Clark would not produce the cheap electricity needed by an aluminium smelter.

Western Australian experts also doubted whether their state held much coal, let alone cheaply mined coal. It was the fashion, in that era when cheap Middle East crude oil was supplanting expensive coal, to underestimate the coal that had been found. Oil was becoming so cheap that deep coal, or coal covered by a depth of overburden, was not payable under the half-mechanised mining methods then prevailing. Coal that would be payable in 1991 was unpayable in 1961. At that time Charles Court was entitled to argue that if his state used the 80 million tonnes of Muja coal in generating electricity to supply the proposed aluminium smelter, then one day in the remote future most factories might be short of coal—if coal should return to favour.

During the debate the Labor Party complained that far more jobs should have been generated by the bauxite and that higher royalties should have been charged for each tonne of bauxite mined. A.R.G. Hawke, the leader of the opposition, regretted the decision to build the smelter outside Western Australia. Whereas Alcoa of Australia would spend 30 million pounds on construction projects in Victoria, the site of the smelter, it would spend only 10 million pounds near Perth.

'What is in it for Western Australia?' was the question naturally asked by the Labor members. A goldfields member replied that the venture, when operating, would directly employ only 400 people in Western Australia or half as many as 'one decent goldmine' in Kalgoorlie. John Tonkin, who as Labor premier of Western Australia in the early 1970s would support the expansion of the aluminium industry, argued that the government was not demanding enough of Alcoa of Australia. Interrupting Charles Court's speech he called out, 'Are these people allowed to write their own agreement?' When Court resumed his speech, Tonkin waited only seconds before calling out: 'The sky is the limit!'.

Sir Charles Court, at the time minister for industrial development in Western Australia, addresses an Alcoa dinner at the Palace Hotel in Perth, probably in the late 1960s. John 'Doc' Mitchell, head of the Aluminum Company of America International Operations, is seated to the left.

The debate in parliament displayed more the fireworks of party politics than deep divisions. It was well known that an aluminium smelter near Perth would have to pay far higher running costs than one in Victoria. Moreover it would have been ill-sited for the fabricating of aluminium products, nearly all of which would then have been sent by railway or ship to Melbourne. At least the aluminium industry gave Western Australia a relative advantage which the rising iron ore industry could not give. Whereas nearly all the iron ore mined in the state was to be exported in a raw condition or treated only slightly, nearly all the bauxite was to be exported only after substantial treatment had taken place, thus giving work to large numbers of Western Australians in the refineries and associated industries. Western Australia was to gain more jobs on its own soil from the processing of each million tonnes of bauxite than from the processing of each million tonnes of iron ore.

The American company, along with the Western Australian and Victorian governments, was an essential collaborator in the project. So too were the Japanese. They were the last to be signed up. The ups and downs of the negotiations between the Japanese and Bill and Fred Morgan have not been fully documented, at least in Australia. Krome George of Pittsburgh recalls a tense moment when he was attending a conference in Melbourne with Mr Hasegawa, the head of Mitsubishi Chemical Industries. Hasegawa clearly intimated that he already had stronger rights than Pittsburgh. Putting his hand into a green bag at his side he plucked out a document stating that the Australians would grant him an option to buy a 20 per cent interest in the bauxite venture. Krome George recalls his reaction on reading the document: 'I almost fainted'. The document, it seems, was not quite a contract but almost a promise. The Americans felt slightly uneasy, to put it mildly, that until such a late stage they had not been adequately informed by the Australians about these negotiations with Japan.

In the end the Mitsubishi did not buy an interest in Alcoa of Australia. Instead it accepted a favourable contract to buy cheap alumina. The cargoes would rise to a total of 120 000 tonnes a year by 1965, thus making Mitsubishi the main outside buyer of alumina. This deal was not as important as the entry of Pittsburgh but, in a way then unseen, it had long-term effects on how the world's aluminium industry developed.

There was one hitch in the series of deals, contracts and under-standings arranged by Lindesay Clark in 1961. The time, in theory, was unfavourable for a new aluminium venture in Australia and, for that matter, almost anywhere. The metal was so plentiful as to be almost a glut. The major aim of the new aluminium ventures was to supply firstly the Australian market, but that market was likely to be over-supplied.

The rival venture operated by Comalco—the offspring of Consolidated Zinc (later CRA) and Kaiser Aluminum & Chemical Company—was already producing on a humble scale. It was planning to develop its big deposits of bauxite at Weipa in Queensland. The capacity of its Tasmanian smelter at Bell Bay was being expanded from a mere 12 750 to 29 000 tonnes a year. It was designing another smelter for the South Island of New Zealand. The *Australian Financial Times* wondered how Australia would manage to sell all its aluminium ingots once the two big projects, Alcoa and Comalco, were competing.

It seemed, in Clark's moment of triumph, that the foundations of Alcoa's expensive venture were being laid at the wrong time.

PART TWO

◆ 7 ◆

The Rise of Kwinana

Americans began to arrive to plan the aluminium venture on both sides of Australia. One of the first to come was Ed Harrison, a talented geologist, who supervised closer drilling of the bauxite deposits. Described by Don Campbell as Pittsburgh's 'world-roving one-man explorer for bauxite', Harrison was more than explorer. He sat down to tackle a problem with the same single mindedness as many people sit down to devour a meal. In the office he looked at a chair or a filing system and said it could be improved; and he improved it, though not always to everyone's satisfaction. In Western Australia he invented a drilling rig that operated on a vacuum rather than a pressure method. It had the advantage of curbing dust and providing a visual sample of the bauxite while the drill was still at work.

Ed Harrison once invited employees to a party at the Perth house he rented. Guests arriving were puzzled to see a large tyre floating on the backyard swimming pool but delighted to find that drinks and food were arranged on the tyre. Harrison encouraged his guests to coax the tyre from one side of the pool to the other and help themselves to drinks from this floating dumb waiter. He was to die in an air accident, and when the news reached Australia many of his former colleagues felt an acute sense of loss.

Alcoa's chief executive, J. Colin Smith, arrived from America in December 1961. At his first board meeting in Melbourne he was elected managing director of Alcoa of Australia Pty Ltd, his appointment being backdated to 1 November. One American colleague described him as 'a gem of a human being', but other colleagues, while liking him personally, thought he was a slightly odd choice as head of a mining, refining and

75

The Australian vacuum drill (model number 5), designed for exploration in the Darling Range. Holes could be drilled rapidly to a depth of 2 metres before the rods and bits had to be altered.

smelting company. He was a salesman, having recently managed sales in New York, and his appointment reflected the belief, later disproved, that Alcoa was more likely to succeed as a producer of smelted aluminium for Australian factories than as a producer of alumina for foreign smelters. One of Smith's special tasks was to sell the Alcoa brand of aluminium to Australian factories.

Smith delighted in entertaining the company's clients. He personally mixed cocktails for his guests at a time when Australians were unaccustomed to cocktails but excited at the thought of tasting them. He said he needed, for his parties, a spacious and expensive house; and in Melbourne the company bought one that perched on a high cliff overlooking the Yarra River. Lindesay Clark, noting the stream of guests knocking at the front door of this busy extrovert, wondered whether he would go on cheerfully mixing cocktails until every businessman in Melbourne had tasted them.

Charles W. Parry arrived to take charge of the financial liaison between Australia and Pittsburgh. He later rose to be head of the parent company in the United States. Like so many of the rising executives of the Aluminum Co. of America, he was an engineer by training and, before coming to Pittsburgh, had served at a plant on the St Lawrence River. At first it was intended that he should base himself at Geelong, where construction of the smelter was commencing, but after six months he moved to Melbourne to be closer to the bankers. He and his family settled into a Cape Cod cottage near Studley Park Road in Kew but soon he was travelling more and more.

The supervision of spending was not Parry's only task. More money had to be raised. The original plan was for Alcoa to borrow from its American partner some 5.7 million Australian pounds in 1962 alone, but that was not enough. The likely costs of the project, both in Western Australia and Victoria, had been estimated with haste, and proved unrealistic, especially as interest rates were rising. Often Parry went to Pittsburgh for financial negotiations. One visit was prolonged to eight weeks. During his brief term in Australia he flew across the Pacific some sixteen times.

Meanwhile in Western Australia the mine and refinery were being planned. With the strong urging of the Western Australian government, Alcoa agreed that the best place for the alumina refinery was the new, dredged port of Kwinana, about 24 kilometres south of Fremantle. Opposite the beach of Kwinana, the long Garden Island served as a natural breakwater shielding the harbour from the ocean swell and the strong westerlies that blew from the Indian Ocean. Ships of 30 000 tonnes could enter the harbour, and for years such ships were considered adequate.

Alcoa acquired a large flat area fronting the sandy beach. Nearby stood British Petroleum's oil refinery, opened in 1955, and the Broken Hill Proprietary Company's new mill for rolling steel. Along the beach, on land leased from the Western Australian government, straggled the holiday cottages and shacks to which many Perth families came in summer. To the dismay of many of the cottage-owners' tenants, the government gave notice that the lazy summer resort on Lilian Beach was to vanish and to be replaced by the alumina refinery and its jetty.

Few aluminium industries in the world possessed such a convenient site. The land was cheap, and the harbour was deep by the standards of the 1950s. Close by, along a new freeway, was Perth from whose half a million people the refinery's workforce could be recruited. Only a short distance to the east, in the low hills, was a large bauxite deposit.

Kwinana was near a sweeping expanse of flat wasteland on which could be deposited the waste from the treatment process, the so-called red mud. As the bauxite was low grade, its treatment in the refinery would yield more waste matter than alumina. The valueless red mud, after being pumped from the refinery, was to be allowed to settle and

White Gold

The first earthworks at Kwinana.

dry before being covered with a layer of sand. Ultimately the red dumps of mud would consolidate and subside, and it was believed that buildings could be eventually erected on the dumps. It was assumed that the reserve of surrounding land would be sufficient to hold all the red mud that came from the refinery. Nobody envisaged the dramatic expansion of the refinery, and the huge quantities of red mud that soon eventuated.

Pittsburgh engineers were in charge of the design of the refinery. They prepared to test the Western Australian bauxite at East St Louis where the Aluminum Co. of America owned a refinery and research laboratory. Samples of typical bauxite were collected and crammed into 44-gallon drums for shipment to the research laboratory. A novel refining process, the ultimate in its attention to detail, was designed for Australia. Some of the American designers, however, were not so well informed about Australia's climate. For Kwinana they designed one building with steep roofs which would easily shed the heavy snow in winter: so far no snow has fallen on those roofs.

As project manager, R.C. Blasingame came to Kwinana from the United States. He had made an earlier, hurried visit to prevent a Pittsburgh trade union from trying to influence trade union activities in Australia. A dozen American technical officers arrived on assignments lasting as long as four years. Some thirty Australians were recruited to

The original unit at the Kwinana refinery, completed in 1963, was designed to process 200 000 tonnes of alumina a year.

supervise the scores of construction contracts, for most tasks were done by contractors.

Bob Freeman, a tough experienced American, was construction manager. He was not willing to accept the Australian phrase 'she'll be right, mate'. Insisting on the highest standards of safety, he instructed his safety officer to 'order workers off site for serious breaches'. The Cavalier Construction Co. a subsidiary of the Aluminum Co. of America, built the refinery, using a host of Australian contractors.

Plans for each building and major item of equipment came by airmail, in large tubes. If there was an urgent need for information the Americans would ring Pittsburgh in the evening—international phone calls were not yet common. Colleen Aspher, who came to work for Cavalier as a secretary, was surprised at the swift flow of information all day long. She learned to fit in with the tempo, and occasionally she drove her black Holden car to the refinery before six in the morning to handle the backlog of work.

Each Sunday hundreds of spectators would set out from Fremantle and Perth to see the progress of the refinery works at what was still called 'Naval Base'. A tall wire fence prevented them from entering the site but they stood beside it, sometimes a hundred or more, and watched the buildings taking shape. Descriptions in the *West Australian* newspapers drew more visitors. 'The hustling colourful site of the Alcoa bauxite refinery at Naval Base is becoming a sightseer's mecca,' readers were told on 21 February 1963. Here they could see, through the wire, 'a vast iron-and-concrete assembly of futuristic forms' and a 'gallery of visual monstrosities that will become a refinery'.

The bauxite mine at Jarrahdale attracted its workforce. The mine itself was a few shallow quarries in clearings in the bush, with contractors working the mechanical shovels and the trucks that hauled ore to the storage bins erected by the new railway. The railway from Jarrahdale to Kwinana, 45 kilometres long, was the first line of any length built in Western Australia since 1933; and indeed the railway and its special aluminium-built ore wagons were the government's main financial contribution to the alumina venture.

Small opening ceremonies for the mine and railway were held in July 1963, and Hubert Opperman, federal minister for shipping and transport in the Menzies Federal government, joined the Western Australian ministers Charles Court and Arthur Griffith in saying a few words. Opperman, once a professional cycling champion, attracted the television cameras almost every time he spoke. As the weeks went by, Western Australians watching the evening television news saw more and more of the mine and refinery and the company's jetty that extended more than 500 metres out to sea.

At the mine, the first train was loaded with bauxite which spilled into the seven rail wagons from a bin overhead: the doors that opened to admit the bauxite were air-operated. That train carried no more than 280 tonnes. About fifteen years later a typical bauxite train was to haul more than thirty times that tonnage. And yet that inaugural train seemed almost too heavy for the new-laid railway track. 'We loaded the first train in great trepidation,' said Wilf Birrell, the mine superintendent; 'our fears were unfounded.'

On 18 July 1963 employees at Kwinana—except those working in noisy places—heard for the first time the whistle of an approaching diesel locomotive with its wagon of freight that would launch the refinery. A small cargo of bauxite shipped from the Americas had already been used in trials and tests. A month later the first cargo of caustic soda, the chemical vital for the refining process, arrived in the *Saga Sea*. As the long jetty was not quite completed, the ship had to anchor nearby and pump liquid caustic soda along a rubber hose laid on the bed of the sea. A total of 11 600 tonnes was pumped from that first ship.

The core of the alumina refinery was the process devised by the long-dead German chemist, Karl Bayer. The bauxite arriving from the mine was already crushed, but it was crushed—indeed pulverised—again until it had the fineness of sand. The solution of caustic soda was mixed with this watered sand, or slurry, and the resultant liquid was pumped to the first refining process, known as digestion. The slurry, or solution, was heated in big vessels called digesters, using steam from the company's own powerhouse. After the solution was heated to 143°C, the bauxite and the caustic soda reacted to produce a 'green liquor' which contained nearly all the alumina.

In the second step in the process, the clarification, most of the waste was removed. Silica and iron oxide formed nearly all of the waste, and they were removed either as coarse sand or as red mud. The process was a great absorber of caustic soda and of steam, and wherever possible the steam and the caustic soda were recycled. The green liquor, having been deprived of most of its waste sand and chemicals, was purified further as it passed through filters. It was now 'supersaturated' with alumina, the material which had to be saved. Stage three consisted of sending the green liquor, now much cooler, through a row of precipitators—tall tanks which looked like silos standing shoulder to shoulder.

For about thirty hours the solution passed through the precipitators, from which were recovered crystals of alumina hydrate. In the fourth, or calcination, stage the crystals were washed, dried and then heated to about 1000°C. The result was a dry crystalline powder—the aluminium oxide or alumina. More than two tonnes of alumina, in a smelter, would be converted into one tonne of aluminium. Much of the process consisted of removing the white sand and iron oxide and then, above all, the water and caustic soda which had been added at the outset to assist the removal of the sand and iron oxide.

In essence, the process consisted of removing the enemies and then the friends of the bauxite. The main enemy was useless red mud which, once it had been excluded, was pumped to the dumps near the refinery. The main friends were the caustic soda and the heat which were saved as much as possible and diverted back into the continuous process. The process gave off intense heat, and so was soothing on a cold winter's night and trying on a hot summer's day for the workers.

By October 1963 the refinery, later known as Unit 1, was almost completed. The powerhouse, with its two secondhand generators of wartime vintage, was burning the fuel oil pumped from the oil refinery along the coast. At the Alcoa works the caustic soda was placed in the circuit and then, on 22 October 1963, the first bauxite was added.

The teething trials were painful, for part of the plant was of radical design. As if to intensify the troubles, the Darling Range bauxite was unusual by North American standards. The precipitators at first produced alumina that appeared to be fair in quality but it proved to be too fine and flour-like for the smelter in Geelong which was already at work. Many new treatment plants built on a large scale experience early hitches which the original testing—on a smaller scale—has not identified. Again and again at Kwinana the managers, foremen and process workers had to busy themselves coping with the unexpected.

The Australian National Line won the contract to ship alumina from the refinery at Kwinana to the smelter at Geelong, on the far side of the continent. At Kwinana the first alumina ship, the *Lake Sorrel*, berthed in the darkness of the early hours of Thursday 20 February 1964.

It was hoped that the loading of the ship would be efficient, for the journalists and television cameras were bound to be there. The company prayed for a still day, for the loading of a ship was certain to raise dust if the wind was blowing. The white powdery alumina, fresh from the refinery, lay in big storage bins near the deepwater, and a conveyor belt extended from beneath the bins all the way to the pier and the ship. For most of the distance to the pier and ship the conveyor belt travelled in the open air. On that first day a 'strong shoreward wind' was blowing and, as feared, it scooped up the dust from the alumina being loaded. Dust blew in white clouds towards the nearby houses, whose residents were not impressed, especially if washed clothes were hanging outside to dry. To the dismay of the company the two Perth dailies featured the dust on the following morning, the official opening day.

Tony Fallace, then a new employee, recalled the first loading. His task was to clean up the alumina that spilled from the conveyor belt to the ground. After he completed his twelve-hour shift nobody arrived to take his place; so he continued working for another twelve hours, his clothes covered with white dust. With all the overtime hours his pay for the day must have seemed princely. At the 25th anniversary of the opening of Kwinana he recalled that dusty loading of the first ship. By then the memory had mellowed a little and he said: 'The work wasn't too hard and I was supplied with great free meals'.

For the opening ceremony of the refinery a dais had been erected, with poles flying Australian and American flags. Aluminium chairs were specially ordered to seat the 200 invited guests, and buses were ready to take guests on a tour of the refinery. The tour was, deliberately, little more than a glimpse. The buses drove at moderate speed past the power-house, the point where the train unloaded the bauxite from the mine, the building that stored the bauxite, the precipitator and kilns, and the other phases of the process. Officials of the Aluminum Co. of America who planned the grand opening were normally secretive, but on this day they were doubly so because part of the process in the refinery was new. They were nervous lest observant visitors—especially the representatives of Mitsubishi, which had just opened a plant in Japan—detected the novelties in the refining process.

The process tank in Building 36 held the main secret. If, as their bus passed by, guests asked what was the purpose of the building, they were to be informed that it was 'part of our clarification system'. The process gave off foam; and if the wind happened to be blowing from the southwest, the foam was likely to blow across the bus route, spattering the bus's windows and drawing attention to the building. Accordingly, an instruction was issued to divert the buses if the wind blew the foam onto the road. The foam, of course, was a nuisance to workmen and they often wore cloths over their mouths when working near the tank.

Secrecy was normal in the aluminium industry, but at Kwinana the secrets could not all be hidden. An industrial spy determined to learn as much as possible could take advantage of the lie of the land. As the project manager, A.B. Kaltwasser, pointed out in a private letter, a spectator or spy standing on a nearby hill and focusing the latest camera with telephoto lens could learn even more about the refinery than was visible to the guests who were actually inside.

A ship carrying the first batches of alumina was about to sail to the Geelong smelter. Near the ship the speeches of celebration were delivered, and David Brand, the premier, officially opened the refinery. Later, afternoon tea and coffee and sandwiches and cakes were served to guests who crowded into the cafeteria, but Lindesay Clark's suggestion that whisky and beer also be served was rejected, probably at the decree of Arthur Lindley, who had come from America to take charge of publicity and hospitality. Each guest, however, did receive an unusual memento: a small hourglass filled with small pieces of alumina and capable of timing the boiling of an egg.

The ship sailed on 22 February 1964 and soon began to cross the Great Australian Bight, one of the roughest stretches of water near the continent. The other outward route for the alumina ships was northwards to the Indonesian archipelago and so to Japan. At first the refinery did not produce enough to supply both Japan and Geelong, and a further shipment of 10 000 tonnes of alumina had to be sent to Geelong from the United States refinery in Mobile, Alabama. 'Kwinana continues to have excessive start-up problems of all kinds,' wrote the manager. Monthly output was low, with only 8000 tonnes produced when double that amount was hoped for. After one problem was fixed, another seemed to emerge.

Slowly the refinery's hiccoughs were cured but its deep hoarse cough was not so easily fixed. The bauxite, because it was different from the kind refined in America, did not act as predicted in the treatment process. The silica prominent in the bauxite was sharp and abrasive. In liquid solution it flowed at high speed along the steel pipes and through the tanks, and after a time it cut its way into sections of hard steel. At some points the flow reached a sharp elbow in the pipe, and as the sharp wet sand changed direction it cut deeply into the bends of the pipes. Such abrasiveness had not been foreseen. Frequent repairs had to be made, causing delays to a process that was normally continuous. And yet much was learned by failure and by experiment. At first the recovery of the alumina in the ore was inadequate: in some months barely 90 per cent of the available alumina in the bauxite was recovered. But by 1966 the recovery rate had risen to a heartening 97 per cent.

Lindesay Clark, as chairman of Alcoa, remained quietly critical of the refinery. His long goldmining experience taught him that it was a mistake to build an expensive plant without making adequate tests in a small-scale pilot plant. He himself had learned that lesson the hard way at the Bullfinch goldmine. He concluded, with some exaggeration, that the large plant at Kwinana was in effect the pilot plant, to which running repairs and alterations were frequently being made at great expense.

Kwinana was slow to achieve the output for which it was designed. It was slow to earn profits. Officials in Pittsburgh excused the early results by explaining that the Western Australian bauxite, being unique, was difficult to handle. A few Australian engineers replied privately that the design of the refinery was partly to blame. But when they learned much later the details of the working costs and the hitches in the new refinery built in Queensland they were not quite so critical of the Americans who designed Kwinana.

A new refinery was like an industrial intestine with its coils and lengths of pipes and conveyor belts, its big volume of heating and circulating liquor, and its special smells. The long intestine was patrolled by a regiment of shift-workers who, labouring around the clock, walked along it to monitor the process or clean up the inevitable spillages.

As many engineers were needed to operate the process, young Australians were employed increasingly to take the place of the departing Americans. Usually recruited in the eastern states, they were flown to Kwinana for an interview before they were offered a firm job. In the refinery their first vivid impression was of the liquid frothing and boiling and the steam rising in the precipitator tanks. At the sight of all that boiling liquid, high above ground level, new employees were slightly nervous. Old employees were also nervous on 14 October 1968, when probably the largest earthquake experienced in Australia in 70 years struck the distant wheatbelt town of Meckering. The tremors reached Kwinana, and in the refinery the tall tanks that were filled with hot caustic soda began to sway. Those employees who were some seventy feet above the ground wondered whether the swaying decking on which they stood would collapse or the boiling caustic soda would pour down on them.

The Rise of Kwinana

*Kwinana refinery, reaching an annual capacity of 1.25 million tonnes in 1970
(the year of this photo), was upgraded to 1.7 million tonnes in 1995.*

In 1964 Alcoa began to search for markets outside Japan. The United
States was an obvious choice. The Reynolds Metals Co., with its head
office in Richmond, Virginia, was a huge aluminium producer but weak
in reserves of bauxite. Reynolds was said to be interested in bidding for
the big bauxite deposits which the Commonwealth government was
offering for sale at Gove in the Northern Territory. Clark's belief was
that alumina made from Darling Range bauxite would be cheaper than
alumina made by Reynolds from Gove bauxite. Why not, he suggested,
make a long-term contract to sell Alcoa alumina to Reynolds? This might
also deter Reynolds from buying Gove, perhaps setting up a refinery and
smelter somewhere in Australia and thus becoming another competitor
in the local industry.

Pittsburgh was apparently not keen on Clark's brainwave of selling
alumina to a rival. Clark responded by suggesting that alumina be sold to
another American company, American Metal Climax known as Amax.
That deal was clinched in March 1965. It was arranged that 200 000
tonnes of alumina a year should be shipped from Kwinana to Amax. This

A view of Jarrahdale, showing the operations for crushing and loading bauxite, with the vehicle workshops in the background.

deal seemed to promise a safe profit, for the alumina would be sold on a cost-plus basis. To determine those costs, a Western Australian price index was devised. Wages at the refinery accounted for 35 per cent of the index, fuel oil accounted for 20 per cent, caustic soda delivered at Kwinana accounted for 20 per cent, and 25 per cent was the miscellaneous component which, for the sake of simplicity, was based on the price of BHP steel. When the cost of any of these items was increased, Amax paid more for its alumina, thus assuring the Kwinana refinery of a profit.

The mines in the Darling Range became busier, and longer trains rolled down the gentle slopes and across the plains to the refinery. In September 1966 another unit of the refinery was opened, doubling the output so that the Amax contract could be met. More and more ships sailed with alumina for Japan as well as for Geelong. In 1965, a total of 65 000 tonnes of alumina was shipped to Japan. In 1970 the annual total shipped to Japan reached 307 000 tonnes—or one and a half times the original capacity of the first refinery.

Australia, where almost no bauxite was mined in 1955, stood high on the world's bauxite ladder ten years later. The West Indies, primarily

Jamaica, was the main miner of bauxite, with nearly 10 million tonnes a year in the mid 1960s. In tropical South America, the neighbouring countries Suriname and Guyana together mined another 7 million tonnes each year in the mid 1960s. Then followed the Soviet Union, which was estimated to produce close to 5 million tonnes, and France, with 2.6 million tonnes. Below those top five nations came a cluster of lesser miners of bauxite: the United States, Jugoslavia, Hungary and former French colonies in Africa. And then, well behind, came Australia, Greece and Malaysia, each of which mined more than 1 million tonnes of bauxite in 1965. Australia was about to climb rapidly up this ladder of producers.

Aluminium was entering a triumphant era. In the 1960s its global output passed that of copper as the main non-ferrous metal. Australia was able to share in this triumph because after a slow start it was becoming one of the more efficient producers of alumina. It was still difficult to predict that Australia would one day challenge Jamaica and the other old bauxite miners in the Caribbean for world dominance—but that day would come.

$$\blacklozenge \quad 8 \quad \blacklozenge$$

Glow at Point Henry

A   s cheap coal and cheap electricity could not be found in Western Australia, the smelter had to be elsewhere. The likely choice seemed to be New South Wales, the home of cheap black coal, but industrial relations on its rich coalfields were not predictable. Nor was the government in Sydney as sympathetic as that in Melbourne to attracting new businesses that created thousands of jobs. It was true that Sydney had a larger range of factories than Melbourne, but the margin in its favour was small. Moreover, in Sydney there was already a competing factory that fabricated aluminium, on a large scale, much of it for the local market. All in all the odds did not favour New South Wales as the site for the smelter, rolling mill and the other plants that would eventually surround a smelter.

Tasmania held possible sites for a smelter. It generated cheap hydro-electric power which had already attracted to Bell Bay the only existing Australian aluminium smelter. From Tasmania, however, shipping to the mainland was expensive. Moreover, it was not clear whether the big blocks of power needed by a smelter could be quickly made available in Tasmania, for a new dam and hydro-electric scheme would take many years to complete. Queensland was another possibility but its magnificent coalfields in the Bowen Basin were not yet developed. That left only Victoria, which was generating electricity from the world's largest known deposits of brown coal. Furthermore, Victoria already had surplus electricity. In addition, once the company operated its own power station at Anglesea the margin in favour of Victoria would seem overwhelming.

The idea of shipping the alumina more than 3000 kilometres to the coal of Victoria worried the Americans. That long voyage was at the

mercy of one of the more volatile, less efficient Australian industries—
coastal shipping. Clark, on the other hand, emphasised the enticement
of Victorian coal in one of his first letters to Pittsburgh: 'I am still
convinced that with an alumina refinery in the West, power based on
our own coalfield and a smelter at Geelong we are less subject to pressure,
will get lower costs and have a better market site.'

The city of Geelong, standing not far from the brown coal of
Anglesea, had a clear advantage over Melbourne as a site for the
aluminium smelter. Fred Morgan, the secretary of the company, was given
the task of finding suitable land near Geelong. By the end of 1960, even
before Clark made his first visit to Pittsburgh, Morgan had selected four
rural sites fronting seawater close to the bay at Geelong. Two sites were
examined on the northern side of the bay, towards the rocky range called
the You Yangs. Point Abeona, with its expanse of rural land, was close
to the Shell oil refinery; but a smelter there would stand so close to the
Geelong Grammar School and suburban houses that approval was
unlikely to be given by the authorities. Point Lillias, the second site,
was further from Geelong and so sparsely inhabited that fears of pollution
could not be taken too seriously. That site, however, had defects: it was
rocky here and marshy there; and it was near the southern approach to
the Avalon airfield. The presence of a smelter with its tall transmission
pylons would not please the aviation authorities. Moreover, if a wharf
were built there, a shipping channel would have to be blasted across
shallow rocks.

Clearly the southern side of the harbour was more favourable. It was
closer to the brown coal mine and the proposed power station and so
the transmission line would not be so long. One of the favoured sites
was on the Leopold coast, close to two caravan parks, and the other was
nearby Point Henry. The harbour master of Geelong favoured these
southern bayside sites. A shipping channel could be dredged from the
harbour almost to the shore, and ships of 30 000 tonnes could load and
unload. Point Henry and its narrow rural headland was the favoured
place. Surrounded by sea on three sides, it did not need a large and
expensive buffer of empty land.

In November 1960 Fred Morgan began to buy land at Point Henry
through estate agents: he spent 23 000 pounds on the first 34 hectares.
This was not dear, for the same sum could have bought two houses in
one of the more fashionable suburbs of Melbourne. By January 1961 he
had acquired 60 hectares. It was not yet certain that a smelter would
ever be built, and it was not even certain that Pittsburgh would join in
an Australian venture. The buying of land, however, was an urgent
priority. If word of the company's intention to build a smelter became
known, the land at Point Henry would suddenly become dearer, and the

price of certain strategic paddocks might become exorbitant as the owners realised their bargaining position. By the time the company was ready to announce its smelting plans, nearly all the required land was in its possession.

On cold days Point Henry was bleak and often windswept. On a warm summer's afternoon, however, it was almost romantic to stand on the narrow beach and see the dazzling blue of Corio Bay and on the opposite shore the rocky ranges, the You Yangs. Point Henry had been the main port for Geelong in the 1840s and in the gold-rush years of the following decade, and a village stood where its piers jutted out into the shallow bay. Not far away had stood the house of Horatio Wills who left in 1860 to take up sheeplands in central Queensland and was a victim of the worst massacre ever inflicted on white people by Aborigines during the pioneering era. Here too, in the 1890s, when the village at Point Henry was almost deserted, a famous inventor of commercial refrigeration, James Harrison, spent his last years. Historic ground, it was now almost deserted.

To build a smelter here called for no environmental report. The prevailing winds would not blow the fumes towards Geelong. Everyone in the city, except perhaps a few fishermen and birdwatchers, was pleased to see the smelter on the drawing board because it promised to provide jobs.

Engineers arrived from the United States. Hundreds of Geelong workmen were recruited for Point Henry. Foundations were dug, with Henry Bolte, the premier of Victoria, motoring down to break the first ground at a short ceremony held on 14 December 1961. The pier at Point Henry was not yet built, the special shipping channel was not yet dredged, and so Geelong's wharves were used. On those wharves were soon stacked the loads of material that were to be carried by trucks through the main streets of Geelong to the smelter on the other side of the bay.

No act of parliament was needed to authorise the smelter and the new port at Point Henry but the mining of coal for the proposed power station called for the signing of an agreement with the Victorian government. It was signed on 22 November 1961, and on that same day it came before the legislative assembly in the form of the Mines (Aluminium) Agreement Bill. The leader of the opposition, Clive Stoneham, who represented the old goldfields area of Castlemaine, was quick to welcome the proposed power station and smelter. The bill, he said, was one of the most important 'to be brought before Parliament for a long time'. His only complaint was that 'this really momentous measure' was being rushed through parliament. Allowed another week to consider the details in the bill, he expressed only one doubt. What, he asked, would

Glow at Point Henry

'*Breaking the ground' for the Point Henry smelter and fabricating plant on 14 December 1961. From left to right: J.C. Smith, Archdeacon Douglas Blake, Sir Henry Bolte, Sir Hubert Opperman, and Sir Lindesay Clark.*

happen if the Victorian government, having granted Alcoa a monopoly of the only important deposit of coal in the western half of Victoria, later decided that a big power station was required for that region? Nonetheless his Labor colleagues were happy to vote for the bill. It would expedite one of the biggest industrial projects to be seen in Victoria with 600 employees at Point Henry and 100 at Anglesea, and hundreds more when the aluminium smelter was enlarged.

The smelter was designed in the United States, on the basis of the Aluminum Co. of America's long experience. Pending the building of the company's own power station at Anglesea, a contract was signed to buy electricity from the State Electricity Commission of Victoria. As is the custom in the international aluminium industry, the exact price of the electricity remained a secret. Questions asked in the Victorian parliament in the following two years drew no new information from the premier, Henry Bolte, who simply replied that 'all costs of supply have been covered' and that the auditor-general was satisfied with the probity of the deal negotiated by Alcoa. Almost invariably, aluminium smelters bought their electricity at special rates because their bargaining position was unusual. Massive consumers of electricity, they used it not just at busy hours on weekdays, when the call on power from factories and households was at its peak, but also through the night and the weekends when demand was low. In Victoria the debate about electricity prices for the aluminium industry would simmer for the next third of a century: it still simmers.

In its opening years the smelter would be uneconomic without a ban against excessive imports of aluminium ingot and fabricated products. For much of the 1950s the Commonwealth government had restricted imports, partly by a system of licensing, but this scheme was on the way out when the smelter was rising at Point Henry. Lindesay Clark, eager that it be retained for aluminium, made his first approach to Canberra just before the federal election of December 1961 which the Menzies government won by a whisker. The election over, Clark increased his calls for government intervention so that an infant industry would not be squashed by cheap foreign aluminium. He did not want a protective tariff but rather import restrictions. If these were granted, Clark promised that Alcoa would supply aluminium to all Australian customers at a price no higher than world prices plus the cost of shipping aluminium to Australia.

To strengthen its lobbying in Canberra, the board of Alcoa, in March 1962, hired A.V. Smith as 'political adviser' at 2000 pounds a year and 'out-of-pocket expenses'. In the Second World War he had been the head of the Department of Supply and Shipping, one of the most powerful posts in the federal bureaucracy. From that post Smith retired early, through ill-health, but later he became an adviser and lobbyist. Smith was one of the country's few experts on how to handle politicians in Canberra or, at times, how to protect his clients from being mishandled. Now in his late sixties, he was a valuable help in the company's campaign to prevent the new smelter as well as the old smelter at Bell Bay from being besieged by imports of foreign ingot.

The company gained the protection it sought. Aluminium from overseas smelters usually had to obtain a licence to enter Australia, and the licence was not readily granted if supplies of Australian ingots were plentiful. At times the Australian ingots were to be sold at higher prices than the imports, and at other times the local and foreign prices were not far apart, but generally the level of protection was not high by Australian standards of the protective 1960s. While licensing was to protect the ingots produced at the smelter until 1971, import duties protected the products fabricated from the aluminium. This initial Commonwealth protection proved crucial, for Point Henry would face strong competition just when its own new plants were suffering from teething troubles.

The construction engineers, working to deadlines, were expected to complete the smelter by March 1963—six months ahead of the refinery at Kwinana. As much of the construction work had to be done in the open air, the weather was watched closely. A burst of hot or windy weather led to absenteeism, and wet weather caused delays, inciting a rush to recover lost time. There were minor skirmishes with the trade unions, and the two main unions—the FIA and the AWU—fought each other, poaching members when possible. Electricians went on strike just before Christmas 1962, by which time the steel towers of the last part of the transmission line were erected, bringing power from Gippsland, about 240 kilometres away.

Plans were afoot to recruit local men who would operate the smelter as foremen and operators. The first six of these men began work on 5 December 1962. Skilled Americans arrived from the Aluminum Co. of America early in the new year to train the newcomers. Although an aluminium smelter was already working at Bell Bay, just across Bass Strait, little if any effort was made to poach its employees.

The first alumina, the raw material for the smelters, was due to arrive on 11 February 1963. It came not from Western Australia—that refinery was not yet open—but from a refinery at Mobile in Alabama. Carrying one of the important cargoes in the long history of Geelong the ship sailed slowly into Corio Bay, docking at the North Corio wharf. She had been tied up only a few hours when the unloading began. Trucks carried the alumina from the wharf to the storage bins at the smelter, and indeed the trucks continued to carry alumina through the city of Geelong to the smelter until the end of 1965 when the company's pier at Point Henry was finally completed and the channel for the incoming ships was dredged.

There was no pool of skilled aluminium engineers in Australia, and so the company had to recruit and train them. Roger Vines, an engineering graduate of Melbourne University, was working as a bridge designer for the Country Roads Board when a friend working at Alcoa sounded him out about changing jobs. 'I didn't apply,' he said, 'they applied to me.' When Vines began work at Point Henry in 1963 he thought that the plant was 'loaded with engineers'. Becoming a production engineer in the carbon plant, he learned the job as he worked. In theory, enough carbon could be made for the smelter in one shift but at first the breakdowns were so common that two shifts were needed. Later he became superintendent of the smelting plant, about which he also knew nothing when he reached Point Henry.

Training has played a very significant part in the company's refineries operations. Four apprentices with their instructor, John Richards.

The deadline for completing the first unit of the smelter was not quite achieved. On 17 March 1963 three experienced smelting foremen arrived from Tennessee to assist the local crews in starting up the plant. The great electrical transformers were energised. On Thursday 4 April, the lines of 52 pots were ready, and the power was switched on at 5.50 in the afternoon. On the following Saturday the pot lining was completed. The first powdery white alumina was added to the pots on the Monday, and the whole plant was under way on Wednesday 10 April when editors of the financial page of the main daily newspapers arrived for a tour: only the Adelaide press was not represented. A week later, on 17 April, the molten metal was poured, and the first load of fourteen tonnes of ingots was sent on to the Australuco factory on 2 May.

Though the early months of smelting were difficult, the new workforce showed a willingness to learn. A cheerful spirit was in the air, recalls Vines. The Spanish and Italians and 'the good old Australian types' worked well together. The succession of crises and breakdowns, almost inevitable in operating new plant and using an unfamiliar technique, added to the fun. Everyone soon knew each other. No barrier separated the salaried staff from workmen—the barrier arose later—and no official of a trade union objected

Glow at Point Henry

The Point Henry smelter was visited on 3 July 1964 by the governor
of Victoria. From left to right: J.C. Smith (managing director), the
governor Sir Rohan Delacombe, R.C. Blasingame (operations director),
Sir Lindesay Clark (chairman).

if at weekends a salaried engineer walked around the smelter with spanner, wrench and screwdriver, doing the work of a trade unionist and repairing what had to be repaired without delay.

At night at Port Kembla and Newcastle the furnace at the steelworks provided spectacular sights, but at Geelong some people felt disappointed that the glow of the smelter could not be seen across the bay. Few Geelong people asked to see the molten metal in the potroom: the process was not dramatic in the eyes of most bystanders.

Whereas direct smelting in a furnace was ideal for removing impurities in iron, copper silver, lead and many other metals, the process was not suited for removing the final impurities from alumina. The aluminium oxide, if treated in a furnace, was converted into aluminium at such a high temperature that most of the aluminium vanished as vapour. Moreover, inside the alumina the atoms of oxygen and of aluminium were knotted together so tightly that traditional metallurgical methods could not part them efficiently.

The electrolytic process has been the method of producing pure aluminium ever since two young men, Paul Héroult in Grenoble, France, and Charles Hall in Ohio, USA, tried it separately, and successfully, in 1886. Indeed the Aluminum Co. of America had been founded largely on Hall's patent. The invention was made possible by the improved performance of the dynamo which, thanks to Edison and others in the 1880s, could produce those strong electric currents which enabled the efficient electrolysis of the alumina. The essence of electrolysis was the use of an electric current to decompose, chemically, substances that were molten or dissolved and to separate their components. The separation depended on the capacity of electricity, through positive or negative electrodes, to attract or repulse each main component.

The process of intense heating took place in long shallow boxes or troughs made of thick steel. Inside the troughs was an array of baked carbon blocks or rods that formed the anode. The ingredients of the carbon anodes were pitch and petroleum coke, imported mainly from North American refineries that had treated crude oil of a heaviness not found in Australia. Point Henry baked its own anodes—ultimately more than 110 000 a year—at a temperature rising to 1150°C. In effect, the direct electric current entered the trough or cell and melted the alumina and the added cryolite, or sodium aluminium fluoride.

Cryolite was almost as vital as the bauxite, both in Hall's era and in the modern era. It is the solvent for the alumina. Originally the southern tip of the Danish colony of Greenland was the source of the cryolite or 'ice rock'. When Germany captured Denmark early in the Second World War there was a fear that it would also capture Greenland, and a special American force was sent to occupy the island, partly because it produced the vital cryolite. When, two decades later, Point Henry began its smelting, it used artificial cryolite made from fluorspar. Ultimately Point Henry was to become an exporter of artificial cryolite.

In a molten bath the melted cryolite had a remarkable capacity to dissolve the alumina, thus preparing the alumina's twin components of aluminium and oxygen for their separation. Through this molten mixture of alumina and cryolite a strong electric current was run continuously. It did what the heat of the blast furnace could not do. In the electrically created heat, rising to 950°C, the process did its work of separating the wanted from the unwanted ingredients. The oxygen, the main impurity, was deposited on the anode (the positive) and was burned away.

The molten aluminium slowly formed a deposit on carbon walls or lining of the cathode (the negative). As the molten aluminium was a little heavier than the molten cryolite, the aluminium gathered in a pool at the bottom of the cell where it could be tapped in its molten state.

After the molten metal was collected, more alumina was added, making the process continuous.

At Point Henry, as in the North American smelters, the entire sequence was highly mechanised. Overhead cranes ran at high speed, setting the carbon anodes in place, carrying the bins of alumina for distribution into the pots and drawing out the molten metal in special crucibles. These crucibles then went away to be cast into ingots or extrusion billets which were stored at high heat in furnaces. Most of the pure aluminium was not used in its full purity, and small quantities of copper, nickel, zinc and other metals were added to make an alloy with specific qualities for special needs.

In effect there were four main ingredients in the initial process: alumina from Western Australia, the cryolite produced from fluorspar, and the petroleum coke and pitch that formed the carbon anodes and lined the pots. To produce one kilogram of aluminium, usually two kilograms of alumina were needed, perhaps 700 grams of carbon, and a small amount of cryolite. And of course a final raw material was the brown coal of Gippsland, from which the electricity that was used was generated. The electrolytic process required a huge amount of electricity each day. Indeed the forerunner of the Aluminum Co. of America was the first customer of the hydro-electric scheme established at the Niagara Falls in 1895.

L.E. (Larry) Curran, the sales manager sent from America, began to drum up customers even before the first ingots were produced at Point Henry. The Melbourne firm, Olympic Cables, he reported, would be a customer for the brand new aluminium. A maker of foil and a maker of medals promised to use Alcoa aluminium. Wunderlich Limited, Australia's largest user of aluminium for architectural purposes, expressed interest. Curran also reported to the board in June that a well-known firm of architects—Buchan, Laird, and Buchan—was involved with Alcoa in designing 'a monumental building' that would use aluminium. It was hoped that Alcoa aluminium would be used for building houses on the island of Nauru, which had little timber of its own. The first firm order received by Alcoa for aluminium ingots came in October 1962 from Metal Manufactures at Port Kembla.

Clark hoped for a ceremonial opening of the smelter and grand publicity for the venture. Robert Menzies, the prime minister, agreed to open it on 6 May 1963, which turned out to be just a few days after the first white ingots were sent away for fabricating. Pittsburgh, however, had different ideas. Grand openings of factories were not so common in the United States where a big factory, mill or smelter had long ceased to be a novelty. Moreover, there was a fear of industrial espionage. From Pittsburgh came the warning that if there was to be a grand opening

White Gold

ceremony, it should be held away from the smelter. Under no condition whatsoever were the official guests allowed to see inside the smelter or any other building. Not even Menzies could set foot in a building where the latest Alcoa processes were to be seen.

It was feared that Japanese experts, already invited to the opening ceremony, would see too much of the working process. Japan was now a strong competitor of the United States in aluminium, and its experts should be given no clues about the latest smelting techniques devised by the Aluminum Co. of America. Pittsburgh advised the Australian directors of Alcoa not to attend the openings of refineries and smelters when they visited Japan; and that abstention would, in effect, exempt them from an obligation to invite Japanese to inspect the new smelter in Australia. Pittsburgh's canny advice reached Melbourne too late. Lindesay Clark, planning a visit to Japan, had already accepted an invitation to attend the opening of a plant owned by Mitsubishi Chemical Industries.

The grand opening did not take place, and the prime minister did not appear. Instead the chairman, Frank Magee, flew out from Pittsburgh to attend a board meeting in Melbourne on Friday 10 May 1963 and to have his first view of the smelter. It was too late to cancel the press tour, but the journalists were not shown as much as they had hoped.

Fortunately the journalists did not realise that a continuous drama was going on inside the smelter as well as inside the publicity machine. On almost every day something went wrong. In the confidential, official reports the over-used phrase was 'operating problems'. Many pots were not operating in the smelter building. The rotary machines that cast the ingots had to be modified. Assays revealed that the first aluminium often contained a little too much iron and silicon. In July, as a result of a cavalcade of errors, the smelter produced only 895 tonnes, or less than half of the planned output. By the first weeks of August many faults had been overcome, the workmen understood their jobs more clearly and production jumped by 25 per cent. Still far from satisfactory, the results were at least improving. The consolation was that most new aluminium smelters had similar troubles.

At first it was not easy to produce aluminium of the highest level of purity, especially if the alumina itself carried more impurities than average. If too many impurities remained after the process of smelting, the resultant batch of aluminium ingot was limited in its usefulness. Slowly the purity of the product was increased. Now and then the manager would announce that his smelter had achieved a new record for purity. Thus 29 December 1966 was to be a special day because the percentage of metal in the ingot reached 99.843 per cent.

Glow at Point Henry

An early view of the potroom at the Point Henry smelter.

The first stage of the smelter—a section with a capacity of 20 000 tonnes of aluminium a year—had been completed almost on schedule. The next section of 20 000 tonnes had been reduced temporarily to 12 000 tonnes and timetabled for November 1963, but even that smaller addition was postponed. With Bell Bay and Point Henry now in competition, Australia was for some time producing more aluminium than it could sell. Alcoa decided it was sensible to eliminate the bottlenecks in the existing smelter before enlarging it. It was in 1964 that Point Henry reached its first goal of 40 000 tonnes a year.

Point Henry had other setbacks in its first years. An aluminium smelter faces chaos when its electricity is unexpectedly cut off, because its potroom is like a long line of large cake ovens, and when the power fails the batch of cakes is ruined and the burned cake turns into hard, useless metal. On the morning of 26 September 1967, at a point between Geelong and the smelter, a transmission cable fell from its tower after a cotter pin had failed. All power was cut off at 11.19 a.m. and the molten metal in the potroom began to cool. It was nearly 4 p.m. when at last the electricity was restored. Almost by a miracle, 45 pots of molten metal were saved, but 57 pots were ruined. In addition, about 1500 anode bars

White Gold

View of the smelter and fabricating plant at Geelong in 1969, after the expansion of the smelter to 90 000 tonnes a year.

had to be repaired, and with the aid of air compressors and jackhammers a mass of once-molten material had to be broken up and carted away. To clear up the mess required 26 000 man-hours. Four weeks passed before nearly all the pots were again in working order. In the meantime an output of 1.1 million kilograms of ingot had been lost because most of the smelter was idle.

The growth of Point Henry was slowed partly by a scarcity of skilled labour. Accordingly, houses had to be built in Geelong to attract new-comers to the city. The Housing Commission agreed to build houses and the company made cash loans, free of interest, to enable selected employees to pay a deposit on a house. In 1964 the company engaged the firm of A.V. Jennings to build houses at the outer Geelong suburb of Newcomb. They were sold or rented to selected employees on easy terms with a low down payment, interest at 5 per cent, and repayments to Alcoa spread over 28 years. Many of the houses were clad with aluminium on the side walls, partly to advertise the versatility of the company's metal, but bouncing cricket balls and footballs soon dinted the aluminium. A list of the employees who bought these houses in 1965 shows such names as Lasmanis, Stalio, De Kryger, Vouk and Lieknier: perhaps half of the houses were sold to 'New Australians' who represented a large part of the workforce in that era of vigorous immigration from Europe.

Alongside the smelter, a new fabricating plant called for several hundred more employees. The Aluminum Co. of America had long been a fabricator, and Australia had to follow that line simply in order to consume many of the ingots it produced. In Australia as in America it was believed that the making of aluminium products was as important as making aluminium itself. The ingot had to be shaped and fabricated if the growing Australian market was to be served by Point Henry rather than by imported aluminium products.

Clark and his colleagues, seeing themselves primarily as mining men, were at first not very interested in fabricating. That activity lay outside their expertise and interests. In addition they knew they would be hard pressed to find their share of the money for a fabricating plant. In the first years, any part of the project they could cut, they gladly cut.

Since a smelter without a fabricating plant was like a dog with three legs, Krome George approached Alcan, the Canadian company which already operated a plant in Sydney. In 1962 the two companies agreed to a 50–50 venture. Fears of infringing the American anti-trust laws made them hesitate. The lawyers on both sides shouted 'no'. In the end the three Australian shareholders of Alcoa of Australia agreed that a fabricating plant should be built at Geelong where work on the smelter was already under way.

The rolling mill—the key to fabricating aluminium for various uses— was built next to the smelter. Les Davey, recently recruited from his teaching post at the Bairnsdale technical college, was the working engineer. The machinery, new or secondhand, was assembled and installed. Much of the equipment came secondhand from the Aluminum Co. of America's plants in the United States. A scalper, worth US$225 000 if bought new, was sold to the Australian firm for US$54 500. A huge item of equipment, it was rehabilitated at a cost of US$12 000, packed for another US$17 000 and freighted to the nearest deepwater port of embarkation for US$6500. A run-out table, worth US$200 000 if new, was sold for US$85 000. A Niagara Shear, a cutting machine, was said to be worth US$14 000. It was sold for US$275, but more than three times that sum had to be spent in packing it in a crate and sending it by train to a port where shipping costs had to be paid by Alcoa of Australia.

A stiff leg crane, a rotary corrugator, and a Cincinatti-Bickford radial drill press were amongst the equipment unloaded at Geelong's wharves. There the cranes were unable to lift the heavier parts of the rolling mill, and so the ship had to employ her own lifting gear to draw them from

White Gold

*The hot reversing mill in the fabricating plant at Point Henry in the 1960s;
aluminium ingot is reduced to slab form for further rolling at the hot
continuous and cold finishing mills.*

the hold and lower them onto low-loader trucks. For all this secondhand equipment Alcoa of Australia did not pay cash to its American parent. The equipment was seen as a contribution of capital and the sum involved was deduced from the capital which the Aluminum Co. of America had promised to provide.

The huge Watson-Stillman extrusion press was first used in the mill in September 1963. Its task was to shape new-made aluminium into sections for use in building, defence, transport and a variety of industries. Like many machines, it refused to behave on its christening day. So arranged as to produce billets of one-and-a-half-inch round bar, it produced a mere two billets on that first day. It was pulled apart—the equivalent of major surgery—and in the course of several months it was reassembled. In February 1970 an even bigger extrusion press, made in Japan, was installed. A monster of 5000 tonnes, and the largest in the land, it extruded aluminium into sections for the manufacture of aluminium lightpoles and other products. It 'was a bit of a white elephant', Ken Mansfield recalls, and was sold after five years.

The smaller extrusion press continued to squeeze out the same product—now called 38.1 mm in the metric system—for twenty years, during

Glow at Point Henry

The 2750 tonne extrusion press at the Point Henry works. A powerful ram pushes heated aluminium billets through dies in the press, thus shaping the aluminium into the required patterns. Extrusions from this press were used extensively in the building, construction and transportation industries.

which time a succession of at least twelve drivers looked after the machine. Horst Engel, with his white steel hat and safety glasses, was the last driver, and when on 9 December 1983 the machine pushed the last round bar down the long table there was a sense of emotion. It was as if an old employee had died. An obituary was published in the Point Henry news magazine paying tribute to 'a gallant and endearing friend'. Old customers were glad to receive, as souvenirs of the last twitching of the muscles of the old machine, strips of round bar with their names inscribed.

It was believed that a rolling mill erected at Point Henry would consume an increasing proportion of the newly made ingots that came from the smelter. Any way of promoting Alcoa aluminium over the two rivals—Alcan and Comalco—brought more sales to the smelter door. The rolling mill began operating on 14 April 1965, producing its first satisfactory sheet after further days of trouble and modification. In the following six years a variety of new processes and machines were added or duplicated, including the light gauge sheet mill, foil mill, direct chill casting unit and coil preparation line.

White Gold

Alcoa promoted aluminium framing for building houses in the late 1960s and 1970s.

Once the smelter, rolling mill and fabricating plant were busy, the safety of employees was a concern. Noise was an early nuisance in the rolling mill, where the extrusion press and the big saw made a din. In the smelter building the jackhammers, which were sometimes called upon to break cold metal in the smelting pots, were just as noisy. In April 1968 at Point Henry, men working in certain areas had to wear earplugs made of wool or fibreglass. Publicity was given to groups who worked for long periods without an accident. On Sunday 5 May 1968 in the mechanical maintenance department, a large group of men notched up 250 000 man-hours without suffering one lost-time accident. It was less than one month since the first Western Australian employee lost his life at work. Arthur Howarth, a former school teacher, was working as a field attendant at the Jarrahdale mine when he was killed in an accident in an ore bin.

The company, even before it made a profit, felt bound to show its commitment to Geelong and district. In 1965 a large donation went to the Infant Welfare Centre at Newcomb where many of the smelter's employees lived, and the next year $24 000 (£12 000)—enough to buy a typical suburban house—was given to the Geelong and District Hospital. Amongst the company's donations during the next few years were

John Harper (president and chief executive of the Aluminum Company of America) and Allen Sheldon (managing director of Alcoa of Australia) viewing the site selected for the power station at Anglesea.

$10 000 worth of aluminium products to those who lost houses in the Hobart bushfires of 1967 and an aluminium surf boat to the Anglesea Surf Life Saving Club which patrolled the beach near the coalmine where the company's powerhouse was being built.

At Anglesea the company mined brown coal for customers in Geelong and Ballarat but delayed building its own power station which would be the main consumer of coal. One advantage of delay at Anglesea was that the expensive projects at Kwinana and Point Henry could have first call on the massive funds required. Point Henry's smelter was thus at work five years before the power station at Anglesea was designed. The contract for designing the power station was signed in June 1964, and the construction began sixteen months later.

It was a construction worker's dream. At the site of the power station the strong sound of surf could be heard on the days when the wind blew inland from the ocean. Some of the finest surfing beaches in the world, including Bell's Beach, were close to the coalmine. The mining areas were on the edge of a charming, straggling holiday resort which had less than 1000 people in winter but at least ten times that number at the height of summer.

White Gold

Proximity to the holiday town was also a difficulty. The mine and powerhouse, if intrusive to eyes and ears, would arouse intense objections. Potentially they were intruders. The mine, being an open cut, would be worked by noisy equipment, though, fortunately, the breaking of barren ground and coal seams called for no explosives. The powerhouse required a tall chimney, but fortunately the prevailing wind would carry the smoke away from the town and the coast.

One of the delights of Anglesea was the river estuary where children paddled. The two creeks that flowed into the estuary actually passed by or flowed over the coal deposits. What if the mining, or discharge of steam or dumping of ash, polluted the estuary? In the next five years, the environment would become a thorny political topic, in America and Australia but in the mid 1960s violations of the environment were rarely thwarted by the existing laws.

Fortunately for Anglesea, the company was a few years ahead of its time. Mistakes were made in planning the project, but by the standards of the time the overall plan was sensitive to the estuary, bushland and nearby town and beach. A creek was successfully diverted from coal-bearing ground and allowed to run and dribble in relative purity towards the estuary. Several attractive coal areas were virtually abandoned so that a permanent ridge of bushland could lie untouched, serving as a barrier between town and mine. Steps were taken, primitive steps at first, to grow new vegetation on ground that was mined out. As for the big power station, it could be placed in the valley, hidden by low hills from most streets in the holiday town. It is a sign of how effectively the mine and power station were hidden that most people in Melbourne have visited or driven through Anglesea but most of them do not know, even in the mid 1990s, that an extensive coal mine has been working at Anglesea for more than a quarter of a century.

The tall power station was not easily disguised. Protected by neither roof nor external walls, it was the first outdoor power station in Australia. The boiler and the turbine housing and the pipes could be seen from a distance, and from close up the steel stairways and stagings resembled the layers of decks of a tall ship. The top of the power station, with its view of the sea, was about as high as an eighteen-storey building. The white concrete chimney, called an 'exhaust stack', with a height of 108 metres, was twice as high again.

By May 1968, $24 million of the projected $30 million had been spent. Houses were being built in the town for newcomers. At the mine five Euclid trucks were removing the overburden of clay and sand to expose the deep coal. The power station was not far from completion, and the foundations were being laid for the steel towers which would transmit the high-voltage electricity 35 kilometres to the smelter at Point

Henry. Designed with a capacity of 150 megawatts, it was expected to lose only 2 per cent of its electricity along the powerlines to Point Henry.

Anglesea was formally opened by the premier of Victoria, Sir Henry Bolte, on the afternoon of 20 March 1969. Two hundred guests came in buses from Melbourne to watch him press a button which gave the impression of setting in motion the delivery of coal up the conveyor belt to the power station. The male guests walked along the open decks of the noisy power station and peered into the furnace from which gusts of orange flame shot upwards, while not far away the women inspected, some with justifiable signs of boredom, the administrative offices and the quiet control room of the power station. A buffet dinner was served in a marquee at 5 p.m. and the buses were boarded at 6.15 for the hour-and-a-half trip back to Melbourne.

A few months later, when all was working smoothly, everyone who lived in Anglesea was invited on a Sunday afternoon to tour the mine and power station and have afternoon tea. The tea party atmosphere did not last long. In November 1969 the members of the Australian Workers Union stopped work for five days and demanded over-award payments; and the mine and powerhouse had to be operated by engineers, senior clerks and other salaried staff.

Anglesea was originally planned to supply nearly all the electricity needed at Point Henry, but there the smelter and fabricating plant grew faster than predicted. By the time Point Henry received its first electricity from Anglesea, it had a second potline at work. That had to rely partly on government electricity from Gippsland, for Anglesea could not produce enough to satisfy Point Henry's growing appetite.

No attempt was made to enlarge Anglesea, but more power was later squeezed out of the existing turbine and generator, lifting its capacity almost to 160 megawatts. As Point Henry grew, it consumed more and more electricity generated from the brown coal of Gippsland. Today nearly 60 per cent of the electricity used at Point Henry comes from Gippsland. Anglesea's power station, while relatively small and antiquated, remains surprisingly efficient. Power stations a quarter-century old are close to the end of their useful lives, but Anglesea is much more reliable and fulfils its capacity far more than State Electricity power stations of the same age.

The company's own power station had been central to Lindesay Clarks' original thinking. As he thought that the smelter would be the ultimate source of profit and as cheap electricity would underwrite the smelter, he placed high emphasis on the brown coal of Anglesea. At a pinch his company could buy bauxite. He did not think, however, that it could acquire another private source of electricity. In the late 1950s he valued Anglesea more highly than the Darling Range. In the early books of Western Aluminium appears an entry which surprises us today:

Value of brown coal at Anglesea: 446 042 pounds
Value of bauxite in Darling Range: 252 691 pounds

By November 1962 the company decided to revalue these assets to 'reflect more accurately their true worth'. Coal and bauxite were deemed equally valuable and each was assigned a value of 2 259 926 pounds. The day would come when the value of the brown coal was only a tiny fraction of the worth of the bauxite. Whereas the bauxite became one of the most productive deposits in the world, the brown coal at Anglesea became a valuable but relatively minor asset.

The Forty-Niners

In the first years Alcoa lost money. The losses persisted long past the stage when profits had been expected. Tension arose between Melbourne and Pittsburgh, for it was only natural that such unexpected losses would lead to arguments and recriminations

For these disappointing results, Clark with some justice blamed the Americans who were largely running the business. In January 1965 he reminded Pittsburgh of its blemished record as a forecaster of profit. The formal prospectus of Alcoa of Australia had promised an annual profit for the calendar year 1965 of 2 347 000 Australian pounds with rising profits thereafter. But there was instead a heavy loss, and at the end of 1965 the accumulated losses were 6 323 000 pounds. Clark was not sure how far he should go in reminding the Americans of their failed promises. In June 1965 he reminded them, more forcibly than was his habit, that the financial results 'came as a great shock'. As Western Mining was only a small company, by Pittsburgh standards, and still depending largely on gold for its fragile profits, the absence of aluminium profits was a bitter blow.

The money lost was not the only cause of conflict. The parent company in Pittsburgh was not accustomed to working with an overseas partner. At times it baulked at the process of learning to cooperate rather than simply giving commands. Sometimes the Melbourne board and its managing director were not consulted adequately. Most of the major decisions were made in Pittsburgh. Even the appointing of a new director to represent the Australian shareholders on the board in Australia required, under clause 4.8 of the common agreement, the formal approval of Pittsburgh. Thus, after Frank Espie died on 9 May 1962, leaving a vacancy in the ranks of those directors representing Australian share-holders, Pittsburgh had to cable its approval before Bill Morgan of Western Mining could join the board.

At the same time Pittsburgh was sensitive to some Australian fears. Members of the American staff working for Alcoa, recalls Parry, were privately told not to buy shares in the Western Mining Corporation, the largest of the minority shareholders. If they were to buy shares in that Australian company they would ignite suspicion that perhaps a complete American takeover was quietly being planned in Pittsburgh.

Melbourne and Pittsburgh usually had cordial relations but the tension paraded itself from time to time. One cause of tension was the habit of the senior Americans working in Australia to take their orders from their department in Pittsburgh rather than from the Melbourne board which, by law, was in charge of the operations. Clark criticised the senior American staff in Kwinana and Geelong for constantly consulting Pittsburgh rather than the Melbourne board which paid their salary. In one sense it was natural that they should look to Pittsburgh because they knew that their chances of advancement lay there. In effect, they were merely on loan to Australia.

Clark was adamant that Pittsburgh should only be consulted when a crucial issue was at stake, but he could be as adamant as he liked: his complaint was barely registered. It was unwise, Clark argued in a letter, for Alcoa to 'be run as an Australian branch of a great American company from 10 000 miles away'. Too much interference could be 'fatal'.

The management style of which Clark complained was almost a tradition within the Aluminum Co. of America. Whereas some big companies faced their fiercest competition from rival companies, a few companies which traditionally faced no outside competition—and Pittsburgh for long was such a company—tended to foster their competition within the company. When the Aluminum Co. of America gloried in its monopoly, it was run almost as four separate companies or divisions: the mining division was run from Philadelphia, but later from the city of New York; the refining division from St Louis; the shipping from New York; and the fabricating from Pittsburgh. The head office in Pittsburgh was in the Gulf Oil building, with its strange pyramid-shaped top, but was superseded in 1952 by the aluminium skyscraper to which all the divisions—previously apart—migrated in a great show of unity. But the unity was largely artificial.

Within the Aluminum Co. of America the divisions remained, even in the early 1960s, and they were acute in its operating plants. While all the heads met daily in the head office, the distant producing plants retained the old rivalry. The big aluminium plants were divided into sections—power, refining, smelting, and mill—and each was more answerable to head office than to a general manager on site. Thus at a big plant the refining section often spoke more with head office than with the smelting section next door.

In a Tennessee company town, aptly named Alcoa, there were three separate Alcoa offices. One office ran the hydro-electric station, another office ran the smelter, and a third office and its staff ran the big rolling mill set up in the war to supply aircraft sheet to Britain. In this industrial centre Alcoa's operating managers did not meet regularly. Cooperation was not the first goal, because each chief reported primarily to a separate head in distant Pittsburgh. Indeed Krome George recalled visiting the town in the 1950s and hearing the chief of the rolling mill actually boast that he had never stepped inside the smelter.

What Krome George saw in Tennessee was repeated to some degree in Australia. The senior staff at Kwinana, all Americans in the first years, reported to Pittsburgh more than to Melbourne. They saw themselves as belonging to their particular division within the American company rather than as members of the Australian-based company. At the same time the Aluminum Co. of America was financing the enterprise and supplying its technology; and so it was reluctant to concede authority to a Melbourne board which, highly competent in so many facets of mining and finance, was not experienced in aluminium.

Clark had specific grievances. Alcoa was paying America too much money in interest. The Americans, while not making profits from Alcoa, were indirectly making them in the form of the interest on the money they had lent. There was some truth in this complaint, but Clark had gladly agreed to the arrangement some years ago. Clark also suggested the time had come to make the Australians and the Americans equal partners, with a 50–50 interest in Alcoa rather than the 51–49 interest which allowed Pittsburgh to dominate. His suggestion was extremely optimistic. The negotiations of 1961, when his bargaining position was fragile, had been very much in his favour.

There was another source of tension, though it was called an 'agreement'. The Victoria Agreement, signed in 1965, arose from the American taxation laws and took its name from one of Pittsburgh's subsidiary companies, called the Victoria, which had its head office at Wilmington in the state of Delaware. The Aluminum Co. of America, in order to comply with the depletion allowance provided for mines by American tax laws, wished to own some of the actual mining leases in the Darling Range. It wished to own half of those leases from which the alumina that went in ships specifically to the west coast of the United States was produced. This wish was loosely, and hurriedly, agreed to in 1961. In 1964 both sides tried to work out the exact details, and they sparred and argued for eighteen months. Finally on 15 December 1965, Alcoa

agreed—in the name of its Australian subsidiary Western Aluminium—
to sell to Pittsburgh a half interest in virgin leases containing 48 million
tonnes of bauxite with 'an available bauxite content of 35 per cent'.

To convert this bauxite into some 200 000 tonnes of alumina a year,
Western Aluminium would virtually have to double the output of the
refinery, financing it with twenty-year loans from Pittsburgh. In turn
Western Aluminium would refine the crushed bauxite at so many dollars
a tonne, the exact price being calculated on a rather tangled formula,
and hand over the alumina for Pittsburgh to use in one of its smelters
outside Australia. The Victoria Agreement was open-ended. If Pittsburgh
wished to buy more alumina it then bought another unmined lease in
the Darling Range, paying the same purchase and treatment price, and
the bauxite was refined in yet another 200 000-tonne unit of the refinery
built with American loans.

The agreement gave a sure profit to the Australian partners. The
difficult question was whether it gave an adequate profit. Lindesay Clark
was inclined to say 'no'. Pittsburgh, listening to him recite his grievances,
couldn't help saying with some justice that he had been a knowing party
to the agreement. Clark replied, also with some justice, that since the
signing of the agreement, fast inflation and a change in the value of the
American dollar had altered the predicted costs of refining. The dispute
was still simmering in 1978 when it was resolved by the recommenda-
tions made in a long report written by Harry Fawcett of Pittsburgh.
Generously and tactfully, Fawcett concluded that his own company truly
had an Australian opponent worthy of its 'steel'.

Clark's periodic protests to Pittsburgh led to action in one vital
matter: the selecting of a new managing director of Alcoa. Clark had
asked for 'one of your best men' in place of the genial, cocktail-shaking
Joe Smith. The man chosen was Allen C. Sheldon. He was seen as an
outsider within the Aluminum Co. of America, which meant that he
had not spent his whole career in that company, but a corporate
outsider—a manager who did not accept the American tribal loyalties
and was willing to swear some allegiance to the new Australian tribe—
was very much needed in Australia at that moment.

After studying chemical engineering at Iowa State University, Sheldon worked with the Pentagon during the war and then studied at the
Harvard Business School. After working for Abbott Laboratories in
Chicago, he learned how to run a business as head of the Rae Magnetic
Wire Co. which made wire that was thinner than a strand of human
hair. When that company was acquired by Pittsburgh in 1960, Sheldon
was voluntarily acquired too.

Sheldon was working at Fort Wayne, in Indiana, in the summer of 1965
when he received a phone call from 'Doc Mitchell', head of the company's

international division. Sheldon promptly hired a pilot and small Cessna aircraft and flew to Pittsburgh. In the head office he was shown a map of Australia, with the alumina refinery and the smelter standing on opposite coasts of the continent. After three-quarters of an hour of talk, Sheldon was offered the post of chief executive in Australia. It would be a high honour, said Mitchell persuasively, to run a fully integrated aluminium industry. 'Why,' he added, 'only John Harper does that.'

Refreshed after halting in Tahiti for a brief holiday, Sheldon landed at Essendon airport in September 1965. Entering the head office in Melbourne, he found that Smith did not wish to vacate his room. Smith would not even speak to Sheldon, and they went their separate ways without a word.

Sheldon slowly achieved more independence for the Australian board on which he now sat. He endorsed Clark's opinion that Alcoa should depend less on Pittsburgh's financial power and instead try to borrow in Europe the money needed for expansion. Sheldon built up the fabricating of aluminium at Geelong and he almost bought a large firm that dealt in aluminium scrap metal. He backed the Australian board's plan for expanding output.

At a time when nearly all the top jobs in Alcoa were held by Americans, Sheldon argued that young Australian engineers in the organisation should be advanced quickly to higher posts. He was impressed with the ability of some of these rising engineers. Roger Vines, for example, second in charge of the smelter at Geelong, and facing chaos after the supply of electricity was suddenly cut off at Point Henry, 'did a wonderful thing', according to Sheldon: 'he jump-started the smelter'. Believing that an Australian should become the next managing director of Alcoa, Sheldon had his eyes on Rod Carnegie, who later became head of the big mining company, Conzinc Riotinto of Australia (CRA).

Enjoying life in Melbourne, Sheldon accepted a seat on the council that governed the new La Trobe University, he sat on the Canberra selection committee which chose the Fulbright scholars and joined Melbourne Rotary and the Australian Club. His wife became vice-president of the Young Women's Christian Association in Melbourne, and each Sunday they went together to the Toorak Presbyterian church— when Sheldon was not overseas, trying to sign up new buyers of alumina. The Sheldons came to fancy contemporary Australian painters and, at the time of writing, they were living in retirement near Pittsburgh with a remarkable collection of 25 Australian paintings, collected largely in pairs and including two Tuckers, two Nolans, and two Percevals.

As managing director answerable equally to Melbourne and Pittsburgh, Sheldon walked a tightrope, indeed a slender magnetic wire. If he leaned too much towards the Australian side, he was likely to be rebuked by Pittsburgh; if he leaned towards the Pittsburgh side, Australian suspicions were likely to grow. Sheldon worked hard to find the balance. After three years he was recalled to America to a senior post. Even today he is not sure why, having been promised five years in Australia, he was recalled at short notice.

Pittsburgh made a vital concession when it agreed that Clark should have a strong say in selecting the successor to Sheldon. While the new man would come from Pittsburgh, he would not come without Lindesay Clark's nod of agreement. The first choice, Joe Bates, flew to Melbourne in May 1968 to meet Clark. It was not his first visit to Australia and he told Clark how as a wartime submarine officer he had landed in Fremantle in 1944, taken rest and recreation in an old converted mansion at Applecross, and then travelled by train and plane to Brisbane before flying back to Pearl Harbor. A mechanical engineer, Bates ran his own business after the war and, like his predecessor Sheldon, was a relative newcomer to the Aluminum Co. of America. Bates had five children and he and his wife were not certain whether they should make the disrupting move to Melbourne. Clark used his charm and logic. Bates, persuaded to accept the post, found he liked Australian life.

Bates had wide-ranging interests, and was able to take a balanced view of the company's needs. Speaking slowly and expressively he could make a powerful case. Normally he took the same side as Lindesay Clark when differences of opinion arose with Pittsburgh. Speaking privately in Pittsburgh a quarter of a century later, he said: 'My siding with Lindesay didn't endear me here'. He thought Clark could be tough but in the end he found him 'lovable'. Together they were to initiate bold plans in Western Australia, though neither was in office when the plans were fulfilled.

The company's profits had begun a year before Bates arrived, and that helped to ease the disagreements. While the company was very healthy, no dividend was yet paid to the Australian and American shareholders. Australia's economy was far and away the main gainer from Alcoa's early years. The exports created, and the imports no longer needed, were big advantages to Australia. There were also the thousands of construction jobs and then the permanent jobs, for the company employed about 1750 people by the end of 1967. It was an industry to be measured more by the wealth created than by the employment created, for aluminium at every step was heavy in the use of machinery and electricity but light in using labour.

In the second half of the 1960s Alcoa's expansion was almost continuous. The Kwinana refinery was doubled between 1965 and 1966. In the following year an outlay of $17 815 000 was needed to build a third unit and so increase the refinery's capacity to 620 000 tonnes of alumina a year. Within months another $17 000 000 was needed to raise refining capacity to 830 000 tonnes. The long-awaited steam powerhouse at the company's own coalmine at Anglesea was now under way, with a capacity of 150 megawatts. That called for another $31 330 000. And there were plans in 1968 for doubling the smelter at Geelong and for building a new refinery in Western Australia. Far more money was needed for these plans than had been spent in setting up the original refinery at Kwinana and the smelter and mills at Point Henry.

So far nearly all the capital had come in loans from the Aluminum Co. of America: little had come from the Australian shareholders. They lacked the required cash, nor did they have the financial strength to borrow, in their own name, huge sums in Australia. The time came in 1968 for a new way of raising big sums. Alcoa was now making a profit, and had big assets in its ore reserves and buildings and machinery. Therefore it could borrow in its own name if necessary. Pittsburgh for its part was no longer so eager to pour money into Australia because it had other calls on its funds. It was not even keen to guarantee loans raised by the Melbourne company. Nor could Pittsburgh always gain official permission from Washington, where an unfavourable balance of payments created a reluctance to encourage the export of capital to Australia and other foreign lands.

For his part, Lindesay Clark did not wish to be an eternal supplicant, relying on Pittsburgh to finance each leap in output. If Alcoa could raise money in its own name it would enhance the independence of its Australian directors and shareholders. The magnitude of the new capital needed was not yet fully realised. In fact at least $A200 million would be spent in the four years ending in December 1970, with tens of millions more to follow.

For funds the company turned towards London. Its decision was influenced by one of the new directors, John Darling. He came from a well-known business family which began with flour mills in South Australia and became prominent in Broken Hill Proprietary where his father had been a long-time chairman. After serving as a pilot in the final phase of the war—his last task was to give protection to the Royal Navy in the recapture of the Channel Islands—John Darling rejoined the flour business and became a buyer of wheat. Deciding that Australia had an opening for merchant bankers, then a new profession here, he commenced in a humble way in Sydney in 1958 and then branched out by forming Darling & Co. which began with four equal partners: the Darling family; Ord Minnett, the sharebrokers; a partnership between the Bank of New South Wales (now Westpac) and Jardine Matheson; and finally the London merchant bankers, Schroder Wagg.

A pioneer of the unofficial money market in Australia, Darling & Co. flourished.

In 1964 John Darling was invited 'out of the blue' to join the board of Alcoa, as a representative of the Americans. As the custom was, he attended an extraordinary general meeting of shareholders of Alcoa in Melbourne on Monday 29 June 1964. The meeting, commencing at 10.30 a.m., was over in an instant. Darling was elected a director in place of the American engineer Perry 'Red' Hartsock, who was returning home, and at 10.45 he took his place at the regular meeting of directors held in the same room. He was still on the board thirty years later. His reputation, a colleague said, embraced many areas, including English grammar: he always detected a split infinitive.

When John Darling joined the board, Denny Marris, working in the office of Lazards in the city of London, let out a murmur of apprehension. He privately told Clark he could see perturbing implications. He feared that Lazards would be supplanted by Schroder Wagg as Alcoa's main financial adviser. When a few years later the time came for Alcoa to raise money in Europe, John Darling's connections were valuable. For sentimental reasons Lazards were Alcoa's first choice, but were not seen as large enough to raise the sums required. So the London firm of J. Henry Schroder Wagg & Co. merchant bankers on the grand scale, was also enlisted.

Ned Pfeifer, a young American who was the finance director of Alcoa, planned the initial fundraising in London. As an expansionist, determined to seize every opportunity to enlarge Alcoa's plants, his formula was simple. Alcoa had contracts to supply alumina on a large scale to overseas smelters, so it was assured of a monthly inflow of cash: indeed the price of the exported alumina was fixed in advance on virtually a cost-plus basis. Therefore Alcoa could probably negotiate a loan from a syndicate of overseas banks on the security of the alumina contract. Then the interest and principal could be repaid regularly to the banks from the money earned by the sale of alumina.

In wintry London early in 1968 the Alcoa party—Sheldon, Pfeifer, and two non-executive directors, Burt and Darling—began negotiations with Lazard and Schroder on the procedures to follow. Details were hammered out, sometimes over dinners that went on so long that Burt would drop off to sleep at the table. Schroder Wagg soon became the main player in the organising of the loans, with one of its directors, Peter Bulfield, the key negotiator. On 29 February 1968, largely through his efforts, a Eurodollar credit facility of $US46 million was secured from a syndicate of British, American and Australian banks. At that time the Australian dollar was much more valuable than the American dollar.

The Forty-Niners

In 1968 a team from Alcoa set out for London to negotiate the first Euro Dollar loan needed for financing the expansion at Kwinana. Calling at South Africa, the team was photographed while visting a gold mine. From left to right are three directors, C.E. Pfeifer, John Darling and Ralph Burt along with a leading Melbourne solicitor, S.G.C. 'Jock' Macindoe.

In 1969, through the combination of Schroder Wagg and Lazard, two further credit facilities totalling $US129.7 million were secured. More loans coped with the expansion of refining in Western Australia. In Sydney, David Clarke and then Richard Griffin were vital links in Alcoa's borrowings, flying to London when negotiations for a new loan began in London. In the raising of loans, several Australian banks played a brave part, either on their own or in a syndicate including American and British banks. Initially the E.S. & A. Bank and the Commercial Bank of Australia were the main Australian banks to help Alcoa's expansion, but the Australian Resources Development Bank was increasingly active. Overseas loans, however, dwarfed Australian loans. In some deals the American banks were the main lenders to Alcoa but their support was arranged through London finance houses and not through Pittsburgh.

Legally, these loans were delicate because Alcoa of Australia (W.A.), the successor to Western Aluminium N.L., formally held the mining leases and the refineries, while the Melbourne company, Alcoa of Australia, owned the smelter, rolling mill and fabricating plant. These loans also posed dangers and difficulties for the overseas financiers. At no stage did they make their loans on the actual security of Alcoa's physical assets. Their 'security' was the cash flow from the shipments of alumina, coupled with covenants restricting what Alcoa could do financially.

More loans were raised. The capital cost of the increased refining capacity and the enlarged smelter at Point Henry seemed never-ending. Indeed by 1971 the company's debt was 3.37 times its equity, a ratio which would now be regarded, in the gloomy light of the experience of the late 1980s, as hazardous.

The ability of Alcoa to raise overseas loans was one sign of its growing independence. Another sign was Lindesay Clark's victory in his campaign to rescue the lower grade bauxite from oblivion. In the Darling Range much of the bauxite near the bottom of each quarry was ignored and bypassed. Whole deposits containing lower grade bauxite were left unmined. At Jarrahdale, bauxite containing less than 35 per cent of alumina was considered too poor to be worth mining. Charles Court and the Western Australian government said: why waste it? Clark agreed with Court wholeheartedly.

It was understandable that in the early years of mining activity much bauxite was discarded. It was simply low in grade by world standards. Now, however, the economics of turning bauxite into alumina were becoming very favourable, and the excess silica—once feared—was being removed with relative ease. What was low grade in the Darling Range was potentially as profitable as high-grade bauxite of a different chemical composition in another part of the world. To mine lower grade bauxite in the Darling Range became an enticing prospect. It would prolong the life of the mine and give more wealth to Western Australia.

Ed Harrison, Pittsburgh's ingenious roving geologist, had seen this possibility at an early stage. While the alumina refinery at Kwinana was designed to treat bauxite containing 35 per cent of recoverable alumina, it might also earn a profit from the huge zones that assayed just over 30 per cent. Harrison had estimated that the bauxite in the 30 to 35 per cent range ran into tens of millions or even hundreds of millions of tonnes. Why waste it? While Ed Harrison was initially seen as a stirrer, his argument made sense to Lindesay Clark. Clark's own previous big venture, as head of Western Mining, had been the attempt to mine very low-grade gold ore at Bullfinch on a considerable scale. Perhaps the Darling Range could be a *successful* version of Bullfinch.

There was now talk of building a second refinery in a new area and opening another mine. Here was a chance to include poorer bauxite. The board in Melbourne was sympathetic to lowering the grade of bauxite from 35 to 31.5 per cent, thus enabling vast blocks of neglected ground to be quarried. Not all the Pittsburgh leaders were convinced.

The capital invested in the second mine and refinery would yield a smaller return if poorer bauxite was treated. Moreover such poor bauxite was not being treated in other mines they competed with.

Clark persevered, and in Pittsburgh one day he confronted Harper, Krome George, Banks Smith and other heads with his argument. Graphs and charts were displayed; the 'no' case was forcefully put by head office; all guns were blazing. Clark listened in silence but was not persuaded. Bob Slagle, who came to Australia more than twenty years later as managing director, was at that time 'just a spear carrier'. Watching the debate as perhaps the youngest person in the room he just had to admire Clark, by far the oldest person present, for his pertinacity and his command of the facts.

In reply Clark put forward more a nationalist argument. The bauxite was a valuable Australian asset, of long-term value to the world. It should be used to its maximum potential. Mined and refined with the latest skills, the poorer bauxite would be profitable. Clark won. It was his greatest victory.

Meanwhile he must have been pondering, with some reluctance, when to step down as chairman. One of the recognised leaders of Australian industry—knighted in 1968 for his services to mining—he still enjoyed the challenges and the arguments. Chairman of three major mining companies—Alcoa, Western Mining and Broken Hill South—he was intensely interested in the detailed operations of each company and gave them nearly his whole working time. At the same time he was now aged 74, an age deemed old for a company chairman.

Clark was now treated often as a father figure. At times he seemed slightly frail, his hair was white and wispy, his cheeks were a cherubic red and his voice, as always, was soft. His words, carefully plucked from his large vocabulary, could be slow and hesitant but at times were as strong as steel. Perhaps he seemed hesitant because he took time in choosing words. And yet his ability to coax the best out of members of his board, his capacity for sorting out the priorities of his company and his command of the loyalty of the board remained formidable.

Meetings chaired by Clark were more like those of a friendly debating society, with the discussion ending when he saw that at last they were reaching a spirit of agreement. How it would be expressed in the minute book was not always decided at the meeting. The company secretary could see that harmony had risen out of the vigorous discussion but he could not be sure how to express the harmony—in short, what did they exactly agree upon? At board meetings, Clark loved to debate the technical matters that were a thorn in his relationships with Pittsburgh. Sometimes he was right, but not always.

In February 1970, he let it be known privately that he was soon

White Gold

The directors of Alcoa of Australia meeting in the head office in Queen Street, Melbourne, in 1970. Seated from left to right: Sir James Forrest, J.R. Burt, J. Darling, W.M. Morgan, J.C. Bates, Sir Lindesay Clark, D.R. Tucker (secretary), R.L. Bowlby, Sir Wilfred Brookes, A.W. Stewart (alternate director), C.E. Pfeifer. Absent were W.H.K. George, J.M.H. Mitchell and R.L. Baillieu.

stepping down as chairman of Alcoa. He would remain as chairman of other gold and base metal companies, and he would serve as deputy chairman of Alcoa. Part of the reason, in addition to his age, was perhaps an inability to get on with the new head of the Aluminum Co. of America, the strong-willed John Harper. He ceased to be chairman at the end of the meeting of the board on Monday 24 August 1970.

Choice of a new chairman was not easy. J. Chester Guest, who represented North Broken Hill on the Alcoa board since its inception, was a close friend of Clark and they sat together on the board of Western Mining. Charming as a negotiator and a good listener, he knew Alcoa's business through long experience. Prominent in Melbourne finance, Guest was chairman of the Commercial Bank of Australia, the third largest of the Melbourne-based banks. At the start of the year when Clark was preparing to retire, Guest was aged 59. He seemed to be in fair health, especially when he played golf, but he had not entirely recovered from his years as a prisoner of war in European camps. He died only a fortnight before Clark announced publicly his own pending resignation as chairman.

Another possibility as chairman was Bill Morgan, a director of Alcoa since 1962 and also a member of the Western Mining stable that was expected to produce the next chairman. He had followed Lindesay Clark as managing director of Western Mining, leading the company to new success as Australia's big nickel miner and smelter. On the Alcoa board he was the expert on Japan, the company's biggest customer. Unlike Clark he preferred Japan to England as a place for doing business; and much of the Japanese business he had personally signed up. As a former senior employee of the State Electricity Commission of Victoria his links there were valuable; he had negotiated the contract to buy big blocks of power from its power stations and he was also prominent in the purchase of the coalmine at Anglesea. He had a way of inviting trust, and the company owed much to what the board minutes called 'his warm personality'.

Morgan tended to be interested more in the commercial side of Alcoa and in the technical side of Western Mining. That was the result of the slightly vague way in which Clark apportioned territory amongst top staff. As Arvi Parbo once noted, 'it was never very clear who was in charge of what'. He added that Lindesay Clark 'tended to be unclear about these sort of things; and yet it worked well'. In such a situation the question of choosing successors was not a first priority. Morgan was likely but not certain to succeed Clark as chairman of Alcoa. But when Clark was about to retire, Morgan's health was beginning to fail. He resigned on 30 November 1971 and died early the following year. His son Hugh was later to become a prominent member of the board.

To the surprise of many observers an outsider, Sir James Forrest, became chairman of Alcoa. Nine years younger than Clark, he was in the process of retiring as senior partner in the well-known Melbourne law firm of Hedderwick Fookes & Alston and had been chairman for many years of several of the country's largest companies, including the National Bank of Australasia and the Australian Consolidated Industries, a major manufacturing firm. He had no particular experience of mining, but about three months before he became chairman of Alcoa of Australia he was invited to join the board of Western Mining Corporation.

Forrest accepted a permanent office in the company's section of the new AMP offices in Bourke Street, where he usually spent two days a week. He liked precision, and orderly relationships. He believed in a structured meeting. The typewritten agenda on the table was the king, and the meeting began on time. He listened, and did not talk unduly. He imparted a benign authority to the chair.

He developed firm views about Alcoa's business. Knowing that the fabricating of aluminium was not very profitable, he wondered at the merit of the small fabricating companies in which Alcoa had a stake. He thought they were a distraction from the main business of mining, refining and smelting which should dominate the company's attention. Forrest, who had a fondness for the old-fashioned sayings, sometimes said of small companies: 'If you mix with dogs you get a flea in the ear'. The small companies, like dogs, could give more trouble than they were worth. Some of the senior managers by the 1970s were reaching the same opinion.

Forrest came to office with scant knowledge of the earlier disagreements between Pittsburgh and Melbourne, and that was an advantage. Holding no grievances towards Pittsburgh, and being lawyer-like in designating which was its realm and which was his, he improved relations between Melbourne and Pittsburgh largely by taking no intense interest in them.

For two years Sir Lindesay Clark remained as deputy chairman on the Alcoa board, and then in May 1972 he wrote a letter of resignation to Forrest. In farewell his colleagues spoke of Clark's vision, leadership and determination, praising also 'the fellowship' he engendered. At the company's request his portrait was painted by Clifton Pugh, for he was rightly seen as the founder.

In his last years his loyal ally had been Joe Bates, the managing director. Bates had been appointed to Australia partly because he was seen as likely to break down the habit of senior Americans of reporting to their head office in America rather than to their real employer in Australia. He enjoyed almost too much success in making Alcoa independent. He worked hard, usually ruling, some said, 'with a rod of iron'. And yet he did not monopolise the decisions, being willing to delegate to others, and eagerly encouraging his staff to improve their qualifications so that they could have more say.

Some of the leaders in Pittsburgh seemed to see Joe Bates as too often an ally of Clark, but others saw him as a talented manager whose services were now needed in the United States. In August 1971, Bates received a telex which named the new managing director of Alcoa. On the day of a scheduled meeting of the board in Melbourne, Bates wrote out his formal resignation as a director of Alcoa. Whether he briefly appeared at the first part of the board meeting is not certain but a warm vote of thanks was expressed to him and noted in the minutes. On returning home he rose high in the Aluminum Co. of America. As we shall see, he was also to leave his green mark on Western Australia.

With the departure of Clark, the ruffled period of relations between Pittsburgh and Melbourne was almost over. In the first years of Alcoa some friction had been almost inevitable, for the opposite sides of the equator possessed different interests and experiences. Pittsburgh, in its desire for close control, was influenced by its memory of the anti-trust laws: it could not afford to put a foot in the wrong place. Moreover, as it had taken the major financial risks in the initial years, it expected to be in unquestioned control. Pittsburgh erred, however, in not paying enough attention to the technical criticisms coming from Australia. It did not quite realise that while its three Australian partners originally knew nothing about aluminium, they represented one of the strongest technical traditions in the history of world mining. In the treating of a difficult low-grade ore they had a distinctive contribution to make.

There was one other underlying cause of unease. Lindesay Clark somehow hoped—it was a futile hope—that his Australian alliance could eventually secure 50 or even 51 per cent, instead of 49 per cent, of the shares. From the outset he was slightly resentful of American control even on those issues where the control was sound. And yet when he ceased in 1972 to be a director, the venture was far larger and more profitable than he could have imagined in the first year. It was producing eight times as much alumina as envisaged in the original stage. After six years of making financial losses, it was earning a high return on the shareholders' equity, averaging 21 per cent in the three years between 1969 and 1971. Above all, it was becoming a producer of world importance.

♦ 10 ♦

'There's Your Sign'

After seven years of continuous mining, the proved reserves of bauxite in the Darling Range were larger than ever. Far more was found than was mined each year. The existence of about 500 million tonnes was proven, and at least another 500 million tonnes were believed with reasonable confidence to be awaiting further drilling. At the present rate of mining, the bauxite could be worked for several hundred years.

The refinery had begun as a single unit with an annual capacity of about 200 000 tonnes. By December 1970 a sixth and almost identical unit had been opened, raising the capacity to 1 250 000 tonnes of alumina a year. Back in 1961 the original act of parliament had insisted that Alcoa had to produce only 120 000 tonnes of alumina a year to justify its right to the bauxite deposits, but it now produced ten times that tonnage. In capacity Kwinana was now well ahead of the oldest refinery, at Bell Bay, the new Gladstone refinery in central Queensland and the almost completed refinery at Gove in the Northern Territory.

At Kwinana more and more ships arrived with caustic soda or, arriving empty, took in cargoes of alumina for Point Henry and for Japanese and North American ports. About five ships a month berthed at the long pier by the refinery and in 1971 a total of 59 ships took away alumina. Dredging of the harbour had allowed bigger ships to arrive. In September 1968 a ship carried away a record 32 000 tonnes of alumina for the Bellingham smelter in Washington State, but only three years later a cargo of 40 600 tonnes was carried away.

For those people living within a few kilometres of the Kwinana refinery and pier, the industry was outliving their original welcome.

Houses were more numerous than when the site of the refinery had been selected ten years earlier. While the noise and fumes from the refinery were rarely seen as a nuisance, the white dust was resented by those living nearby. Those nearby householders who dried their washed clothes on wirelines in the backyards of their houses sometimes complained. In the Western Australian parliament in October 1969 the dust was strongly criticised by Colin Jamieson, member for Belmont and for ten years the state president of the Australian Labor Party. He pointed out that whereas the iron ore loaded into ships at Port Hedland, far to the north, released annoying clouds of red dust, the lighter alumina at Kwinana pier was even more easily picked up by a breeze and carried to nearby streets. When the wind blew from the sea, he said, 'the hotel and some homes were covered with dust'.

Day and night the Kwinana refinery disgorged a flow of red mud—the thick liquid waste of iron and sand from which the alumina had been extracted. As the Western Australian bauxite was very low in alumina, it was correspondingly high in waste. Perhaps no refinery in the world produced so much waste for each million tonnes of bauxite treated. Indeed the year would come when Alcoa calculated that its three refineries in Western Australia produced 35 per cent of the world's red mud.

Even before Kwinana was working on a huge scale, it had to buy several nearby houses and demolish them so that room was available for the mud lakes and for the protective buffer zone of land surrounding them. In 1967 more dumping ground was bought along the Hope Valley Road. On the hundreds of acres of dumping ground the refinery mud dried in the sun, and then fresh mud was laid on top, like a red sandwich cake. On top as, a final icing, was placed a layer of 60 centimetres of waste sand pumped as a slurry from the refinery. So these 'lakes' grew wider, covering large areas. Under the Alumina Refinery Agreement, signed in June 1961, the layers of mud were supposed to harden so that eventually they would 'support buildings for light industry'. So far no factory sits on the dumps.

Kwinana's refinery grew faster than anyone had predicted when the wire fence was erected around the empty site. Now parts of the site were jammed with buildings, and expansion was impossible. Even if there had been room to expand, the environment case against building a second refinery nearby would have been powerful.

At Pinjarra, about 64 kilometres to the south of Kwinana, a site was selected for the second refinery. Unlike Kwinana, the new refinery would be about twenty kilometres inland, at the foot of the escarpment of the Darling Range. To be away from the sea was an advantage. The sea breezes, though pleasant for the refinery workers on hot days, could also add to the expense. As much of the Kwinana refinery had no outer walls, thus allowing the sea wind to be felt by men at work, more energy was need to maintain the intense heat required by the rows of heating and 'cooking' tanks. Moreover, the salt air corroded the vast extent of metal piping.

The second refinery, being closer to the bauxite deposits that extended along the Darling Range, would gain from cheaper transport. As a refinery needed roughly three tonnes of bauxite to produce one tonne of alumina, there was merit in building the refinery near the mine. In contrast, the long distance between the mine at Jarrahdale and the refinery at Kwinana meant that the millions of tonnes of waste material mixed with the aluminium oxide had to be railed at considerable cost all the way to the coast before it was separated and sent to the red mud heaps. Curiously, the international practice was not to build the refinery near a bauxite mine. Alcan's decision in 1953 to build a refinery next to a bauxite deposit in Jamaica was revolutionary at the time, but it proved sensible. For Alcoa, the decision to build the second refinery close to bauxite deposits was even more sensible.

Land at Pinjarra was much cheaper than at urban Kwinana. The clay below the soil was ideal for the holding of the red mud, thus preventing the escape of effluent into the creeks that crossed the plains. The district had another advantage for Alcoa: it was not far from the alternative harbour of Bunbury which the Western Australian government was eager to deepen. Eventually the Pinjarra refinery would have the option of sending its alumina by railway to one of two different ports, thus ensuring that it always had an outlet, even if one port or loading pier was temporarily out of action. As overseas smelters depended on receiving regular shipments of alumina, and receiving them on time, there was additional security in having two Western Australian alumina ports.

The error made at Kwinana, where the nearby wasteland was inadequate, was not repeated at Pinjarra. It was resolved that some 5000 hectares, mostly farmland, had to be acquired to allow room for the mud lakes and a protective corridor around the extensive site. Standing near the foot of the Darling Range, the farmland must be bought secretly. Once it was announced that Alcoa was coming, the prices of the remaining islands of unbought land were sure to soar.

Joe Bates and some of his engineers began to inspect Pinjarra farms, sometimes examining them from the road and sometimes walking inside the paddocks. Bates recalls that they had broadly designated the best area and were sitting under a tree, eating their sandwiches, when a flock of galahs noisily landed on the tree. 'There's your sign,' said Bates to Jim Langford, the mine manager. That land was to become the heart of the refinery.

Meanwhile, an estate agent in Perth was buying up farms for Alcoa. About twenty owners had to be persuaded to sell. In the end only one family refused to sell, and remained obstinate until an enticing sum was offered.

By chance a tiny area of crucial land was overlooked during the buying spree. The refinery was being designed before someone within the company realised that about half a hectare of land near the middle of the refinery was still in private hands. The owner, Bates recalled, 'had us over a barrel'. If she had lived in the United States, he added, and if she had followed American commercial practices, she would have demanded a fortune. As it turned out, she was willing to sell at a moderate price.

The presence of adequate bauxite in the range just above the site of the Pinjarra refinery could almost be taken for granted. After the exact site of the refinery was decided upon, deposits of bauxite were found and drilled on the company's mining leases, only eight kilometres away. Nearby was the timber-milling town of Dwellingup, where a fire had recently burned the main mill and many houses. Most shopkeepers in Dwellingup gave three cheers when they heard that a mine would soon appear near their doorsteps.

At Kwinana the company had not built streets of houses for its employees and had supplied few if any civic amenities. But the opening of the iron ore in the Pilbara had set a precedent for companies, rather than the government, to finance towns and suburbs and many of their amenities. Charles Court, still the minister for industrial development, decided that Alcoa, like the iron companies of the northwest, should take on new responsibilities. Joe Bates was taken aback. He told Court that these demands were normally not made on an industrial company in the United States. Court merely smiled. He really did not have to explain—for Bates knew—that the Western Australian government had already granted Alcoa a huge area of bauxite at a low rent. The amenities Alcoa now had to provide were an additional form of rent.

Alcoa had to provide its own water and electricity for the new refinery. Whereas the government had built the railway from the first bauxite mine at Jarrahdale, the company now had to provide its own transport from the new mine to the new refinery. In addition, the company had to pay its share of the cost of the large town of Pinjarra's expanding facilities—the sewerage, hospital, school and the fire and police stations which the refinery workers and their families would require.

A company town was also planned on the open park-like country to the north of Pinjarra. Christened Carcoola, said to mean 'land of the gum trees' in the local Aboriginal language, the planned town was closer to the refinery than to Pinjarra town. Jean Verschuer, who had helped to plan the new nickel town of Kambalda near Kalgoorlie, became the landscape architect. Insisting on retaining most of the stately old gum trees, she enhanced Carcoola by planting thousands of trees. Two hundred houses with aluminium frames were built or almost ready when the refinery opened. There was space for hundreds more, but Carcoola was not as successful as was hoped. There the husband usually drove the family car to work, leaving the wife stranded in a town too small to have its own amenities and too far from Pinjarra with its shops and services.

Contrary to expectations, a large part of the workforce did not come from Perth or from other states. As Charles Court recalled, the planners overlooked the fact that this farming district already held a 'pool of healthy, strong' men who were eager to build and then work in the refinery. Many farmers continued to run a small farm, supplementing their income by 35 or 40 hours of well-paid work at the refinery. Moreover, large numbers of the outsiders coming to construct the refinery preferred to live at Mandurah, a rising seaside town that was only a fifteen minutes' drive away. The predictions made in 1969—that in the next two decades the refinery would help lift the combined population of Pinjarra and Carcoola from 8000 to 23 000—were far too confident.

There were new methods at the rising refinery, for several hard lessons had been learned from Kwinana. In October 1969 Lindesay Clark had emphasised the deficiencies of Kwinana in a letter he wrote to John Mitchell in Pittsburgh: 'What the total waste in capital and operating costs has amounted to over the years—and is still continuing—I have not attempted to assess but it must be very large'. After nearly six years, Kwinana was still suffering from original defects which had simply been repeated in the duplicate plants built there. Thus the peculiar bauxite of the Darling Range gave trouble in the pipes and processes at Kwinana partly because it was not crushed finely enough in the rod mills. Colin Kleeman, the chief metallurgist at Western Mining's gold plants, thought it was odd that Kalgoorlie's old mills could effectively treat gold-bearing ores that were heavy with sand, while Kwinana with the latest equipment was less effective in treating bauxite that was heavy with sand. He decided that the new process of autogenous grinding was needed at the alumina refineries.

Clark called on other experts. As chairman of Broken Hill South, the third largest shareholder in Alcoa, he was able to consult South's metallurgist, Len Fielding, who had proved the success of an autogenous grinding process at the new copper mine near Cobar, New South Wales. There, Fielding treated samples of bauxite sent from Western Australia, and concluded that they would gain from the same kind of grinding. Fielding inspected Kwinana and made numerous criticisms of the rod mill and the thickeners. He then went to the United States to meet refinery experts. The argument was won. The rod mills were replaced by autogenous grinding in the rising Pinjarra refinery.

'There's Your Sign'

The method of transporting the bauxite from the mine to the refinery was another debate in which Pittsburgh was willing to concede. Whereas American consultants had favoured the building of a railway from the bauxite deposits on the Darling Range to the Pinjarra refinery on the plain below, Jim Langford of Alcoa favoured the wide conveyor belt. Bill Morgan, managing director of Western Mining, had experience of conveyor belts

The construction of the second Western Australian refinery at Pinjarra was well advanced in July 1971. The new conveyor belt can be seen coming from the mine (bottom right).

when in charge of mining brown coal for the State Electricity Commission of Victoria, and he concluded that a fast conveyor belt was the cheapest way of moving bauxite across the hills to the Pinjarra refinery. E.D.J. (Doug) Stewart of the State Electricity Commission became consultant, and forecast a large saving in capital and labour if the fast conveyor belt were built. The decision proved correct, and the sight of the heavy conveyor belt travelling through the bush, up and down steep hills, was to fascinate engineers from around the world.

The Pinjarra refinery was seen as so important that John D. Harper, chairman and chief executive of the Aluminum Co. of America, organised his first visit to Western Australia for five years. Harper, aged 60, was a national name in American industry and a long-time Alcoa man, having worked as a fifteen-year-old in school vacations at the smelting town of Alcoa in his native Tennessee before studying electrical engineering and joining the company's staff.

Harper set out with R. Banks Smith, vice-president of the international division, in one of the company's four aircraft, the *Grumman Gulfstream*, with its aluminium body and its decorations of red and blue, the company's colours. Seating twelve, it was fitted with a special table where Mr and Mrs Harper and Mr and Mrs Banks Smith could sit and talk during the long flight. On Friday 6 November 1970 their aircraft called at Darwin and Mount Isa, and next day it 'buzzed' Ayers Rock in central Australia before flying on to Perth where the new Australian chairman, Sir James Forrest, and his wife were waiting to welcome them. On Sunday they saw the rising works at Pinjarra where more than 1000 construction workers were normally working. On Monday they called on the state's two leading politicians, David Brand and Charles Court, went to the Kwinana refinery for lunch and entertained Mr and Mrs Court to dinner at the Weld Club. The next day they set out for Melbourne where they were to meet the Alcoa directors.

In January 1972 a bauxite mine was opened at Del Park, in the ranges above the refinery. Trucks carried the big lumps of bauxite to a huge mobile crushing plant made in Germany. The crusher, almost a mechanical dinosaur, could walk to a new position on its 'lift and stride pads' at a pace of over ninety metres an hour. The bauxite, crushed into smaller pieces, was dropped onto the long covered conveyor belt that ran along the plateau and down the steep hill for a distance of six or seven kilometres to the refinery. There the autogenous grinders were ready to reduce the bauxite to a slurry, enabling the alumina to be slowly extracted in a series of steps.

With the initial unit of the refinery almost completed, workmen were recruited and taught their job by visiting operators from Kwinana. Whereas more than half of the recruits at Kwinana had been British migrants, most at Pinjarra were rural Western Australians. Mostly practical men, they did not mind—contrary to union rules—jumping in to do the work that traditionally belonged to a member of another union. If a valve failed, they fixed it without waiting for a specialist fitter to arrive. Skilled in using fencing wire and other old remedies, they sometimes tackled breakdowns in their own rough and ready ways. Being farmers they used a dash of oil in their repairs. 'The place was flooded with oil,' one foreman recalls.

The day of the official opening was Wednesday 3 May 1972. Buses carried the guests from the new Parmelia Hotel, the pride of Perth, to Pinjarra where they briefly saw the refinery and its alumina, which was setting out for Kwinana pier in sealed railway trucks. John Tonkin, leader of the Labor Party, which had won office at the recent state election, was pleased to open the refinery. As overseas grandees of the aluminium industry had assembled, more speeches were called for. Sir James Forrest of Alcoa and Mr John Harper of the Aluminum Co. of America each stepped forward, and were followed by Mr Shinojima of Mitsubishi Chemical Industries and Mr Ohsumi of Furalco, presidents of Japanese companies which would buy much of the alumina produced at Pinjarra.

The premier of Western Australia, the Hon. J. Tonkin, opens the Pinjarra refinery on 3 May 1972.

White Gold

At the Parmelia Hotel that evening 55 guests dined their way through what is now a museum-piece menu of the era: one dozen Sydney rock oysters, fillets of sole caprice, roast duckling with orange sauce, tartufo ice cream, cheese and coffee along with Australian wines, port and cigars. In these celebrations some guests observed Alcoa adding a touch of the folksy for the first time. Thus one press release announced that Forrest, as Alcoa's chairman, 'drives Holdens and smokes a pipe'.

The Pinjarra refinery needed fewer people than Kwinana for comparable tasks. Employing only about half the number originally contemplated, its sheer efficiency helped to explain why the population of the Pinjarra district did not expand at the pace predicted. Soon the refinery was working at a rate well above its official capacity. The design engineers in Pittsburgh, conscious perhaps of the complaints made when Kwinana took so long to achieve its planned output, had quietly built in their own safety factor. The new refinery, though working well below its full efficiency, was even then capable of far exceeding its planned output. More alumina was being produced than at first was needed.

Apart from its well-concealed outlay of additional capital the refinery had its own defects. Engineers and metallurgists, recruited from other

Operators in the control room at the Pinjarra power station, 1989.

Australian mining fields to work at Pinjarra, soon realised that the refining of alumina was more difficult than the comparable treatment steps at most gold and base metal mines. Neil Bennett, a young engineer from Broken Hill, called alumina refining 'a bitch of a process'. Hitch after hitch appeared. Sometimes the experts who were brought in to confer would disagree when prescribing a cure for a sluggish step in the process. The low-grade ore, and the tree roots and fibres mixed with the ore, continued to pose problems.

Pinjarra was soon the showplace and its margin of superiority over Kwinana grew and grew. Being smaller, it lacked the advantage of economies of scale, but its costs of production for each tonne of alumina were only two-thirds those of the older refinery. Its equipment was tailored to the peculiar ore, the boilers in the powerhouse had a higher pressure and it required a smaller staff. The clay and soil on which the refinery was built was more capable than the sandy subsoil of Kwinana of safely containing the mud lakes without the aid of expensive precautions. Poor Kwinana was now hidden in the shadows. It was almost an embarrassment, though the financial statistics were not made public. Despite the hiccoughs and hacking coughs that sometimes impeded production, Pinjarra was extracting alumina from bauxite with an efficiency that few other companies in the world could equal.

The Spinning Seventies

I n 1972 the company seemed to have overcome its early setbacks. It was becoming one of the world's leading producers of alumina, though it was not at the top of the list. Its two refineries in Western Australia were, for the first time, being noticed by other companies eager to reach higher standards. Its smelter at Geelong was exporting heavily to east Asia and its milled products were gaining a higher share of the booming aluminium market in Australia. Its power station at Anglesea was setting Australian standards for efficiency in converting brown coal into electricity. The new alliance with Pittsburgh was working more smoothly than before. New orders were pouring in. Pinjarra was no sooner opened than it was about to be invaded again by builders and contractors.

For years the company had been absorbed in just growing. It resembled a builder who started erecting a medium-sized house and kept on adding rooms and verandahs and then whole wings. But the builder was so busy just hammering and sawing that he had no time to enjoy the house. Alcoa was like that. For all its efforts, for all its huge investments, its profit was small.

Few other companies in Australia, during their first decade, had spent so much on new buildings and plant. The late 1960s were even more energetic than the early 1960s when Kwinana and Point Henry were built. In the four years from 1968 to 1971 Alcoa spent a total of $247 million on construction. This boom was largely based on expansion at Kwinana, on the new Pinjarra, and on extensions in Victoria. It was followed by two quiet years, when only $41 million was spent on construction.

In this quiet period Waldo Porter, another American engineer, replaced Joe Bates as managing director of Alcoa. Reared in North Carolina, Porter had started work in 1936 in the company town of Alcoa, Tennessee, and was one of the designers of aluminium smelters that were built during the Second World War. In 1958 he returned to Pittsburgh as the American Aluminum Co.'s power manager, and in 1968 he went to Suriname, the Dutch colony in tropical South America. There, Porter ran a big bauxite mine, a refinery, a hydro-scheme and a smelter about the size of Point Henry: he was the most powerful man in the entire economy. Tall, quietly spoken, personable, Waldo Porter was a skilled and patient negotiator—a talent soon to be in demand. Already he had a global web of contacts, for on many evenings he sat at his short-wave transmitter and contacted radio 'hams' around the world. As a city, Melbourne was slightly familiar to Waldo Porter, for in 1966–67 he had negotiated a power contract with the State Electricity Commission. Nonetheless, in August 1971 he returned to Melbourne against his will, for he had found stimulus and satisfaction in Suriname. Soon, however, after settling into the big company house in Heyington Place, Toorak, he had the same feelings towards Australia. In the next seven years he made so many overseas trips on behalf of Alcoa that he began to regret his absences from Australia.

Alcoa was so skilled in producing alumina that it was tempted into an allied field. The alumina refineries were huge importers of caustic soda, which in some months cost more than all the salaries and wages paid by the Western Australian refineries. The volume of caustic soda actually at work in a refinery at any time ran into several hundred thousand tonnes, and eventually 600 000 tonnes of caustic soda solution would be circulating in the Pinjarra refinery at the one time. This was the equivalent of the liquid carried by fifteen to twenty seagoing tankers.

The price of caustic soda fluctuated widely and could soar, multiplying by five times in the space of a year or two. Its price was volatile partly because it could not be readily stockpiled. It was closely linked to chlorine, and if the demand for chlorine was heavy then the supply of caustic soda and chlorine rose together, often leading to a glut of caustic soda. Glut was then followed by scarcity.

Alcoa was such a large consumer of caustic soda that it wondered whether it should make the product. In 1970 it combined with Mitsubishi Chemical Industries to plan a caustic soda plant in Western Australia. The plan faded, and then in 1973 the price of caustic soda soared, reviving the syndicate. Hopes now moved to South Australia and its potential supply of the crucial ingredients: salt, sulphur dioxide and the hydrocarbons in natural gas. Imperial Chemical Industries of Australia and New Zealand, with its big salt works near Adelaide, joined the syndicate. The Commonwealth government promised finance, the South

White Gold

Australian government promised a power station and port and Delhi-Santos would supply the natural gas by pipeline from the Cooper basin in the far interior to the South Australian coast. Alcoa would then ship the caustic soda to the Western Austalian refineries and the ship would carry alumina back to Geelong and then sail in ballast to South Australia to take in another cargo of caustic soda.

By 1974 the plan was bolder. The Redcliff Chemical Complex, as the syndicate was now called, aimed to make 515 000 tonnes of caustic a year. In capital outlay this would be almost as expensive as the building of an alumina refinery. In 1975, however, the plan began to fall apart. The price of caustic soda fell, taking away much of the incentive. The Whitlam government went ahead with plans to control the use of natural gas and to sponsor the expensive task of converting natural gas to petrol for use in motor vehicles. Thus the likely costs of the Redcliff project began to rise at the very time when the estimated income was falling rapidly. In July, Alcoa decided to withdraw from the project, and the partners went their separate ways. Alcoa in the end was inclined to think that it was lucky to be out of the project, with a loss of only $933 000. In 1981 a similar plan was revived briefly in Western Australia where natural gas was about to provide cheaper energy.

The growth of Pinjarra was a response to unexpected changes in the world's aluminium industry. In 1960 the big producers were giants which owned everything from the mine to the refinery and power station, smelter and products' mill. These giants were integrated—they were jacks of all trades; and they bought their own alumina from their own refinery. By 1970, however, the giants were joined by smaller specialist producers. There was now an opportunity for refineries to supply alumina to a wide variety of non-integrated smelters which owned neither a mine nor a refinery. Japanese smelters formed probably the first large market for alumina sold on the open market, and Alcoa grew partly by serving Japan as well as North American companies that had no connection with the Aluminum Co. of America. The rise of Middle East smelters, which used the cheap natural gas that ran to waste at their oil wells and oil refineries, provided another market for alumina. By the time Pinjarra was opened, Alcoa was in the remarkable position, being attached to a global giant, of supplying alumina to that giant in North America and also shipping even more alumina to independent smelters in other nations. Alcoa, in catering for the independents, was beginning to change the structure of the world's aluminium industry.

At Pinjarra the refinery initially supplied big annual orders to Amax in the United States. When the refinery was enlarged, it supported smelters in Japan, North and South America, and the Persian Gulf. In the four years from 1973 to 1976 the output of Pinjarra was multiplied by eight. To supply the bauxite a third mine was opened, and down the steep hill from the Darling Range came a flow of crushed bauxite on two parallel, covered conveyor belts—one from Del Park and the other from the new Huntly mine.

Here in 1976 was one of the largest refineries the world had seen, with a capacity of 2 million tonnes compared with Kwinana's 1.4 million tonnes. Together the Alcoa refineries produced one-seventh of the non-communist world's alumina, while almost another seventh came from the other refineries at Gladstone in Queensland, Gove in the Northern Territory and Bell Bay in Tasmania. Australia was overtaking North America as the world's main producer of alumina.

The company borrowed heavily to finance Pinjarra. During the four calendar years from 1969 to 1972 the ratio of debt to shareholders' equity was high, averaging about three to one, but they were smooth years in retrospect. High debts are most dangerous when commercial confidence sags, and by 1975 the confidence was sagging. Admittedly the company's debt to equity ratio had slipped down from a record 3.37 in 1971 to a safer 2.53 four years later, but in the jittery financial mood of 1975 the lower ratio was probably far more dangerous than was the very high ratio in what had been a confident year. The Eurodollar loans raised to finance the expansion of Pinjarra were weighing heavily on the company, for the business was less profitable. Late in 1975 the company had to scurry for new bank loans and facilities for credit.

The sheer weight of debt was a worry. After the breakdown of Bretton Woods the exchange rates of most currencies began to fluctuate, and that affected the income received by Alcoa from foreign sales of alumina. When the American dollar fell in relation to the Australian dollar the revenue from the sale of each tonne of alumina to America, being expressed in a depreciating American dollar, was smaller. In the year 1973, simply through movements in the exchange rate, the company lost $A13.5 million of export revenue. On the other hand the company gained $A11.1 million because it was busily repaying loans, and an Australian dollar bought more American dollars than usual.

To finance part of Pinjarra's expansion, the company had borrowed money in Swiss francs. When the Australian dollar fell in relation to the Swiss franc, more Australian dollars than envisaged were needed to repay the loans. In 1976 the potential due simply to altered Swiss–Australian exchange rates, would be about $13 million if the loans were repaid at once. At three meetings the directors debated the question of whether to repay the loan now and accept the heavy loss, or wait in the hope that the Australian dollar would rise against the Swiss franc.

In the boardroom in Melbourne the chairman, Sir James Forrest, was in favour of promptly repaying the Swiss francs. He argued that Alcoa's staff were not specialists in foreign currencies and so they should take no further risks. 'If you don't know what you are doing,' he added, 'don't do it.' He won the argument, and a total of $13.6 million was written off as a potential loss. Today the sum does not seem large but at that time it was almost equal to the after-tax profit of the previous year. The Australian dollar was devalued further by the Fraser government in November 1976, and so the loss on the Swiss transaction was even higher by the time the loans were repaid. In the hope of preventing similar losses, the directors resolved to borrow mostly in United States dollars, since most of Alcoa's revenue came from sales contracts which, irrespective of whether the customer was American or Arab, were written in United States dollars.

At the same time the company's debts were also affected because the aluminium industry in Japan was entering a crisis. Alcoa's contracts for the sale of alumina to Japan were vulnerable, for they were based on the assumptions of the early 1960s. Then it had reasonably been assumed that inflation would be moderate, that there would never again be a serious economic downturn in the Western world, and that the cost of producing alumina in Western Australia would not increase dramatically in any one year. Relying on these assumptions it was possible to sign a contract that was close to the cost-plus contract so common in Australian business during the Second World War. Accordingly, if the costs of mining and refining in Western Australia increased, the Japanese buyer would pay them—within reason. These assumptions made it possible to sign detailed contacts running for ten or twenty years. Those contracts enabled Alcoa to borrow huge sums of money from banks and merchant banks, for the profits from the alumina produced were certain enough to convince the banks that their loans were sound. Alcoa was built on such contracts. In the mid 1970s, unfortunately, the international economic stability on which these contracts were based began to crumble.

Mitsubishi Chemical Industries held a typical long-standing contract with Alcoa. It stipulated that if Alcoa's cost of producing alumina went up, the price of alumina would rise too. But this pioneering contract of 1961 imposed a ceiling on the amount by which alumina could increase in any one year. Ten years later, with inflation beginning to sprint, this contract was highly unfavourable for Alcoa. Under the escalating clauses, Mitsubishi Chemical Industries was paying $56 for a tonne of alumina which on the world market was worth about $70. On this original contract, Alcoa was a loser.

It was always the task of the managing director to conduct the vital negotiations with Japan. Joe Bates, as the commander of a United States submarine in the Second World War, had felt uneasy when first visiting Japan on behalf of Alcoa. 'I had spent a lot of time being depth-charged by the Imperial Japanese Navy,' he said, recalling his wartime years. Soon he began to mix more easily with Japanese people, eventually declaring that 'the Japanese are marvellous hosts'. Fortunately his successor, Waldo Porter, in the ten or so visits he made annually to Japan, could feel at ease because he had no wartime naval memories. But Porter did not feel at ease when he saw the task facing him.

At least three Japanese producers of aluminium—Nippon, Sumitomo and Mitsubishi—had involved Alcoa in their plans to expand early in the 1970s. Then the world wanted more aluminium ingots. But when in 1973 and 1974 the price of oil quadrupled, and pushed up the price of Japanese electricity, the smelters became vulnerable because their existence depended on cheap electricity. Suddenly Porter learned that Japan was not sure that it wanted to buy all the alumina it was committed to buying in that year.

The energy crisis continued to thump Japan. Aluminium smelters that had been highly competitive in the 1960s, when oil was cheap, now struggled to compete with smelting nations which had cheap hydro-electricity or coal. Japanese firms began to close down potlines in their smelters and to order less alumina. And yet they had promised to buy more alumina; the contracts were emphatic about that. At first, Mitsubishi's two aluminium smelters ordered a lower tonnage of alumina from Western Australia. For this breach of contract some strange excuses, perhaps fuzzed in the process of translation, reached Australia by a roundabout route: 'The propeller has fallen off the ship. That is why the ship has not reached Kwinana to take on more alumina'. Whatever the real reason, the contract was being violated. For Alcoa the potential loss of revenue was stunningly large. It had borrowed huge sums to expand its refineries in order to supply Japan, and the regular sales of alumina to Japan were vital if those debts were to be repaid.

The advice of senior lawyers in Melbourne was sought. They agreed that Mitsubishi was in breach of two alumina contracts. A total of 555 000 tonnes of alumina a year was contracted for but not likely to be paid for. Waldo Porter, flying to Japan, sought an appointment at the head office of Mitsubishi Chemical Industries where he explained, with grave courtesy, that the contract was being infringed. He did not need to explain that in the late 1960s Alcoa had honoured a similar contract even though it thereby incurred financial losses. On 1 September 1975 the board in Melbourne heard a report from Porter, just back from Japan, that Mitsubishi did not appear to appreciate 'the seriousness' of the breach of contract.

'We took the bull by the horns,' said Porter. He flew to Japan with a new contract that offered concessions to Mitsubishi if it agreed to take part of what, years ago, it had unequivocally promised to buy. At a large formal conference he urged its leaders to sign a revised contract which offered concessions. 'It was a sad day for Mitsubishi: they all put their heads down on the table.' They were allowed to take lower tonnages of alumina each year but, as penalty, the price of each tonne was higher. The new deal was signed with relief by both sides.

Sir Wilfred Brookes, Alcoa's senior director, recalled that the Japanese crisis came at a time when the company was deeply in debt. 'In October 1975, without many of the Board then being aware of it, we were in a position almost of default.' In short, the company might not be able to meet its obligations to banks and others.

Money was borrowed, savings were made and payment of the dividend was deferred. 'Fortunately,' wrote Brookes, 'we just scraped through by the skin of our teeth.' The risk was not that Alcoa would go bankrupt—its Pittsburgh partner would have come to the rescue—but that the Australian partners might have to sell a proportion of their shares at a low price.

Since 1965 the Japanese smelters had bought an increasing tonnage of Alcoa alumina, and in only two years, 1973 and 1975, was there a slight slump in their purchases. But now they were wondering whether to retreat from the aluminium industry. They held on for several more years in the hope that the price of oil and electricity would fall again. The busiest year for Japanese purchases was actually 1977 when 947 000 tonnes of Alcoa alumina arrived.

Aluminium smelters in Japan began to close. In the four years to 1981 the Japanese purchases of Alcoa alumina were more than halved. In the next four years the purchases crumbled, falling to a mere 7000 tonnes in 1985. Next year no ship carried Alcoa's alumina to Japan. The market had lasted for almost a quarter of a century.

The decline of the Japanese market coincided with a new form of money-raising by Alcoa. At head office, as at the refineries and smelter, Australians were taking over many of the responsibilities once held by Americans; and finance became the responsibility of Phil Spry-Bailey in 1975. A graduate in science, engineering and, later, business administration, he had managed the Vacuum oil terminal at Newcastle and worked for Lend Lease and then the Department of Trade before coming to Alcoa, where he soon became the company's secretary.

Spry-Bailey was visiting London in the winter of 1976–77 and called at Lazard's office to see the Honourable Tom Manners, who had taken over Denny Marris's role as adviser to Alcoa. Manners said simply: 'Isn't it about time you did away with all this project financing?'. 'Why not,' he suggested, 'borrow on your balance sheet?'

Hitherto large sums had been borrowed on the strength of each new alumina project, with the revenue from the sale of the alumina under-

The Spinning Seventies

U.S. $80,000,000

Alcoa of Australia Limited

ALCOA
AUSTRALIA

12% Bonds Due 1988

Payable as to 25 per cent. on 4th September, 1980 and 75 per cent. on 15th January, 1981

Credit Suisse First Boston Limited

Deutsche Bank
Aktiengesellschaft

J. Henry Schroder Wagg & Co.
Limited

In the era of continuous loan-raising, the fluctuations in the rate of interest were all-important to Alcoa. The cartoon (above), in the London Financial Times *in 1980, highlighted Alcoa's hopes and fears when it was making its first deferred Eurobond issue.*

writing the loan that built or expanded the refinery. Manners argued that Alcoa, possessing a strong financial name, should borrow not on the strength of the coming revenue stream for each new project but on the strength of its own growing financial reputation. The money so raised would be slightly cheaper. The company decided to borrow on the basis of its growing financial reputation. In addition the company decided to live with a permanently lower level of debt, and 1976 was the last year in which its debt was twice as large as its equity.

Tom Manners also suggested that it was time for Alcoa to tidy up its own structure. For a long time it had operated through two Australian companies. One was Alcoa of Australia (W.A.) Limited, which owned the bauxite leases in the West and had taken over all Western Australian government contracts from the original company of the 1950s, Western Aluminium No Liability. The other company was the operating company, Alcoa of Australia. Hitherto all borrowing had been complicated because each of the two companies had to sign cross-guarantees for money borrowed overseas. Following Manners' suggestion, the two companies merged under the name of Alcoa of Australia Limited. The merger came into effect on 29 December 1977. A day later the assets of the new company were revalued upwards by $302 million, and an issue of bonus shares was made.

The company, in its own name, now became the main borrower of the funds it needed, raising loans in Australia and across the world. In the European commercial market, Alcoa was guided by the newly merged firm of Credit Suisse First Boston. In 1979 Alcoa began to borrow in the form of European bonds at cheaper interest than normal. A dozen years later its credit rating—and therefore the ease and price with which it could borrow—was higher than that of any other aluminium company.

For nearly two decades the financial history of Alcoa was a history of borrowing, whereas Lindesay Clark had naturally predicted that it would be more a history of dividends. Where, the Australian partners increasingly asked, were the promised profits? The three Australian partners were mining companies and sometimes they needed capital for their own Australian mines and their own clamouring shareholders. A large profit at Alcoa would have been a delight. Net profits of Alcoa, however, remained small for a company of its size. Profits increased from $5.8 million in 1969 to $17.1 million two years later. Another five years passed before they reached $17 million again, and that sum of course was earned on a much bigger capital, a far bigger output, and earned in dollars that, due to inflation, were worth less. Alcoa so far, while not unsuccessful, was not one of Australia's financial triumphs. Success was always around the next corner.

For the Australian companies which owned nearly 49 per cent of Alcoa the delay in reaching a steady level of profits was vexing because, even when occasionally the profit was satisfactory, very little of it was handed to them. Nearly all profit was needed for expanding the business or reducing its debt. Usually, as much profit as possible was withheld from the outstretched hands of the Australian shareholders and paid to overseas banks and other firms which had lent money. As the ratio of debt to equity was too high for safety's sake, this postponing of dividends made excellent sense.

Back in the early 1960s, while the company was being set up, Sir Lindesay Clark had expressed fears that when the profits finally came, they might be apportioned primarily in accordance with the preferences of the Americans, who held 51 per cent of the shares. To quell his worries it was stipulated in the foundation agreement that at least 33 per cent of the after-tax profits should be paid out as a dividend. This did not happen. Repayment of the loans was seen as urgent. Sir Wilfred Brookes, the member of the board who virtually possessed the company's memory, protested at this infringement. His protest eventually succeeded, partly because the debts were diminishing and profits were rising.

After the nightmare of the confrontation with Japan was over, Alcoa's after-tax profit began to recover. In 1976 it reached $43 million, and the next year it was $65 million. In 1977 the dividend paid to shareholders was more than six times that of the best dividend of the period 1961–75. With Brookes' protest still ringing in Pittsburgh's ears, $33.3 million was paid in dividends and $125 million in bonus shares. In effect this first large dividend was closer to 200 per cent than 100 per cent. In addition, the Australian nation was earning a dividend in different forms: in the jobs created, in taxes collected by governments and in the purchases made from Australian industries. Another gain for the nation was cheap aluminium for local customers. For eight out of the last nine years, Australians had been able to buy an ingot of aluminium at less than the world price.

Despite the financial troubles of the mid 1970s, other alumina projects were now planned in Western Australia. There the centre of gravity of the alumina industry was slowly moving south. The large untapped deposits of bauxite lay well to the south of Pinjarra, and as the mining moved south the new port of Kwinana became less accessible than the old southerly port of Bunbury. The company was committed to sending the Pinjarra alumina by railway to Bunbury as soon as that port was ready to receive larger ships. One of the West's oldest ports, and the third largest city, Bunbury had operated superphosphate works since the 1920s and its exports included wheat, coal, mineral sands and timber, especially jarrah. Its harbour required a deeper shipping channel and a turning basin, and Alcoa and the woodchip industry were called on to help finance the harbour works. Once the harbour was completed in 1976, Alcoa could send the alumina from its Pinjarra refinery along the government railway, either to its own wharves and loading facilities at Kwinana, or to Bunbury.

Alumina ship departing from the Bunbury terminal in 1989.

The new Bunbury harbour and loading facilities were a mixed blessing for Alcoa. Within easy railing distance of Bunbury were promising bauxite deposits which, so far unmined, were not owned by Alcoa. Bunbury was a Trojan Horse that seemed likely to admit a rival into an industry which Alcoa had dominated.

Alcoa knew that someday strong competitors might arise in its own bauxite region. In the beginning it had selected nearly all the promising bauxite but some low-grade deposits remained outside its huge prospecting area. As Alcoa possessed more than enough bauxite to last for several hundred years, judged by the initial rate of mining, it saw no point in holding additional ground. It saw no point in paying to the Western Australian government a rent for leases which it might not use even in the next century.

As Alcoa had deliberately pegged all the visible bauxite lying on the westerly or coastal side of the Darling Range, only the remote deposits were available for latecomers. Eventually they were pegged by another syndicate. The leases were offered to Joe Bates in the late 1960s for $50 000, which was cheap. Bates in turn raised the matter with Lindesay Clark, who said thoughtfully that 'it is not a bad idea to have a competitor'. Presumably Clark argued that there were political dangers in Alcoa being seen as a monopoly. The bauxite leases were then sold to another private party.

Later, Bates was approached by the holder of the outlying bauxite leases. He met him in his Melbourne office one hot Sunday when the air conditioning was not working. The seller, Bates recalls, was Rupert Murdoch who was head of News Corporation and owner of Australian newspapers, but not yet a world figure in finance. Murdoch was interested in coming to an arrangement with Alcoa to develop the leases, but no deal was made. Bates' recollection is that he did not even bother to tell Clark, guessing that his answer would again be 'no'.

Alcoa was to have another chance to buy these leases at Mount Saddleback and thus eliminate local opposition. A vigorous debate took place around the table at a meeting held when the board was visiting Kwinana. Sir Lindesay Clark, supported by Sir Wilfred Brookes, was keen for his company to be rid of any possible rival. The opponents of the purchase said that the bauxite was far from Bunbury and was therefore second best. 'We already have enough bauxite,' argued the majority of directors. The decision was 'no'.

Murdoch made a successful approach to Broken Hill Proprietary, which had no experience of aluminium but enormous experience in iron, base metals, oil and other minerals. By 1970, BHP and News Corporation were trying to organise an aluminium venture known as Alwest. Their main asset was about 5000 square kilometres of bauxite territory to the east of the Alcoa mining leases. Lying on the inland side of the Darling Range, its bauxite rested mostly on slopes that were steeper than those enclosing Alcoa's bauxite. Some of the bauxite was in state forest and some on private farms growing wheat and wool: permission to mine on the farms had been secured, either through direct purchase or through compensation in cash. Compared to the bauxite being mined by Alcoa, Mount Saddleback's bauxite tended to be high in iron and low in reactive silica, and so the treatment process would have to be modified. While much smaller than Alcoa's reserves of bauxite, the Alwest deposits were still impressive.

An ingenious plan was drawn up to bring together this isolated bauxite territory and an isolated coalmine, both of which had been rejected by Alcoa in its early days. The mine was to be at Mount Saddleback, about 120 kilometres northeast of Bunbury. The coalmine would be at Collie and they would annually send 700 000 tonnes of black coal to the port of Bunbury—if the Western Australian government would upgrade the railway. A power station at the port of Bunbury would generate cheap electricity and a refinery built nearby would treat the bauxite transported from distant Mount Saddleback. Variations of this scheme—including an inland refinery at Worsley instead of a coastal refinery at Bunbury—were examined. These promising but seemingly risky schemes lacked one ingredient: they did not have the support of any of the aluminium giants. That was remedied. Eventually the Reynolds Metal Co., the fourth largest aluminium company in the world, took a share in Alwest and its leases, finally becoming the driving partner. Here was the very competition which Alcoa had overlooked.

In 1974 the premier of Western Australia, Sir Charles Court—he had been knighted two years previously—began to think that it would be best for his state if Alcoa and Alwest cooperated. Having regained power from Tonkin's Labor government, he personally held the portfolios of premier, treasurer and minister coordinating economic and regional development. At his urging, Alcoa and Alwest came together to discuss a united mine and refinery based on Bunbury as the outlet. Bunbury port was soon to be enlarged: this was the time for action.

Under the plan Alwest would not go ahead with the building of its own refinery. Instead there would be a combined refinery at Wagerup, a rural town standing near the steep coastal escarpment south of Pinjarra. Alcoa would build and manage the joint refinery, each partner would supply finance, and each would take its revenue and profit in actual alumina rather than in dividends. The alumina would then be railed to Bunbury and shipped from Alcoa's new wharf.

As Alwest's leases lay far from the proposed refinery, Court suggested that Alcoa and Alwest should exchange some of their leases. Alcoa would receive a large area around Mount Saddleback, and in return Alcoa would give to Alwest some of its bauxite leases near the new refinery. In that way the bauxite could be mined from an area close to the refinery, thus providing bauxite of better grade and, in addition, lowering the transport costs from mine to refinery. It could be argued that under this slightly one-sided arrangement Alcoa was swapping cream for skimmed milk. On the other hand Alcoa knew that it depended in many ways on the goodwill and cooperation of the Western Australian government which had always been fair and at times generous. So Alcoa seriously discussed the plan.

Would the two partners consent? Nowhere in the world had the two American giants, Reynolds and the Aluminum Co. of America, previously shared the same bed. It was a tribute to the persuasion and persistence of Charles Court that they even thought of snuggling down together. On 1 March 1976 the matter was carefully discussed at a board meeting to which R. Banks Smith had come from Pittsburgh. The decision was that the joint project was 'not attractive at this time'. The rejection was not emphatic. Discussions continued.

Maybe the marriage was more likely to benefit the Reynolds Metal Co. and its syndicate. Instead of having to open a remote mine, Reynolds

*Alcoa of Australia's board in 1976 with Sir James Forrest in the
foreground. Seated from left to right: R.L. Baillieu, Waldo Porter Jr,
Sir Wilfred Brookes and H.M. Morgan. Standing from left to right:
H.McE. Scambler, Sir Archibald Glenn and E.W. Lussky. Absent were
J. Darling, L.C. Brodie-Hall, J.C. Bates and C.W. Parry.*

could treat a section of Alcoa's bauxite lying close to the refinery. Instead
of having to build its own wharf and silos and conveyor belts at Bunbury
it could use Alcoa's. Instead of having to experiment with unusual ore
it could use Alcoa's experience, for Alcoa would run both the mine and
the refinery. Reynolds was not entirely convinced by these arguments.
It said privately in August 1976 that, if necessary, it would build its own
refinery and stand alone. The fourth biggest producer of aluminium in
the world, it did not relish the idea of being a junior partner.

White Gold

The gain for Alcoa was not as clear. In its boardroom in Bourke Street, Melbourne, its directors weighed the arguments, for and against, during most months of 1976. To swap mineral leases was a novel idea, perhaps not previously tried by major companies in Australia. As Sir Archie Glenn, one of the newer directors pointed out, the company already possessed government approval to mine huge, accessible areas along the Darling Range. Was it therefore sensible to swap some of that approved bauxite for an area where mining could ultimately be banned for environmental reasons? What if, in twenty years' time, Alcoa found that its approval to mine its swap leases at Mount Saddleback was withdrawn because of a heightened public concern about the environment? As the year went on, the rising world market for alumina gave a boost to those who thought that each company should build its own separate refinery. Money could easily be raided for big ventures. Mac Scambler, another of Alcoa's newer directors, suggested that perhaps this was the first opportunity to give individual Australian investors the chance to buy shares directly in a Western Australian alumina project.

In Perth, Sir Charles Court was the persuasive marriage broker. A combined refinery, he thought, was in the interests of Western Australia. It would boost the exports from the new harbour at Bunbury which he had formally opened on 2 April 1976. A large combined refinery would produce cheaper alumina. It would enable his state to lead the world in producing alumina, and with cheap alumina Bunbury might even become the site, one day, for an aluminium smelter. The combined refinery would also boost the Collie coalfield, some ninety kilometres away, for the Collie and its much-enlarged coal reserves could at last produce a competitive fuel now that oil from the Middle East was so expensive. The coal would be mined in the open cut and converted to electricity, which would be transmitted to the refinery. It was ironical that Collie was again to the fore, because a pessimistic assessment of it in 1960 had helped to tip the scales, persuading Lindesay Clark to move to eastern Australia for the cheap electricity needed by the initial Alcoa project.

At the end of 1976, Alcoa of Australia and the Reynolds Metal Co. signed a memorandum of agreement. Plans for their new Wagerup refinery caused excitement in Perth. Its initial target was 900 000 tonnes of alumina, which was not as much as Pinjarra or Kwinana produced. The refinery was to expand in steps, perhaps reaching a yearly total of 4 million tonnes of alumina, of which Alcoa would be entitled to take half for its own smelters or customers.

In March 1977 the capital cost was estimated to be $463 million, another busy exercise in borrowing. As the construction of the refinery would take nearly four years and as inflation in Australia was anticipated to average 15 per cent a year in 1977 and 1978, before falling to 10 per

Early earthworks at the Wagerup refinery in 1979.

cent, the final cost of the combined refinery was estimated to be $666 million. The economic gains for the district, for Bunbury city and its new inner harbour, and for Western Australia, would be high. Moreover, the combined project, to be commenced in the second half of 1977, would create numerous jobs in what had become the nation's first decade of widespread unemployment since the Second World War.

Legal doubts in the United States suddenly clouded the plan. The anti-trust laws might be invoked to terminate a partnership involving two American aluminium giants. On 22 June 1977 the board in Melbourne heard that for legal reasons, not set down in the minute book, the project was 'not practical'. Eventually, in September 1980, the Reynolds Metal Co. and its main partner, BHP, began building their own refinery at Worsley, to be served by one of the world's longest conveyor belts, extending from Mount Saddleback to the refinery. The plan was completed in 1984 and the alumina was railed west to the harbour of Bunbury.

Alcoa in turn took up the discarded plan for Wagerup, spending $14 million on land alone. There in 1979 it began to build its third refinery. But first it had to fight dedicated opponents in a war which nobody could have foreseen when bauxite was first mined in Western Australia.

PART THREE

Plate 1   Sir Lindesay Clark, painted by Clifton Pugh in 1970.

Plate 2 Loading alumina at Kwinana, about 1990. One ship is about to dock while the other ship is unloading caustic soda.

Plate 3 Pinjarra, with a capacity of 3 million tonnes a year, is the largest refinery in the Alcoa worldwide group.

Plate 4 A mined area at Jarrahdale in 1981, after the bauxite had been removed, prior to rehabilitation. The pit walls would have been contoured and the mine floor deep-ripped after the topsoil was replaced.

Plate 5 The same mined area at Jarrahdale in 1987, with an established tree cover and a vigorous understorey providing habitat for the returning fauna.

Plate 6 Directors visiting the Pinjarra refinery in 1979 (from left to right): J.C. Bates, Sir Archibald Glenn, H.M. Morgan, G.T. Haymaker, Sir Arvi Parbo (chairman), R.L. Baillieu, H.McE. Scambler, L.C. Brodie-Hall, J. Darling, Sir Wilfred Brookes. Absent: R.L. Fischer, G.W. Parry.

Plate 7 View of the Point Henry smelter and fabricating plant following the construction of the third potline, which increased the capacity of the smelter to 180 000 tonnes a year. A new carbon bake area can be seen in the upper left quadrant.

Plate 8   The 150 megawatt power station opened at Anglesea in 1969.

Plate 9 Sir James Forrest, painted by William Boissevain in 1978.

Plate 10   The first refining unit at Wagerup, completed in 1982, did not operate until the world's aluminium markets recovered in 1984.

Plate 11 The Portland smelter was completed in 1986 and the landscaping was about to be commenced.

Plate 12 Directors of the Aluminum Company of America visited the operations of Alcoa of Australia in 1993 and attended a board meeting. In the foreground are chairmen Paul O'Neill and Sir Arvi Parbo.

Plate 13 Hedges gold mine in the early phase when the mining was shallow.

Plate 14 R.F. Slagle (managing director), Sir Arvi Parbo (chairman) amd P. Spry-Bailey (executive director, finance and administration) at a board meeting in 1995, with a painting by Sidney Nolan in the background. (Photo courtesy of Erin Jonasson, Australian Financial Review)

Plate 15 The last board meeting chaired by Sir Arvi Parbo, 6 June 1996. From left to right: Jose Rodolfo Lopes, John Sibly, John Phillips, Sir Laurence Muir, Roger Vines, Sir Arvi Parbo, Philip Spry-Bailey, Hugh Morgan, Professor Adrienne E. Clarke and Donald M. Morley.

Plate 16   Sir Arvi Parbo, painted by Sir William Dargie in 1993.

◆ 12 ◆

The Flip Top

A lcoa was divided in its hopes and goals. While some of its leaders fixed their eyes on the exporting of alumina to Japan, the United States and other foreign markets, other leaders believed that Alcoa's future lay in its Victorian smelter and fabricating plant which tried to meet the growing appetite for aluminium in an industrialising Australia. In the boardroom in Melbourne in the 1960s most directors sensed that the Australian market would prove the more important. Pittsburgh shared that view, though events were to challenge it.

In Australia, Alcoa already faced one strong competitor, Comalco, whose smelter produced aluminium ingots. Comalco and the Canadian firm of Alcan, which owned a plant in Sydney, also fabricated the aluminium ingots for a variety of Australian customers and so competed directly with Point Henry. Alcoa from the start knew that this competition would be tough. The fast-expanding market was simply not large enough to satisfy all three.

To cope with these competitors, Bob Bowlby was sent out by the Aluminum Co. of America as director of sales and marketing for Alcoa. As a young engineer he had originally been hired in Philadelphia in 1950 to persuade companies to switch from copper and steel to aluminium. Later he controlled international sales from an office in Lausanne, Switzerland, and so his appointment to Australia was a sign of how seriously Pittsburgh viewed the competition. He arrived at Alcoa's head office in Queen Street Melbourne in 1967. It was so crowded, he observed, that the staff 'were stumbling over each other'.

He found that the selling of aluminium products in Australia was harder than in the United States, for the local market was small, and the manufacturing runs for many products were not large enough to earn a profit. In effect the profit was a long-term goal. Even so he could see that the demand for aluminium products was widening more rapidly in Australia than in most nations. Thus, aluminium was being used to make air-conditioners: the metal's ability to resist corrosion was as vital as its lightness. Aluminium was used in reading lamps, in ladders, in light suitcases, in the windows of buses and houses, and in fly-wire doors and venetian blinds. It was replacing copper in insulated cable and electrical conductors.

Aluminium invaded almost every section of the transport industry and also the building industry where the flat-rib roofing sheet became popular in the late 1960s. In essence, the old 'tin' roof had a new competitor. On walls of existing wooden houses the aluminium cladding—at first sight it resembled weatherboards—was being tried. A house that used aluminium for both the frame and the roofing was designed in 1970. Christened Alcoa Alframe, it was unveiled in Geelong in the hope that 'this revolutionary' product would be seen in every wide-awake suburb.

The North Pinjarra estate at Carcoola was being built using Alcoa Alframe in 1971 to house workers employed at the rising Pinjarra refinery.

The Flip Top

As more than one-third of all aluminium used in Australia went into buildings, Alcoa in 1966 decided to take over Dowell Australia Limited, which supplied aluminium to the building industry. When Overseas Corporation (Australia) Limited merged its parallel interests with Dowell, the combined company became a vehicle for promoting aluminium amongst builders. The facades of many of the tall office towers of the 1970s were made by Dowell from Alcoa aluminium. Australia's tallest building, the new AMP office on the harbour front in Sydney, was faced with a curtain wall of aluminium. Later the Allendale tower in Perth used 450 tonnes of Alcoa aluminium, mostly in a panelled facade extending up to the 34th storey. With factories in all states and in New Guinea and Hong Kong, Dowell produced aluminium doors and windows on a large scale. Alcoa operated Dowell until 1988, when Point Henry ceased to extrude the aluminium used for many products in the building industry.

When Point Henry was young, the new uses for aluminium were countless. Thus surveyors, in their work out of doors, were replacing the heavy wooden staves with 'lightweight telescope levelling staffs'. On the roads the latest cars contained more aluminium than ever before, and it gleamed in the ornate grills of the Torana, Fairlane and Valiant in the late 1960s. The invasion of aluminium into so many crannies was so swift and often so unobtrusive that the public barely noticed it. Many typical Australians might watch ten episodes of the detective series *Homicide* without seeing one item which they instantly identified as aluminium; and yet such items were constantly appearing in the shots filmed. Point Henry aluminium was sometimes seen in the television footage of the Vietnam War shown on the nightly news: Point Henry rolled and heat-treated the aluminium fins that, in other factories, were fixed to bombs in order to delay their descent.

Aluminium was even expected to replace steel and wood in suburban and country lightpoles. When hit by a car the lightweight aluminium pole would merely snap at the base whereas the steel pole could sometimes smash the car and kill or injure its passengers. In 1973 Alcoa paid for a one-third interest in an Adelaide company that manufactured the lightweight lightpole. One million dollars was spent on the factory but not one commercial pole was produced. The company belatedly realised, when all was ready to go, that the cost of persuading hundreds of different municipalities in Australia to modify their electrical equipment would be astronomical.

Alcoa promoted the use of its metal on the racecourses, and by 1967 nearly all the starting gates on Australian courses were made in part from Alcoa aluminium sheet shaped by an enterprising firm at Murray Bridge in South Australia. One year later Warrnambool became the first racecourse to use a running rail of aluminium. Extending over ten furlongs, and cheaper than Oregon timber, it did not require coats of white paint and did not splinter when hit by a running horse. Alcoa in 1968 made an aluminium case for the new plinth that supported the Davis Cup, the most famous trophy in world tennis. In Melbourne on 8 March 1969, when the boxer Lionel Rose defended his world bantam-weight championship, he fought in a boxing ring made of Alcoa's aluminium flooring. In 1970 the Australian yacht *Gretel II*, about to compete for the America's Cup, was fitted with a light aluminium mast made in four sections at Point Henry.

In the shops and new supermarkets, aluminium foil was used more and more. Butter and frankfurts were wrapped in aluminium. The bottle full of milk—not yet challenged by the carton—was sealed with a thin lid of aluminium. When placed by the travelling milkman by the letter box or at the front gate of suburban houses, the cap was so shiny that birds sometimes pecked at it. The aluminium foil replaced the so called 'silver paper' in cigarette packs, and in 1969 Alcoa boasted that such popular brands as Turf, Capstan, Kool, Craven Filter and State Express were 'overwrapped in foil', while inside the pack a non-porous foil retained the cigarette's flavour and moisture.

Australia was consuming more and more aluminium. The statistics were dramatic. The average Australian used less than 500 grams of the metal in the year 1940, about two kilograms in 1950, about five and a half kilograms in 1960, and eleven kilograms of aluminium in 1970. A growing proportion of that aluminium was made from Australian ingots. When in the late 1950s the first samples of bauxite were chipped from the outcrops in the Darling Range, Australia had been essentially an importer of aluminium, but now it was a supplier to the world. In 1970 Australia exported nearly eight times as much aluminium metal as it imported; and this did not include the shiploads of alumina that left Kwinana regularly for foreign ports.

With the demand for aluminium products so voracious, plans were made for a second potline at Point Henry. Officially opened on 13 November 1969, it raised the capacity of the smelter to 90 000 tonnes of aluminium a year. One-third of its annual output of aluminium ingots was to be shipped to the Furukawa Aluminium Co. of Japan, but nearly all the remainder was to be used in Australia where that novelty, the drink can, was becoming the dynamic consumer of aluminium. It was John Harper, Pittsburgh's chief executive since 1963, who saw a future for the aluminium can and pushed his American company into the mass production of rolled can sheet for processors of food and drink. His company, which was traditionally a refiner and smelter of aluminium, thus moved closer to the daily wants of the American consumer.

The Flip Top

Guests who attended a private Alcoa dinner at the Esplanade Hotel in Perth in February 1964 were amongst the first Australians to glimpse what would happen to the packaging of beer and soft drinks. After dinner the guest speaker was John Mitchell, on a flying visit from Pittsburgh, and he explained how, just thirteen months earlier, his company had introduced to Americans a novelty not yet seen in Australia. It was a steel beer can with an aluminium top. He called it 'the tab-opening' can. To the surprise of some of his Perth listeners, he pointed out that the new can could be opened without a tin-opener.

At that time in Australia the steel can was used less for liquids than for vegetables, soup and preserved fruits, which were simply tipped into a saucepan or bowl. The bottle was the normal container, and a can containing beer and soft drink was still a novelty, though in fact the first beer can made of tin-plated steel had appeared in the United States as early as 1935. In the early 1960s the few beer cans seen in Australia were opened by a metal device held in the hand by the barman. The device forced open a small neat hole in the can and enabled the beer to be poured into a glass.

Those listening to Mitchell were not quite sure how the new flip-top can was actually opened. His explanation was simple: 'The can snaps open when a specially designed tab is lifted and pulled'. He confided that few products had ever snatched a big slice of the national market so quickly. Within a year nearly all of the 26 major brewers in the United States were adapting the new device to one of their brands of beer. More than 40 per cent of the canned beer sold in America was now in cans consisting of tinplate steel on the bottom and sides, and aluminium at the top or opening end. Cans were displacing bottles as containers for beer and held 80 per cent of the market by 1968.

The dinner audience in Perth was not told the huge sum which the company in Pittsburgh had poured into research on this new venture nor how much it was spending on the sheet mill at Warrick, Indiana, which would produce metal of the required thinness and strength. Many problems had to be overcome. An aluminium–magnesium alloy was needed for the high-speed rolling process which slowly turned thick ingots of metal into continuous strips that were almost as thin as paper. Telling arguments were needed to persuade the brewers and soft drink factories to change their production line in whole or in part from the familiar tin-plate steel to the new aluminium. The new can was actually a little dearer than the old, but to the surprise of many customers the beer in a steel can with an aluminium top stayed fresher than beer in an all-steel can. In the United States the aluminium top on a steel can took the beer market by storm. Holding 40 per cent of the market at the end of 1963, it held 80 per cent in 1968.

White Gold

Mitchell confided that his Aluminum Co. of America was now making not only the aluminium tab for the top of the beer can but, at the request of one big American brewer, a 12-ounce (340 mL) can which consisted entirely of aluminium. There were additional benefits if aluminium constituted the whole can. It could be chilled more quickly than a steel can. The can did not rust, and was lighter, thus saving costs in transport. Moreover, it could easily be recycled—though that argument did not carry much weight in the wasteful 1960s.

Australia moved first to the all-steel can and then to the aluminium flip top. The first tops were imported from the Aluminum Co. of America but in 1967 the Point Henry mill began to roll aluminium can-sheet for Containers Limited, which at Footscray made Australia's first cans with an aluminium end and a flip-top opener. Breweries were soon attracted to the idea. Indeed N.R. Hall, Alcoa's advertising manager, was visiting the office of the Cascade brewery in Hobart on a selling mission on 7 February 1967, a day of bushfires in which the brewery itself caught fire. The Cascade brewery, rebuilt in the space of months, was one of the first to sell beer with the aluminium 'easy open can top'. The beer can was still of steel while the 'easy-open end' was of aluminium, but these tiny aluminium devices were made on such a large scale that Point Henry's new can-sheet line was soon devouring tonnes of ingots as raw material. The ordering of products from Point Henry was now easy, for in July 1967 the factory office had a telex machine capable of sending and receiving printed and written messages.

By 1968 two large manufacturers of soft drinks, the Coca Cola and the Passiona companies, were using the aluminium end and flip top on their cans. In the following year the first all-aluminium can was made in Australia. To Alcoa's disappointment, it was made by Comalco in Sydney.

At first there was no agreement on how to describe the flip top. It was variously called 'easy open end', or 'touch 'n go', or 'ring pull end', or 'aluminium convenience opening'. The first such cans, used in 1968 by Courage Bitter, were described with a cumbersome collection of words: 'this convenient opening device—the wide angle super ring pull easy-open end'. As many people did not know what to do when confronted with them, the cans carried detailed instructions on how to pull the metal ring.

This can that required no old-fashioned tin-opener was also used for food. In 1974 Alcoa widely advertised its special can with a white, hygienic, inside lining. It was said to be ideal for single, small helpings of food, especially desserts. Like all the new aluminium products, it carried a long name that was not easily remembered. Often it was called the 'Lightweight Single-serve, All-aluminium Easycan', but sometimes it answered to the name of the 'aluminium shallow drawn can'.

The aluminium can captured Australia. By the late 1970s the cans and foil and other forms of aluminium 'packaging' were running second to the building industry as a consumer of the metal within Australia. Over half of all the beer and soft drink in Australia was consumed from all-aluminium cans, many of which ended up on the side of the road or amongst the seats at sporting grounds. Alcoa began to collect these discarded aluminium cans in 1977. At depots in the larger New South Wales and Victorian cities it paid 30 cents for each kilogram of empty cans—usually 45 cans weighed one kilogram. City councils and local charities set up depots for the collecting of old cans and children wanting pocket money joined in the pursuit. Alcoa publicised the new game, and more and more joined in. During the first half of 1978 about 22 million cans were collected, but in 1980 the year's total was 267 million. In Australia half of all the cans sold were being collected and remelted—a higher proportion than in any other nation.

The argument for collecting and recycling these empty, discarded cans was made more powerful by the fact that aluminium was a high user of energy: to melt down a can and remake it was a saver of electricity in a decade which was conscious of the soaring costs of oil and other

In the late 1960s the company displayed the diversity of aluminium products on every possible occasion.

White Gold

forms of energy. To convert one discarded can into aluminium consumed only 5 per cent of the electricity required to smelt the aluminium needed for one brand-new can. In the collecting and recycling of aluminium cans Alcoa became an expert. It was called on to advise the can-maker Kian Joo on Malaysia's first systematic attempt to recycle cans, and to help the Loving Aluminium Corporation of Taiwan in a campaign to recycle cans on a large scale.

The semi-fabricating plant at Point Henry acquired more specialist machines in order to turn aluminium into different shapes. It remained, however, the maker of materials rather than finished products. Thus Point Henry did not make the beer cans but made and rolled the aluminium alloy that went in the form of rigid container sheet to the can-makers.

The making of the alloy, a delicate task, called for tight control of the temperature if the metal in each rigid container sheet was to be uniform in its qualities. To the outsider the various presses and mills at Point Henry seemed to work in an automatic and self-regulating way, but watchfulness was vital. Even when the process was well established at Point Henry, the operators had to be alert. Alex Butwilowski, operating the controls of the cold rolling mill, observed in 1980 that the

A selection of flip top aluminium cans made from Alcoa metal.

coils of metal that entered his mill were never quite identical. Each day, he said, he had to know the 'feel' of the batch of aluminium that his big mill was rolling into shape. 'Cold rolling is a job you never finish learning,' he said. By then the computer was reducing the risk of error but the penalty for error was still expensive, whether in wasted electricity and wasted time and metal or in disappointed customers.

Pittsburgh had believed in the 1960s that it was not enough to concentrate on refining bauxite and smelting alumina. If that idea was true in the United States, it was less so in Australia. For Alcoa the return on capital was becoming lower at Point Henry than in the large-scale mining and refining activities in Western Australia. The Australian market for most of the end products was too small, and too many firms were competing for that market. Virtually only the can-sheet, demand for which was soaring, was produced on an impressive scale at Point Henry.

Admittedly, some products could be exported. In 1972 the company took pride in announcing that its ingots, billet, sheet and semi-fabricated extrusions were exported to fourteen lands, ranging from Guam and Papua New Guinea to China and Japan. In Indonesia the coins ranging from one to five rupiahs were made from Point Henry's strip aluminium, and in thousands of Javanese villages the new pot and saucepan were often made of sheet aluminium from Point Henry. But by the late 1970s Australia's expansive and optimistic era of manufacturing was passing away, the tariff against imported aluminium products was falling, and Alcoa was seeing its future more as a refiner and smelter.

◆ 13 ◆

Dieback

The long Darling Range is not one of Australia's ten natural wonders but it has a host of admirers. To many orchardists, botanists, foresters, bushwalkers and picnickers, it is one of the most attractive parts of Western Australia. The only range of any height in the vicinity of Perth, it collects and dams half of the water which that city normally consumes.

Only a small part of the Darling Range—mostly the western slopes—was scarred in the first years of the bauxite mining. The mines were merely a cluster of quarries that occupied only a tiny fraction of the total hillsides.

Most mines were shallow with steep crooked edges that sometimes rose seven metres above the bottom. Visually they formed scars, and they were also unkempt. Many of the abandoned quarries also held what Joe Bates called 'islands of poor grade material standing up there in the centre of the pit'. The pits or quarries soon accumulated water, and after heavy rain the water cascaded towards the scattered orchards, becoming a muddy torrent on the way. These muddy streams were soon tamed but the abandoned holes in the ground remained.

Within seven years the small quarries, abandoned or active, were dotted along the range. From the air they were unsightly, even though the empty pits were levelled out a little and the mined ground was covered with young bushes. If similar scars had been inflicted on the dry goldfields in the interior, nobody would have protested, for that was seen primarily as mining country. But in the lightly timbered country close to Perth, the scars seemed more out of place.

Even before the mines were opened, a few residents of the towns along the Darling Range expressed concern for the fate of the jarrah trees that grew on the slopes. Jarrah is a tall, handsome stringy-bark, and from the straight trunk the long strands of the bark fall away like thick grey streamers. Along with the taller, more majestic karri tree, the jarrah is the pride of Western Australia. The finest jarrah trees grow as tall as 56 metres, or as high as perhaps an eighteen-storey office block. In contrast a stunted variety, growing in the Stirling Ranges near Albany, reaches only a couple of metres in height. Some of the tallest, stoutest jarrah trees are believed to be 350 years old: they were saplings when sailors in Dutch ships bound for Java first saw the dry coast of Western Australia.

In spring and early summer the younger jarrah trees caught the eye, for their flowers were a daring white. As a hardwood timber, jarrah was also unusual. It could survive for decades in the ground, as a building post or railway sleeper, and not be eaten by the white ants. Deep red, it was a striking sight when freshly laid as flooring boards. Jarrah was the basis of a big timber-milling industry along the range, and in fact more Western Australians depended on jarrah for their livelihood than depended on the aluminium industry—at least in its first decade.

In September 1961, when the parliament in Perth debated the bill to permit the creation of the alumina industry, several members felt uneasy. Joseph Rowberry, a Scottish immigrant who had come to the timber belt in the 1920s, lived in Manjimup, which was a timber and apple town outside the proposed mining areas, but he decided to speak in the hope that members of his Timber Workers Union would not lose work as a result of the competition between the alumina and the jarrah forest. Rising to his feet when the debate was almost over, he made the only strong conservationist speech heard during the discussion. He drew attention to the belief of the state's conservator of forests that 'when an area of jarrah forest is properly cleared, it is lost beyond recall'. He repeated the recent warning by Perth's best known geographer, Dr. J. Gentilli, that the water catchment as well as most of the prime jarrah forest could be affected by mining.

Would the mining affect the water which Perth drank? Several politicians feared that mining, by clearing the bush and undergrowth and the thin carpet of leaves and twigs, might indirectly add salt to the topsoils and so to the drinking water. Would the mines make ugly scars on the ranges? In the upper house Norman Baxter, a former farmer, warned that a hundred years of mining could lead to a larger scarring than was visible on the Greenbushes tinfield, where many visitors got the impression that 'oversize rabbits had been burrowing'. Charles Court, the minister who explained the bill, tried to allay the fears. Those jarrah trees standing in the way of a mine would be inspected by the Forestry Department and the sound ones would be bulldozed by the mining contractors and the logs carted to the timber mills. Trees would be planted after each area was mined, and fertiliser or trace elements would be added to the soil to help these young trees to grow.

It was not yet envisaged that bauxite would be mined on a large scale. If Alcoa were to mine 550 000 tonnes of bauxite a year—not a large annual tonnage by world standards—then only about ten hectares of ground would be excavated annually. At that rate the scattered quarries would cover little more than three square kilometres of ground during the next thirty years. In fact the pace of mining was to leap ahead of reasonable expectations. In the Darling Range, by the mid 1990s, as much ground was being mined in one year as was originally expected to be mined in about a quarter of a century.

In the early years of mining, not many jarrah trees were lost. Accordingly, when in 1969 Charles Court introduced his bill to allow the building of the refinery at Pinjarra and extend the mines further along the range, few members had fears for the health of the forest. Certainly a few were concerned about the effects of the bulldozers, excavators and trucks. The Labor politician, H.D. Evans, a native of Wales who had become a school teacher at Manjimup, spoke on behalf of the jarrah forests. Pointing out that Australia imported more timber than it exported, and that jarrah was one of the most useful native timbers, he said that jarrah trees should be protected as much as possible. He was worried partly because jarrah trees actually preferred the slopes where the bauxite lay. He spoke commonsense. He did not go so far as to call for the project to be halted. So the bill was passed with relative ease.

Jim Langford, a former New Zealander, was in charge of mining, and as the years went by he did not like the multiplying mess. He thought trees standing very near the proposed areas of mining should not be felled or bulldozed when they did not actually stand in the way of effective mining. He instructed the operators to clear only the trees that stood in the area to be mined.

Charles Court observed the extensive eyesore in the late 1960s and raised the question of a different approach. He did not force Alcoa to act but he occasionally reminded its chairman and managing director that as good citizens they should care for the landscape. After all it was close to the water catchment of a big city and it embraced hill country much used by the city people for recreation.

Bates and Langford were sympathetic to Court's argument. Langford, however, was answerable to the head of the Kwinana refinery, an American engineer who was interested more in the grade and quantity of ore delivered to his refinery and the costs of mining each tonne than in the scars extending across the hills. Moreover, the refinery head tended to report direct to Pittsburgh, the real centre of power, and so it was not

J.C. Bates (managing director), Sir James Forrest and Sir Lindesay Clark
discuss the company's plan to reafforest the mined areas at Jarrahdale,
about 1970.

easy for Bates, who was stationed in Melbourne, to intervene. In the
end Bates announced that he, as managing director of Alcoa, was in
charge of Langford who should report direct to him. Clark supported this
snub to the authority of Pittsburgh. It was the first step towards viewing
the environment more seriously. Bill Morgan, managing director of
Western Mining and a member of the Alcoa board, went further and
suggested at the board meeting on 1 September 1969 that the company
give a high priority to reafforestation.

The Western Australian Forests Department initially had the task of
planting trees, and usually planted imported species of pine in worked-out
areas. Their hope was to create a commercial softwood plantation, but
the trees were not very suitable for the climate and terrain. As the heavy
mining machinery had stamped down the rock and soil, the saplings did
not readily send down roots. About one in every six pines were blown
over by heavy winds.

Wherever part of the original topsoil was restored, the trees fared
slightly better. Accordingly, Langford collected the thin layer of top soil

and set it aside before the heavy mining machinery lumbered into each new area. After a quarry was worked out, and it was only a matter of months, the overburden was carted back to fill much of the hole, and the topsoil was then added before the pines were planted.

There had been virtually no hint of environmental concern in the earliest of Alcoa's published annual reports. The concern crept in, slowly, in the early 1970s, as the new green movement gained followers around Australia. Much of the company's concern was at first aesthetic. How could the rugged holes in the Darling Range be greened over? And how could a refinery be made more presentable? The outskirts of new Pinjarra refinery were marked out for greening. In 1970 thousands of trees were planted in clumps along the roads leading to the site of the refinery. To build a buffer around the refinery and to allow room for expansion, the company bought a large area, and 5000 hectares was turned into a farm with the sheep and cattle grazing within sight of the refinery. The company was proud of this rural scheme and pointed to the farm as a sign of its 'declared policy of helping to protect the environment'.

In 1970 Alcoa took what it saw as a bold step by recruiting its own forester, George White, and allowing him to employ additional staff. Next year, the company spent $115 000 on a Caterpillar D9 to help with the moving, levelling and landscaping. White realised that the tendency for trees to blow over in the wind was due in part to the heavy compacting of the rehabilitated ground by the mining machinery. So the bulldozer began to deep-rip the ground at some depth before the replanting took place. A nursery was established at Jarrahdale in 1971 to grow seedlings, and tens of thousands of native trees were planted each year.

The official responsibility for planting the trees in newly mined areas was transferred from the Forests Department to Alcoa. On those expanses of clay and rock and boulders—almost like a desert in its bareness—the original topsoil was spread, and thousands of young native trees were carried from the company's new plant nursery and set out in neat rows. After a few years the forest began to resemble the forest of old, though certainly not in the eyes of the purists. Most of the trees were eucalypt species imported from eastern Australia. Jarrah, the noblest tree in the ranges, was rarely planted.

One of the replanted areas was attractive enough to be turned into a picnic ground. With its pond and its fringe of green grass clipped short by kangaroos, it was ideal for picnics. Opened in February 1975 and named Langford Park, it proved a fine advertisement for the company. In appearance it was quite unlike the original bush, but visitors thought it was actually superior to the native bushland which they drove through on their way to the picnic. The pond did much to enhance the scene

Langford Park, one of the original minesites, was dramatically transformed into a recreational area.

in visitors' eyes. The dedicated members of the Dark Green movement were not in the least impressed, saying the company must do better.

There was a deeper fear in the minds both of those who loved the forest in its original state and those who made their living there. They observed that many of the jarrah trees in the Darling Range suffered increasingly from a disease with the vivid name of dieback. Some evidence suggested that mining activities might be assisting to spread this infection. Within the state's forests perhaps three of every ten adult jarrah trees actually grew in the same rock that held the bauxite, and most of the other jarrah trees in Western Australia were not far from mining operations. Therefore in the long term the mining activity—if it was the main culprit—might, directly or indirectly, endanger many parts of the jarrah forests.

Dieback was first identified in Java and Sumatra where it attacked cinnamon trees as far back as 1922. It was later noticed to be attacking pineapples in Hawaii and tall pine trees in the United States. After the Second World War another variation of the disease—a tiny fungus known formally as *Phytophthora cinnamoni*—savagely attacked Dutch elm trees in the northern hemisphere. Not until the early 1960s did a forestry expert, Frank Podger, clearly identify this fungus in the jarrah forests of Western Australia. Possibly it had been quietly at work in the timber-milling districts as early as the First World War. When later it spread through small parts of the forest on the Darling Range, its spread was initially attributed to bushfires.

The diseased parts of the forest were easily recognised. The fungus attacked the roots, and the tree slowly lost vigour. While many jarrah trees continued to survive, those that died might stand for years, their light-coloured, dead limbs sticking out from the trunk like witches' fingers. Some observers, on first seeing the forest, thought that every second tree had been ringbarked. On many other trees the leaves near the top were falling, and soon the top branches were almost bald. 'Jarrah dieback' was the common name for the disease but banksia, blackboy, zamia palms and several other native trees also suffered from the fungus.

The infection was thriving in the Darling Range long before the first bauxite was mined, and probably the logging industry helped to spread it. Those who dug roadmaking material from the range also spread it. Sometimes, not wishing to take gravel from areas where the forest flourished, they excavated rock and gravel from patches where the jarrah had died. In that way they probably helped to spread the disease to areas far from the source of the gravel. In certain areas the cartage of baux-ite—even the accidental dropping of bauxite from the back of ore trucks—probably helped to spread the dieback, for diseased tree roots were frequently mined with the bauxite. By 1973, there was a deep suspicion that mining was one of the human activities—perhaps the main activity—that accelerated the spread of the infection.

Alcoa was slow to view the dieback with urgency. To do so might be to accept blame. L.C. Brodie-Hall, who was executive director of Western Mining Corporation's activities in the state of Western Australia, privately said to some of his colleagues that Alcoa itself must promote research into dieback. In November 1973, by which time he was a director of Alcoa, he persuaded the board that dieback was a menace, for it was even spreading to the young forests with their radiata and pinaster pines. In 1974 Colin Agnew, who was mining manager at Jarrahdale, joined with George White, the company's own forester, in writing a useful analysis of the threat.

When a jarrah tree is infected by dieback, the foliage progressively dies.

Specialists were recruited to tackle these widening environmental fears. Graham Slessar came as an hydrologist: salinity was his problem.

Warren Tacey, the first ecologist to work for Alcoa, began to ask why the company should not set its goals higher and try to do the impossible: restore the original plants in all their diversity to the mined-out areas.

Dieback was now taken seriously by a wide circle of experts within Alcoa. Outside the company the fears increased when it was realised by even the most cautious that dieback was affecting, mildly or vigorously, about one-tenth of the whole jarrah forest. In April 1975 Dr S.R. Shea, a leading forester, gave an alarming verdict on the way dieback seemed to be affecting not only jarrah trees but most other plants growing in the jarrah forest. 'It is this almost total destruction that has led many plant pathologists throughout the world to recognise jarrah dieback as the worst plant disease ever recorded.' There was even a fear that the dieback might impair the quality of the water consumed in Perth. Rarely discussed in 1970, the topic was incessantly debated towards the end of that decade.

The spread of dieback was now attributed to a mixture of factors. The infected soil was disturbed by the excavating of gravel, the building of powerlines, the making of reservoirs and the mining of bauxite. As a culprit the bauxite mining became foremost in the public mind, though so far the mining activities had stripped only about 2 per cent of the ground where the northern jarrah forest grew. Even if mining were to be banned, it was feared that the dieback would continue to spread into new areas.

Dieback seemed to be less virulent in the extremes of climate. It lay low in the cold of late winter and the high heat of summer. Only in about six months of the year, when the soil was moist and the temperature was middling, did the pathogen really become dangerous. Then it reproduced itself and spread swiftly.

To arrest the infection, perhaps a fungicide could be sprayed? But the jarrah forest was too huge: the expense would be colossal. Perhaps bushfires might control the spread indirectly by encouraging the spread of leguminous plants after rain fell on the burned ground. Southeast of Dwellingup a bushfire was lit by the Forests Department in March 1980, and 2000 hectares of jarrah forest were burned, but it would be some years before the effect could be assessed. It was observed that the disease was worst where a certain species of banksia flourished. That bush, susceptible to the fungus, perhaps served to foster the disease. Where feasible, *Banksia grandis* was cut out and thinned, but that in itself was a huge task. In a bolder experiment about two-fifths of the entire forest was quarantined and vehicles were not permitted to enter except under stringent conditions: the tyres were believed to be carrying and spreading the infection.

In 1977 Alcoa's annual report printed for the first time a photograph of replanted areas. Readers of the report could see bushy young eucalypts growing at one of the first areas to be mined at the new Del Park mine near Pinjarra. Nobody could say it was a doctored photograph, for the light brown soil and other signs of the massive earth-moving operation were more visible than the trees. Next year's annual report showed a full-page photo of the older eucalypts at Jarrahdale mine with a caption pointing to the 'natural understorey emerging strongly'. A fern was in the foreground. It seemed just the place for a picnic.

The company continued to plant a small selection of native trees on the ground that had been mined. Spotted gum, sugar gum, salmon gum, the Western Australian wandoo and various other native trees and shrubs did not suffer from the dieback, and so they were planted with some confidence. Many of the earliest areas to be replanted with natives were soon pleasing to the eye. The mining scars were camouflaged by young trees and a spreading bushland which, in the eyes of strangers, seemed to have been always there. Foresters and ecologists, however, were entitled to argue that Alcoa's record of planting a total of one million trees in the 1970s was not sufficient. It was not restoration, but renovation. Meanwhile many old jarrah trees slowly died. They died far from the site of mining activities, for all kinds of traffic were spreading the fungus. In some parts of the forest, however, the fungus had been quietly at work long before mining commenced, but was just now being observed for the first time.

George White hired more experts for his team of environmentalists. Barry Carbon was recruited from the Commonwealth Scientific and Industrial Research Organisation to investigate the plant disease afflicting the ranges; and when White moved into private practice Carbon became the manager of Alcoa's environment department and later the head of the Environment Protection Authority in Western Australia. In 1978 the company gave a first grant of $500 000 to promote research into dieback by a public committee chaired by the government's conservator of forests. At the end of 1978, Alcoa had 52 employees working full-time on the environment. In the following year it established a centralised nursery at Marrinup to grow seedlings and do field research. For a time jarrah seedlings were grown and then planted in the mined ground. Then the experiment was halted: many transplanted jarrah seemed to be dying, perhaps because the infection was already in the nursery or carried there in muddy boots or truck tyres. Later the broadcasting of native seeds over the mined and landscaped areas—a technique largely learned from Comalco in Queensland—replaced the growing and transplanting of seedlings.

Alcoa became an increasing target for conservationists, whose numbers were multiplying almost everywhere in Australia. On several fronts Alcoa was attacked by the organisation Friends of the Earth. It was claimed that the red muds discharged in huge quantities from the Kwinana refinery 'pose a serious threat' to the underground water on which Perth partly depended. Along the Darling Range the mining operations, it was rightly said, were shrinking the forest and endangering the surviving trees. Alcoa itself, it was alleged, was receiving massive and secret subsidies from the government and paying low royalties in return for the privilege of mining the bauxite. The allegation of subsidies was untrue but the royalties paid by Alcoa were relatively low.

Throughout the world the 1970s was a decade of expensive energy. It was a prelude—warned many conservationists—to the energy famine of the future. Alcoa was denounced as a waster of energy. It was pointed out that the alumina industry as a whole used 16 per cent of the total primary energy in Western Australia but employed only 0.5 per cent of the workforce. This was largely true: the aluminium industry, and especially its smelters, was by its very nature a glutton for energy. And yet the fact remained that if the world wanted aluminium, some nations— whether Australia or India or Norway—had to consume much energy in order to produce it. If no aluminium were produced then all aircraft and cars, trains and trucks would be much heavier, and so they would consume much more fuel simply to propel their own weight.

The fierce criticism of aluminium and its hunger for electricity was really an indirect attack on modern civilisation, the widening web of international trade and travel, and the fact that the more prosperous nations devoured energy in massive quantities. In the opinion of the Friends of the Earth, fossil fuel in Western Australia was likely to be scarce by the mid 1990s, leading to 'the spectre of a nuclear future'. This was a very exaggerated warning even in terms of the knowledge then available. The warning now seems completely astray because of Western Australia's later discoveries of coal and natural gas on land and offshore.

In pointing to the perils facing the jarrah forest, as distinct from the perils facing Western Australia's economy if its supplies of energy ran low, the campaigners had substance to their viewpoint. Much forest, though only a small percentage, was being destroyed by the mining of bauxite. The forest was also a catchment for Perth's water, and there were rising fears—probably exaggerated—that the water from the nearby reservoirs was becoming salty.

How a government adjudicated between these rival claims and conflicting needs of forestry, scenery, water and aluminium was a knotty task. The government could only find what seemed a sensible balance, weighing the claims of the jarrah forest as a place of beauty and recreation and as a water catchment on the one hand, and as a vital source of mineral wealth and employment for Western Australians on the other hand.

Alcoa was now designing a third alumina refinery at Wagerup, in place of the combined southern refinery initially discussed with Reynolds. Obviously, another refinery would multiply the demand for bauxite and therefore increase the pressure on the jarrah forest. Many conservationists decided to fight the refinery: they resolved that this was a battle they must win. If they could prevent the construction of a major refinery, they would win one of the major victories in the short history of the green movement.

In April 1978 the Court government introduced a bill permitting a refinery under stringent conditions, including a prior statement confirming that the likely impact of the refinery on the environment would be tolerable, and a stipulation that all mining must be carefully monitored by the government's agencies. The refinery could grow to 2 million tonnes a year, over a period of fifteen years, but further expansion was not guaranteed.

The Labor Party called for caution. Several of its members had inspected the mined ground and, while expressing astonishment at the regrowth of the bush, wondered whether the healing of the ground was permanent. They called for a royal commission to investigate dieback, salinity and other dangers. Only if the report were favourable would they consent to another refinery. Their demand was defeated in parliament. Permission was granted to build a refinery at Wagerup, once its environmental impact had been decreed to be satisfactory.

In the face of this defeat, the group conducting the 'Campaign to Save Native Forests' became militant. In February 1979, and again in May, protesters occupied the refinery site and disrupted work. The episodes gained intense publicity on television. On those days when the blockaders planned a confrontation they rang the television stations, and their cameras and crews would appear in Wagerup, all in readiness. Bob Hornbeck, the general manager in charge of Western Australian operations, minimised the publicity by avoiding even the hint of a confrontation until after 4 p.m. when the cameras were on their way back to Perth. Film footage of a late afternoon clash would reach Perth too late for the main evening news. In the end the police moved in—after 4 p.m.—and arrested many protesters who refused to leave the site.

A large section of silent opinion in Perth wanted Wagerup to be built, partly because it signalled jobs and prosperity. Wagerup would also ensure a supply of natural gas to Perth itself and its people would gain for the first time cheap energy for electric light, cooking, hot water and the heating or cooling of houses. The building of Wagerup was probably essential to guarantee the construction of the biggest pipeline project in Australia's history: 1500 kilometres of steel pipeline conveying natural gas from the North West Shelf to Perth and the alumina refineries further

White Gold

south. Alcoa's refineries agreed to buy half of the natural gas that would come along that pipeline in its first years. Indeed the new refinery at Wagerup was to be the terminus for the gas pipeline completed in 1984. Without Alcoa's backing, the pipeline, so important to Perth, probably would have been uneconomical.

The disruption at Wagerup, and the adverse publicity, were a shock to Alcoa's leaders. Most had assumed that they should make few concessions to the militant green movement and especially its strong anti-capitalist and anti-mining stance. Inside Alcoa, however, there was a growing view that the green movement had both a valid argument, which should be heeded, and an invalid argument, which should be criticised. This compromise approach was favoured by the new chairman, Arvi Parbo, and the new managing director, George Haymaker. They saw the need for a constructive response to green issues as well as the strenuous publicising of what the company had already done. 'We had a story to tell: we hadn't told it,' admitted one senior engineer.

During the blockade of the rising Wagerup refinery the company realised that most of its own employees had not seen the bauxite mines and the encircling forest that was now the hub of the controversy. Miners saw it each workday but they were a tiny part of the company's workforce. Accordingly, it was resolved that virtually all the Western Australian employees—three thousand in all—should be taken on bus tours of the mined areas. Citizen groups also were taken in buses to the mined areas. Visitors flocked in to see: 45 000 came in 1981. Most were impressed with what they saw.

Green critics were especially invited to join the tours, sometimes with astonishing results. The green movement in its more extreme publicity had exaggerated the damage to the bushlands in the Darling Range. On television the dying trees and the mining scars were shown more often than the revegetated areas. Most visitors were pleasantly surprised to find bush rather than man-made wasteland. Of course they were not experts—they missed much—but they were voters.

The Conservation Council of Western Australia had called for large areas of the Darling Range to be placed out of bounds. It demanded that the reserved forest—in which mining was banned—be enlarged from 2400 hectares to 77 000 hectares. With some overstatement it claimed that, without prompt controls on mining, 'it will be impossible for any future Government to control this juggernaut industry'. After the Court government refused to extend the forest reserves, the Conservation Council decided on the boldest of steps. It appealed to the United States District Court, thus initiating the kind of class action not possible in Australian courts. In Perth town hall on 4 March 1981 an appeal was launched to finance the case. Ten days later on the 'Four Corners' programme on ABC television, the deputy prime minister, Doug Anthony, and Sir Arvi Parbo, chairman of Alcoa, debated the burning question with green leaders. The president of the Conservation Council was Neil Bartholomaeus, an immunologist at the University of Western Australia, and in the televised debate he confidently predicted that there would be 'an aluminium rebellion throughout Australia' and the aluminium giants would be defeated and dethroned.

Dr Bartholomaeus went to Pittsburgh to organise what was called 'the Jarrah Class Action'. But the idea of citizens calling on a United States court to control events in Australia aroused hostility. In the federal parliament both the Fraser government and the Labor opposition eventually agreed to condemn the idea of Australians appealing to an American court. Senator Gareth Evans, who two years later was to become attorney-general in the new Labor government, said passionately that Australians of all viewpoints should join in fighting the 'growing enthusiasm of US Courts for minding everybody else's business'. Judicial imperialism, he added, is as offensive as military imperialism. Ironically, Alcoa, having long suffered in Australia because 51 per cent of its shares were owned in America, now gained prestige because it opposed the idea of an American court interfering in an Australian dispute.

In the court in Pittsburgh the formal defendants were two American companies: the Reynolds Metal Co. which was planning its own bauxite venture near Bunbury; and the Aluminum Co. of America, which owned 51 per cent of the shares in Alcoa of Australia. The affidavit called on them to halt all mining within the state forest until it was proved, scientifically, that the 'ecological system' would not be damaged by the mines. In June 1981, at a press conference held in the Hilton Hotel in Pittsburgh, Bartholomaeus announced that the defendants were already 'panicking'.

The court heard the evidence on 18 June 1981, and Sir Arvi Parbo was one of the many Australians who attended as spectators. When the news of the court's proceedings was flashed to Australian television, there was amusement that the conservationists' lawyer, in ignorance, had called Western Australia 'a colony'. Three weeks later the judge ruled that the case lay outside the jurisdiction of the United States.

The company, while continuing to build the refinery at Wagerup, knew that it had every incentive to accept a high level of responsibility for the health or ill-health of the forest, even in those places where the forest had been damaged before Alcoa was formed. More money was spent in studying the causes of the dieback; and by the end of 1992 the cost of that research alone was to exceed $2 million. In addition another $12 million a year was spent on rehabilitating the mined areas and replanting them. On average, the cost of rehabilitating each 100 hectares was to be $1 450 000.

Success came, not resoundingly, but more than had been anticipated. At first it was thought that most of the native plants could not be replanted successfully on mined-out slopes where they had once reigned. Then, as the confidence grew, the seeds of numerous natives of the area were broadcast on the ground. Marris and bullich seeds, blackbutt, and jarrah itself, took root. Seeds of various low-growing bushes were collected and planted in the areas that had been mined. The natives took over, and by the late 1980s the planting of eastern Australian trees and shrubs had ceased completely.

The prospect that the seeds would sprout and grow was increased when novel procedures were adopted. To protect the topsoil that had been replaced on the newly landscaped areas from erosion after heavy rains, earthen banks were bulldozed into place on higher ground. In 1984 another way of ripping or ploughing the ground—before the native seeds were sown—showed promise. The rock and soil of the reclaimed ground had been pressed down too tightly by the heavy earth-moving and mining machinery, and so a way of loosening the ground at depth was experimented with by Jim Croton, a civil engineer. Known locally as a 'whiz kid', Croton devised a heavy steel winged tine. Shaped like a T turned upside down, the winged tine was pulled through the restored ground by a bulldozer. It effectively loosened the compacted rock and

The winged tine was devised to deep-rip the soil prior to the replanting of vegetation on mined land.

clay at a depth of about one and a half metres, but it did not seriously disturb the surface.

On a thin layer of topsoil and a deep layer of rubble the replanted forest slowly began to thrive. Special fertilisers, it was discovered, helped the growth; and so helicopters flew overhead and dropped nitrogen and phosphate and other nutrients onto the rough ground. The unusual plough allowed infant trees to put down roots into soil and rock that were now better drained.

A hundred ideas, minor and major, slowly aided the regrowing of the original forest and the limiting of the spread of dieback. Some ideas were borrowed from overseas; some arose from research financed by Alcoa at local universities; some came from the new Western Australian government department called Conservation and Land Management or CALM; and some were the ideas of people working at the mines or in the forest. In searching for solutions, all the investigators and decision-makers had really begun with the mindset of agriculturalists. But landscaping, plough-ing and seeding called more for an imitation of nature than of farming. So the unorthodox plough was devised; and likewise the growing and planting of seedlings by hand gave way to the broadcasting of the seed from the air. Whereas 625 seedlings were originally planted by hand in each hectare, 2000 trees sprang up through direct seeding under the new technique.

In replanted ground the young jarrah trees were found to be free from the fungus. In the early 1990s jarrah was the main species growing in most of the reafforested ground. It seemed as if the process of mining was actually impeding the fungus. The ground, once the bauxite was removed and the ploughing was completed, appeared to lack the condi-tions that once favoured the spread of the fungus. The mined ground appeared to suit the jarrah even more than the unmined ground. By 1990 about seven of every ten plant species that had once been growing in the jarrah forest were again flourishing. Green critics were entitled to ask: what about the other three? At the same time the spread of the dieback was now slower. In 1995 it was estimated that 84 per cent of the jarrah forest was not infected.

While the young jarrah trees flourished in the replanted forest, the old unmined forest was still at risk. Much had been learned—but not enough—about the fungus. Clearly it was being spread by orchardists, forest workers, mining trucks, tourists on picnics and vehicles travelling on the bitumen or gravel roads. Any tyres that came from a dieback area could carry the fungus to a relatively unharmed part of forest. It was decided that the tyres themselves should be disinfected.

The Huntly quarries, sending their bauxite to the nearby Pinjarra refinery, had to produce bauxite on the grand scale because they supplied what was now the largest refinery in the world; and their gravel and earthen roads as wide as highways ran through the forest, and huge trucks rumbled along the roads. The risk of spreading dieback into the adjacent forest was magnified because this wheeled equipment went in and out of the mining zone. In an attempt to prevent the fungus from spreading, the company set up a wash-down station which hosed all vehicles that arrived, irrespective of the corner of the forest they had traversed. The process was repeated at other mines. The capacity of the fungus to spread with ease was at last appreciated.

Research was disclosing more about the dangerous fungus. Seen through a powerful microscope it was a sperm with two tails. In the soil it was attracted to the chemicals that secreted sugar from the tree roots, and it settled on roots and fed on the woody cells. In effect it prevented the water from passing up to the leaves. So the tree slowly died as if in a drought.

The fungus bred rapidly in warm, moist weather. After heavy rains in summer the water gravitated to the cap of the hard rock, rich in bauxite and lying just below the surface. These moist conditions within the warm rock and soil favoured the fungus. Indeed the ground around the root system of the jarrah trees became a hothouse for growing the fungus. But once the cap rock was mined, the water ceased to gather there in summer. Jarrah could therefore be planted in the mined area with more chance of thriving than in unmined ground. Hundreds of thousands of small jarrah trees began to flourish. Of all the species growing in the region before the mining began, eight out of every ten were being restored.

Fauna did not return to the mined-out ground as quickly as the flora: this was confirmed when Alcoa began to monitor the native wildlife. Spiders were amongst the first to return and snakes were amongst the last: snakes waited until old hollow logs and an increase of ground litter gave them protection. Amongst the surprising colonies found in restored mine sites were the quokkas—small wallabies that settled on swampy ground. The most northerly colony of quokkas in Western Australia was recently found near the Jarrahdale mine.

Monitoring of the wildlife in 1992 revealed an alarming decline in the numbers of certain species. Foxes were believed to be the culprits. As the Darling Range was wedged between expanding Perth and outlying towns on the coastal side and the farmlands on the dry inland side, pressure from both sides was possibly driving the foxes into the bushland of the Darling Range. The fox population, tempted by the baits set out for them in the forest, is now declining. The fear is that feral cats, previously kept down by foxes, will take their place. The plan to restore the habitat has no conceivable ending.

Alcoa's other mining region lay at Anglesea in coastal Victoria where

*A colony of the rare marsupials, quokkas, was recently found in a
revegetated area near the Jarrahdale mine.*

brown coal was mined, though not on the same scale as the bauxite in
Western Australia. From the start it was feared that the Anglesea mine
could endanger the surroundings, because it stood at the gateway to one
of the nation's most spectacular tourist routes, the Great Ocean Road.
Accordingly landscaping of the abandoned parts of the mine was carefully
planned. As large areas of clay and sand had to be removed before the
brown coal, sitting some twenty or thirty metres below, could be exposed
for open-cut mining, it was decided to truck the clay and sand to large
overburden dumps and store it in readiness for the landscaping. The coal
was then mined, layer by layer, and when all the accessible coal from
an area had been sent to the power station, only a deep rectangular
crater remained. From the overburden dumps the waste clay and sand
was carted to the crater as filling. Once the filled ground had settled
down, the replanting was begun. It was not very successful, partly because
the thin layer of original topsoil had vanished in the earth-moving
operations. Many of the new trees that did flourish were Tasmanian blue
gums and Western Australian natives, which were alien to the region.
Revegetation was still an infant art.

Much was learned from the rehabilitation experience in Western Australia. The value of saving the topsoil at the earliest opportunity was one vital lesson. So, before removing the clay and sand that overlay the coal, the thin layer of sandy topsoil and its buried seeds were carefully collected and stored on one side. Likewise the subsoil was collected. When the coal had been mined from another section, leaving only a deep hole, the layers of overburden originally taken from the hole were replaced in the correct sequence, with waste ash from the power station placed on the bottom, clay and soil placed in the middle, and finally the thin layer of topsoil and seeds. The effect was dramatic. The original ground cover of grasses and shrubs largely returned. Not every native plant flourished, but most did.

To restore the bushland and heathland on the fringes of a working mine and power station was a double-edged victory. On 16 February 1983 bushfires began to burn in many parts of Victoria. Early in the afternoon a fire was reported about twenty kilometres from the Anglesea power station. The summer had been dry, a strong hot wind was blowing and the bushfire raced towards the sea resort of Lorne. Though the direction of the wind made the power station and mine seem out of the fire's reach, the mine foreman, Don Taylor, halted the mining and carting of coal, sent the trucks and equipment to the safest position and deployed men to run out spray lines and hoses to the exposed faces of inflammable coal.

Shortly before dark, at about 7.30 p.m., the blustery wind changed to the southwest. The bushfire began to race along the bushland near the coast. Even when the fire was far from Anglesea, the wind carried glowing cinders and ashes far ahead of it and dropped them on the coal mine. The mine would have been ablaze but for the efforts of men who carried water in knapsacks.

The wind was now rushing at almost 100 kilometres an hour. At about 8.30 p.m. a ball of fire came towards the mine, making a noise like 'the mad firing of bullets', according to the company's fire protection officer, Don Bennett. In many places the bush caught fire. The flames seized the exposed equipment—cables, rubbish bins, piles of mined coal, the electrical workshop, and even the coal on the conveyor belt near the power station. The mine was evacuated. All effort went into saving the power station.

At 9.31 p.m. the safety valves in the big boiler blew out with a roar. There was a flashing of alarms and the sounding of warning hooters and bells. Inside the building all was darkness, for suddenly the generating of electricity had ceased. Geoff Temple recalled that it was eerie to be in charge of the dark control room, filled with the smell of burning, and to know that if he made one error and turned the wrong switches he

Dieback

Alcoa employees extinguishing embers at the Anglesea coal mine and power station, following the bushfires of February 1983.

might wreck about $50 million worth of equipment. Of course the bushfire, if it set fire to the power station, might destroy even more.

Miraculously the power station was saved by firefighters, including a crew and firetruck rushed from Point Henry. During the night the fires were controlled. By daybreak the wind had died and none of the separate fires was burning dangerously. Around the mine was a waste of blackened bushland which, when rains fell, began the slow process of recovery.

Mining of coal went on as before. The latest sections of the open cut were filled with the collected waste, and the replanting of the distinctive native species of the district was more and more successful. Tiger snakes returned to the restored bushland and heathland. The native birds multiplied. In 1993, on a steep clay wall of the open cut, two peregrine falcons made their nest, in sight and sound of the heavy excavators and trucks that worked for twelve hours each day. The peregrine falcons made the most of their home and, when hunting, perched on the high powerlines or the powerhouse and swooped on passing birds. With the aid of field glasses, three female chicks could later be seen in the falcons' cliff-side nest.

The company's bauxite, more than its coal, was the main target of public criticism. Western Australia was the more vulnerable because Alcoa's engineers not only had to restore the ground that had been mined but they had to dispose of the waste material that poured out of the refineries. The company produced far more red mud than was originally envisaged. For each three tonnes of bauxite that reached a refinery, the end result was one tonne of alumina and two tonnes of muddy waste. The alumina was shipped to distant ports but the 'mud' remained, close to the refineries.

Large areas were needed to hold the mud. At Kwinana the government originally supplied much of the dumping land but soon the company was buying more. At Pinjarra in 1982 the company spent $22 million on new land for dumps, and a year later it spent another $2.3 million to buy the old Fairbridge Farm which stood in the path of red dust that sometimes blew from the dumps.

The mud also gave rise to other difficulties. Each plateau of red mud had to settle down and dry out before an attempt could be made to plant grasses and bushes on the top. While the top was drying out, it was occasionally turned into dust by a succession of summer days and by strong, dry winds. Far below, the bottom layers of the dump might remain wet, and the risk remained that the chemicals that filtered their way down the dump might seep into the underground water that was widely used in Perth and the coastal plain.

By placing a layer of clay—and a plastic lining—at the bottom of a new residue dump, not so much of the caustic soda seeped down and found its way to the subsoil. There was a risk that water below could be contaminated, and so holes were systematically bored on the perimeters of the dumps to test the purity of the water. In 1987 the technique of 'dry stacking' was adopted. About half of the moisture was removed from the residue, and then the mud was spread thinly over a wide area so that it could be dried more quickly by sun and wind. Some of that mud, when dry, was used to fertilise the lean sandy soils on the coastal plain. More pasture grew on land that was fertilised with the mud residue, but the cost of carting the dry mud to farms was an impediment.

There was also a financial incentive to recover the liquid caustic soda which stayed in large quantities in the dumps. If it was recovered the need for costly imports from foreign ports was lowered. In the early 1980s, 35 old-time windmills were erected at Kwinana to help in the recovery of the valuable liquor. The rate of recovery improved. More and more caustic soda, once salvaged, was recirculated within the refineries, finding its way again to the dumps and being recycled again. One problem, then, was solved, but the solution—the recovery of caustic soda from the mud dumps—created a harder problem. The caustic soda, when it returned from the dumps to the refinery process, was a carrier of impurities that poisoned and clogged the refineries.

These impurities, originally in the bauxite, had been detected long ago but were not widely recognised as major obstacles. The impurities came from the soil, clay, vegetation and leaf litter covering the bauxite, and they included the roots of trees that had grown on the bauxite. In places, the organic impurities were seemingly leached right into the bauxite. The proportion of this unwanted organic matter varied from ore body to ore body but was generally much higher than in bauxite deposits in other parts of the world. Mined with the top layer of bauxite, these impurities went to the refineries and entered the liquor circuit where they formed sodium oxalate—a poison in the liquor stream. Don Campbell, Western Mining's chief geologist, had noticed these impurities in the bauxite in the late 1950s. The first tests at the Bell Bay refinery had also detected them, leading to brief fears that the bauxite might be unsellable.

Six refining units at Kwinana were fully at work before attempts were made to remove the organic matter: the first steps did not go far. In any case the increasing attempts to recover the diluted caustic soda that was pumped with the red mud to the dumps resulted in organic matter as well as caustic soda returning to the liquor stream in the refineries. The big financial saving made by recovering the caustic soda from the dumps was partly lost by the simultaneous recovery of impure organic matter. The unwanted impurities might remain in a refinery's liquor stream for years.

While Pinjarra had quick success in scavenging used caustic soda, it was also more effective in recovering the organic matter that came, uninvited, with it. So the problem was compounded. Wagerup refinery was designed with more knowledge of the organic dilemma but the difficulty remained. Kwinana faced a crisis in 1987, so pervasive was the organic matter in the recycled caustic soda. The refinery was capable of producing 1 500 000 tonnes of alumina annually but its output had fallen almost to 1 200 000 tonnes, partly because of the 'rapid build up in organic carbon in the Bayer liquor stream'. Output was not the only loser. More energy was used and the maintenance costs were higher. About one-sixth of the alumina that was produced was still holding so much unwanted soda and silica that it had to be retreated so that the process of crystallisation could take place.

Theoretically it was possible to remove the organic matter completely, but it was too expensive. As a compromise $11 million was spent at Kwinana in improving the rate of removal of organic impurities. In effect this liquor-burning plant was the kidney which removed impurities from the refinery's blood stream. As more knowledge was needed of the exact composition of the bauxite being mined each day, tests were regularly made of the percentage of organic material it carried, thus alerting the refinery.

*School students at an Alcoa display during a visit to Bunbury by Prince
Charles in March 1979.*

One by one the dumps of red mud and sand ceased to be an eyesore.
Each dump, when completed and drained, was planted; and the old
dumps at Kwinana were fit even for pastures to be sown or vegetables
planted. The dumps at the two newer refineries were largely concealed,
moreover, by Alcoa's wide buffer zone of farmland. By 1981 Alcoa's farms,
covering 5000 hectares at Pinjarra and 3000 hectares at Wagerup, grazed
thousands of cattle and sheep. For several years the rate of return from
farming was higher than from the mines and refineries.

The company moved more and more into conservation. It set up Alcoa
Landcare Projects in Western Australia in 1989 and Victoria in 1990, and
tackled such rural problems as salinity, erosion and the degradation of
farmland and bushland. In the Western Australian wheatbelt six conservation sites were set up to experiment in and demonstrate ways of reducing
salinity.

Not far from the Kwinana refinery, on a plain where clay had been
mined from shallow pits as a lining of the residue dumps, the company
created the Wellard Wetlands, a reed-lined lake which became the home
for red-capped plovers and great crested grebes and 80 other species of
birds. These young wetlands received a high award from the United States

The United Nations Environment Programme's 'Global 500 Roll of Honour'.

organisation, the Wildlife Habitat Enhancement Council. The environs around the new Portland smelter were to receive a similar award, making them the first industrial site outside the United States to be so honoured. In addition, for its total efforts Alcoa won Australia's National Landcare Award. Its conservation experiments at mines, refineries and smelters were becoming known far from Australia, and in almost every year in the early 1990s came a new international award. Kwinana became the first alumina refinery in the world to receive 'Quality Endorsement', and the prime minister, Paul Keating, went to Western Australia to take part in the ceremony. When in 1995 the Aluminum Co. of America itself received a major award it was seen partly as a recognition of Alcoa's performance in Australia.

The mines in the Darling Range, where the company was first forced to face painful ecological facts, received the most prized award. In 1990, on World Environment Day, the United Nations commended Alcoa's work in trying to recreate the jarrah forests. The first mining company in the world to be acclaimed for the way it tackled an environmental hazard, Alcoa was presented in Mexico City with a citation praising its 'outstanding practical achievements in the protection and improvement of the environment'.

White Gold

Dr Mostafa K. Tolba, executive director of UNEP, presenting Alcoa's membership certificate of the Global 500 to the executive director of Western Australian operations, Roger Vines, in 1990.

On hearing the news of this United Nations award many green crusaders felt outraged. 'Somebody in the UN has made a colossal mistake,' said the best-known green politician in Australia, Dr Bob Brown of Tasmania. Talking with Andrew Olle on ABC radio on the morning of 7 June 1990, Brown wondered just how the United Nations could seriously reward a company which had been 'the villains on the W.A. scene for so long'. Sir Arvi Parbo, Alcoa's chairman, replied that his company's work in the Darling Range spoke for itself. 'Please,' he invited Dr Brown, 'come and see for yourself.' Brown replied that he had already flown over the forests, emphasising his knowledge by describing them as 'karri' forests. Brown had a legitimate point of view but his view from the aircraft was not quite as clear as he imagined. Parbo explained that the forest was jarrah.

In retrospect the Darling Range was the centre of one of the most daunting environmental problems in the history of Australian mining. The scale of the mining operations exposed a large area. The fact that the bauxite was mined in a chain of shallow and scattered open cuts multiplied the total area at risk. The risk to the surrounding forest was increased by the prior presence of the forest dieback, an infection that was so little understood. There was another source of peril: here was the only large-scale mining operation taking place in the water catchment of an Australian capital city. In trying to grapple with these risks the company had had to discover its own answers more often than borrow them.

When the jarrah crisis became widely known in the 1970s, Alcoa lost the respect of many Western Australians. Slowly it regained that respect by making an expensive effort to learn more about the forest in which it mined. Eventually many conservationists arrived to inspect the results. Some were suspicious, even peeved. Others were impressed that Alcoa was trying to heal not only scars of its own making but damage that had been done long before the bauxite was first mined.

◆ 14 ◆

The Spectre of Stonehenge

Sir James Forrest stepped down as chairman on the eve of his 73rd birthday, and attended his last meeting of the board on the morning of 24 February 1978. In Pittsburgh the occasion was deemed such a landmark that Krome George, the chief executive, flew out to be present, adding his thanks for the efficient and friendly manner in which Forrest had led the company over the last eight years. In the same room that afternoon the company held its annual general meeting, and Sir Arvi Parbo was elected a director in place of Forrest. After the short meeting was over, the same room was used for another meeting of the board at which a chairman was elected.

Sir Arvi Parbo, the new chairman, had just turned 52. Estonian by birth, he had worked in German mines before emigrating to Australia, where he gained an honours degree in engineering at the University of Adelaide. Moving to Western Australia in 1956 he worked for Western Mining as an underground surveyor at the Bullfinch goldmine and as underground manager at the Nevoria mine. Two of his three children were born in the country hospital at the wheat and gold town of Southern Cross. In 1960 he was promoted to be technical assistant to Bill Morgan at the head office but before he moved to Melbourne with his family he was sent to the Darling Range to become familiar with the bauxite then being investigated. Experience there, it was thought, would be valuable, for Western Mining was still managing the venture.

At that time the future of Western Australia's bauxite was up in the air. Were the deposits big enough and rich enough? Nobody could give a sure answer. 'It was like a big cake with a lot of little raisins,' Parbo noted. There was doubt whether even the raisins were worth extracting.

Certainly the best areas of bauxite were promising. 'We knew it wasn't a wash-out,' Parbo recalls.

While based in Melbourne, Parbo was occasionally asked by Bill Morgan to help with the baby bauxite project. When Ralph Derr, the retired refinery man, arrived from Pittsburgh in October 1960 to make an assessment of the project, he was allocated the services of Parbo whose task was to obtain any information requested and do the calculations. In that way Parbo learned about the aluminium industry. Derr's report was received favourably in Pittsburgh, and when—as a result—Lindesay Clark was invited in April 1961 to meet the heads of the Aluminum Co. of America in the hope of negotiating a partnership, Parbo went with him as technical assistant. He was then only a junior engineer, and the Americans were puzzled to receive the telegram saying that Mr and Mrs Clark would be arriving on a particular flight, accompanied by 'Parbo'. Later Parbo learned that the telegram 'threw Pittsburgh office into a turmoil because no one could work out who or what "Parbo" was, the guesses ranging from Mrs Clark's pet poodle to various other possibilities'. In the end it was decided that whatever a Parbo was, a room should be booked in its name at the Pittsburgh Hilton.

Once Alcoa was formed, nearly all of Western Mining's technical staff—except those engaged in exploration—ceased to work on the bauxite project; and Parbo saw little of it. But in 1971 he became managing director of Western Mining, in succession to Bill Morgan, and three years later he became its chairman in succession to Lindesay Clark. He thus had a special interest in the success of Alcoa, for Western Mining would receive one-fifth of the profits—when at last worthwhile dividends began to flow.

After becoming chairman of Alcoa, Parbo set about smoothing relations with Pittsburgh. Representatives of all the shareholders met for two days. The history of the negotiations that led to the forming of the company and the arrangements made in later years were carefully recorded in what came to be known, because of its cover, as 'The Blue Book'. When the views of the contracting parties differed, the respective versions were recorded. The differences were narrowed down to a small number of issues, and all the disagreements were resolved. Even the contentious Victoria agreement, which had met Pittsburgh's need to acquire a formal interest in the bauxite leases in Western Australia and so satisfy the United States tax laws, was slowly clarified and resolved, to the satisfaction of both sides. The arguments ceased.

In the same year as Parbo became chairman of Alcoa a new chief executive took office. After a record term of office Waldo Porter gave way to George Haymaker Jr, who was straight from Pittsburgh and full of bounce. A graduate of the Massachusetts Institute of Technology and the University of Southern California, he had risen rapidly to treasurer of the Aluminum Co. of America before he was posted, at the age of 40, to Australia. Some said privately he was destined for the top place in head office.

An enthusiast, Haymaker looked far ahead. He wanted to achieve things, and achieve them before the deadline. He handled paper with ease but was impatient if a conference dawdled. In Australia he gained a reputation for not always listening to what was said to him, but that impression arose partly from his habit of doing two things simultaneously. For example, when chairing a meeting, he would glance at other business papers for nourishment. Once his mind was made up, it was changed only by an earthquake. His self-confidence was sometimes vexing to those around him but most members of staff gained confidence from his strong sense of direction and his sheer competence. He was also likeable, which was slightly unusual in one so single-minded.

The double change at Alcoa's helm in 1978 also coincided with a short period of expansion in Australia's aluminium industry. The key to producing cheap aluminium was cheap electricity for the smelter; and Australia, which had generated electricity in the middle of the international price range, was becoming a relatively cheap producer of electricity in the late 1970s. The energy crisis, and the expensive oil, tipped the scales in favour of Australia and its chain of huge coal deposits, both brown and black. In contrast, North America and Europe, the major *smelters* of aluminium, were hit by the new economics of electricity. As they now lacked major sites for hydro-electric projects, and as any remaining site was likely to be defended with passion by the new green movement, they could no longer develop this cheapest form of power. Nuclear power was also falling from favour and becoming a target for the green movement following the accident at Three Mile Island in the United States. Moreover, oil and natural gas had costed themselves out of the market; and in 1982 the Aluminum Co. of America was to close down a smelter—at Point Comfort in Texas—that was powered by natural gas.

Haymaker told the directors that the world had entered a new era of 'energy economics'. Here, he proclaimed, was 'a window of opportunity'. Most of the new smelters would not be in Europe and Japan and North America—producers of most of the world's aluminium ingots—but in 'new, relatively energy-rich areas'. Australia was now one of those favoured areas. Haymaker believed, as did most international businessmen, that a scarcity and high price of energy would be a sobering hallmark of the final decades of the twentieth century.

At the same time Japan was slowly being driven out of the smelting of aluminium by the high cost of imported oil and coal. Japan was capable

The Spectre of Stonehenge

of producing 1.6 million tonnes of ingots a year but less than half of its smelting capacity was likely to survive the new economic pressures. Its smelters, said Haymaker, were in 'serious financial straits'. They were likely to buy less alumina, and so the Western Australian refineries, having expanded partly to serve Japan, now had to find new markets.

Hitherto Australia had specialised in mining bauxite and converting it into alumina for sale to overseas smelters. In 1980 Australia mined 35 per cent of the world's bauxite and also produced 26 per cent of the world's alumina, topping the world in both products. As a producer of the aluminium metal, Australian smelters were humbler, supplying only 3 per cent of the world's annual total. With the retreat of Japan, perhaps Australia should smelt more of its own abundant alumina. The Fraser government in Canberra and some of the state governments agreed.

Queensland had plenty of coal near the coast, and that meant relatively cheap electricity. At the port of Gladstone, in central Queensland, plans for a large powerhouse and aluminium smelter were announced in 1978. The main sponsor was Alcoa's oldest rival, Comalco, the owner of the rich bauxite deposits at Weipa in north Queensland. In the Gladstone smelter, Comalco held 30 per cent of the shares, Kaiser 20 per cent, Sumitomo 17 per cent, and four other Japanese companies held the remaining 33 per cent. An expansion of aluminium smelting was also announced by Alumax and Alcan near the black coalfield of the Hunter Valley near Newcastle.

In Victoria the government was eager to expand its output of electricity based on the huge brown coal deposits. The Loy Yang A power station, then being constructed, offered to supply reasonably priced electricity. In this mood of optimism, Alcoa decided in November 1978 to extend the Point Henry smelter. Already it was producing about 104 000 tonnes of ingot a year, of which 64 000 tonnes were sold as ingots and some 40 000 tonnes were rolled or half-fabricated into materials for can-making and the building industry. A third potline would raise the annual capacity to 161 000 tonnes, much of which would be shipped to east Asia. Haymaker assured them that the investment of $85 million would be repaid in a mere nine and a half years. Rapid inflation was to upset that calculation, and the final cost of the extension was closer to $110 million.

As Point Henry's smelter was requiring larger shipments of alumina each month from the refineries in Western Australia, Alcoa made new shipping plans for the Great Australian Bight, which was one of the more expensive of the world's sea routes. After using the Australian National Line for a decade, Alcoa had bought the motor vessel *Wollongong* in 1973, renaming her the *Myarra*. Now, with a third potline in sight, a larger and faster ship was needed to carry alumina from the

The first ship purchased by the company in 1973 was the SS Wollongong.
Renamed the Myarra, *she was painted with the company's shipping logo—a
swan in flight.*

West. The company bought the *Iron Gerringong*, built in Whyalla in
1965, and excised the word *Iron* from her name. Her rated capacity was
29 000 tonnes but for some years she was limited to 16 000 tonnes
because of the bulkiness of the alumina and the shallowness of the
channel to the smelter at Point Henry. She carried a crew of 43—about
double the number who would man the same ship after the coastal trade
was reformed a decade later.

So that the *Gerringong* could supply all the alumina needed at the
smelter she sailed to a tight timetable, completing the round trip every
sixteen days. But if she was late in arriving at Point Henry she could
miss the high tide which she required in order to glide safely along the
channel dredged through mud. Likewise, if the unloading at Point Henry
was too slow, she faced a low tide that delayed her departure for Western
Australia. The arrival at the alumina wharf at Bunbury could also cause
delay: if she arrived in the evening she had to wait until daylight before
berthing inside the dredged harbour. As she also lost time through
industrial disputes and emergency repairs, the odds were to be eventually

The Spectre of Stonehenge

The first purpose built alumina ship ordered by the company was the
Lindesay Clark, *built in South Korea and launched in 1985.*

weighted heavily against her. Much later, in February 1984, the board
was to order in South Korea the building of a larger bulk-carrier, *Lindesay
Clark*, to carry alumina from Western Australia to Victoria. Another new
ship, *Pathfinder II*, was bought for a long triangular voyage—the carrying
of American petroleum coke to Point Henry, caustic soda to the Western
Australian ports, and alumina to the United States smelters. Both ships
were to make their maiden voyage to Point Henry in 1985.

The expansion begun at Point Henry, and completed in 1981, was
not viewed as momentous by the standards of that over-optimistic period
in the global aluminium industry. To add 55 per cent to capacity seemed
almost timid compared to the plans of other international companies
operating in Australia. Haymaker was soon making up for the deficiency.
Always thinking in capital letters, he persuaded the board that Victoria
needed another aluminium smelter. No such persuasion was needed at
Pittsburgh where Krome George felt sure that the world's electricity
would remain expensive. 'Lights Out' was his description of what he saw
as the world's coming era of dear electricity. As the lights might be dim
for decades, the United States should be superseded as a site for new
aluminium smelters by Australia with its cheap coal, Brazil with its cheap
hydro-electricity, and the Middle East and the Soviet Union where
prolific natural gas reserves were running to waste.

Where in Australia should the next smelter be built? Point Henry
lacked room for expansion. The narrow headland with its smelter and
rolling mill was hemmed in by sea and by marsh. If there was to be a
second smelter, the harbour of Westernport, on the other side of Melbourne, was perhaps the ideal choice. It was close to the powerlines
flowing from the brown coal fields of Gippsland. It was, however, close

White Gold

to bayside suburbs and holiday resorts. Complaints on environmental grounds were likely to be indignant: the green crusade was growing.

Distant Portland, in the far southwest, was finally chosen as the site for Alcoa's second smelter. The oldest port in Victoria, Portland had been settled by the Henty family one year before Melbourne became a village, but it did not build on its flying start and, after flourishing briefly, fell into neglect. Finally in 1961 it was modernised with two breakwaters that could shelter ships of 70 000 tonnes from the strong westerlies of the southern Indian Ocean. From the new Portland went wheat, barley and woodchips to foreign ports and live sheep to the Middle East. Into the harbour came ships loaded with petrol and potash, phosphate rock and fertilisers. Nonetheless it remained a town of less than 10 000 people, patiently waiting for something to happen. Aluminium provided the happening.

It is not clear how much Portland was the decision of the Victorian government and how much it was the decision of Alcoa. Probably the Victorian government had the stronger say. The Liberals, led by Sir Rupert Hamer, were conscious of environmental issues—no other state Liberal government was more alert to them. An aluminium smelter at

The site of the Portland smelter in 1979. The ship outlined at the bottom of the photograph marks the location of the unloading facility to be built at Portland Harbour.

rural Portland was safer; any pollution it might emit would be experienced by fewer people than if the smelter were at Geelong or
Westernport.

Some observers said that the choice of Portland was swayed by a
Victorian minister, Digby Crozier MLC, the member for Western Prov-
ince and minister for decentralisation, who wished to make his seat safer.
It is doubtful, however, whether the arrival in Portland of construction
gangs would have added as many Liberal voters as Labor voters. That
the Crozier argument was sometimes raised in private conversation was
more a sign that observers remained puzzled by the choice of Portland
as a smelting site.

Economically, Portland was not the ideal site. The cost of building
twin powerlines across country from Melbourne to Portland was high,
and many farming families would have to be persuaded to continue living
in the shadow of the steel pylons. On the other hand, 4400 hectares of
land at Portland was cheap, and industrial relations might be slightly
better, though Portland already had a few militants in its workforce.

George Haymaker and his many advisers agreed with the selection
of Portland. If he had said the site was unfit, the government would
have accepted his word. He had one unusual theoretical reason in favour
of Portland. Just as in Western Australia the three alumina refineries
and two ports of shipment—Kwinana and Bunbury—had enabled Alcoa
to supply its overseas customers with more certainty, so in Victoria two
distinct smelters and ports offered a similar assurance. A strike at one
smelter or one port would not be completely dislocating if Alcoa had an
alternative outlet for overseas customers.

For the Portland smelter, Haymaker negotiated an electricity deal
with the State Electricity Commission of Victoria. Offered a special
contract at slightly below the real cost of the electricity, he refused.
Instead he signed up on Tariff X which had been in use since 1938 and
numbered 74 industrial and commercial users. Unlike Alcoa's earlier
electricity deals, these were made public.

It was rare in the international aluminium industry for a government
and a smelter to make public the terms on which electricity was being
sold. It was also rare for a big aluminium company to buy power at
normal rates. Being a huge consumer, day and night, an aluminium
smelter normally sought the cheapest of all rates. In Victoria, however,
Alcoa wanted no government subsidy. It simply wanted Victoria to
produce the cheapest possible electricity, thus allowing Portland to
export its aluminium to highly competitive markets.

The premier of Victoria, Sir Rupert Hamer, outlined the Portland
scheme to his parliament on 25 March 1980. The economics had been
studied, the effect on the environment had been studied and only the

town airport would have to be rebuilt elsewhere. Hamer hoped that the first stage of the smelter, with a capacity of 130 000 tonnes a year, would be completed in exactly three years. At the peak, 1500 construction workers would be employed. It was expected to be the largest manufacturing venture Victoria had seen, with four separate stages of expansion. By 1988, if all went according to plan, Portland would be one of the world's big smelters, producing 530 000 tonnes of aluminium metal a year.

Meanwhile, the sailing was smooth for Alcoa. The future looked infinitely brighter than the present. The big refinery was under way at Wagerup, while in Victoria the extensions at Point Henry were virtually completed. All kinds of expansionist schemes were absorbing Haymaker's time. In Western Australia he toyed with the possibility of building and managing another smelter on behalf of an international syndicate. Sir Charles Court, premier of Western Australia, had long dreamed of a smelter for his own state. His government was enlarging the coal-burning power station at Muja, and he hoped that there would be enough cheap electricity to attract a smelter. Nothing came of the scheme, but in optimistic 1980 it seemed feasible.

The decline in the alumina market in Japan no longer seemed such a setback for Alcoa. Almost every month, Haymaker was pleased to be able to show the board the new contracts being signed for the sale of Western Australian alumina. In the middle of 1980 Kenneth R. Peacock, one of the general managers, reported that he was negotiating to supply large tonnages of alumina to Holland, Japan, Norway and Canada, as well as to Japanese companies who were partners in the Alumax venture in New South Wales. Everyone seemed to want alumina for their smelters. By the end of the year, however, the sheen was fainter. The world economy was less vigorous. If fewer cars and fewer cans of beverage were bought, would the new smelters be able to sell all of their aluminium?

In August 1980, just before construction was about to begin on the windy headland at Portland, Alcoa heard worrying news. The Victorian government's charge for electricity jumped more than expected, rising by 15 per cent. A second jump, in the following year, was to be 25 per cent. Even in these years of world-wide inflation, the rise in Victoria was exceptionally steep. Victoria's electricity industry was vulnerable, wages and costs were rising and its unions were showing their muscle. Each of the three power stations built at Yallourn in the 1970s was completed two years behind schedule, and the fourth was late and uncompleted. At the construction site of Loy Yang A, the big station on which Portland would depend for electricity, the same industrial upheavals were visible in 1980. Overtime bans by concrete layers led to a lockout which lasted for six months. In addition the power stations already operating were over-manned. It was almost inevitable that electricity should be dearer than predicted.

The government's announcement of rises in electricity affected every house, office and factory in Victoria. People complained at their higher electricity bills. It did not take long for critics to point out that big users of electricity were paying less for each unit than were pensioners in their high-rise apartments. Alcoa was the biggest single private user of electricity in Victoria and was soon to be an even bigger consumer, and now it was claimed that it was paying less than many similar smelters were paying in the United States and Europe and other places where coal was the main source of electricity. Though far from the whole truth, these specific arguments had a punch.

The *Age* newspaper argued that Victoria was selling electricity too cheaply to Alcoa. Why should Victorian taxpayers subsidise a big multinational company? The Labor Party, confident of winning power after more than a quarter of a century out of office, joined in the attack. In the Alcoa boardroom the attacks were analysed. According to the confidential statistics placed on the boardroom table in March 1981, Victorian electricity was actually dearer than that sold in New South Wales by the Labor government led by Neville Wran. Oddly, opinion polls showed that there was more public unease in Victoria than in New South Wales, where aluminium smelters got a better bargain. On the central coast of New South Wales, Labor won by-elections partly because it was seen to be positively attracting aluminium smelters to the region.

The directors of Alcoa realised they were almost caught in a trap. Public opinion was turning against the Portland smelter that was now under construction. The Labor Party continued its criticisms of the power deal. And yet Alcoa's slowly rising smelter needed support from public opinion and support from the Labor Party, which was to win the state election in April 1982.

Sir Arvi Parbo, as chairman of Alcoa, tried to win public support. He knew the need to explain everything with the utmost clarity—perhaps the fact that English was not his native language made him especially aware of the need for simplicity and clarity. When he spoke about the mining industry or the economy he took nothing for granted. He decided which were the key points to be made and hammered them home with decisive thumps. Opponents did not have to accept his arguments, but at least they heard them.

An argument widely used against Alcoa and the other aluminium companies in Australia was that they were foreigners but were obtaining cheaper electricity than Australians. In a nationalist climate the anti-American feelings had to be taken seriously; indeed Americans voiced the same type of argument against Japanese companies operating in the United States. Parbo simply replied that 49 per cent of the shares in Alcoa were held by Australians, 'by far the highest Australian ownership in any major aluminium company'. The senior staff were Australians. Of the top 70 executives only eight were Americans, and they were 'on loan from our US partner'. That the chief executive was always an American slightly weakened his argument. On the other hand it was true that eight of the twelve directors were Australian. Parbo added that he knew of no decision where the American owners of 51 per cent of the shares used their voting power 'against the wishes' of those Australian shareholders who held 49 per cent.

As for the huge profits reportedly being sent from Australia, Parbo explained that in the last year, 1980, the Alcoa dividends paid to Pittsburgh were $23 million whereas a total of $666 million was actually spent by Alcoa in Australia—spent on wages, in buying materials and electricity, and paying taxes and royalties to Australian governments. 'Can anyone tell me,' he asked, 'where the exorbitant returns to share-holders are?'

It was beyond dispute that Alcoa was obtaining relatively cheap power. Without it Alcoa would not have even dreamed in 1978 of expanding the existing smelter near Geelong and building a new one at Portland. At the same time the wages and many of the other costs of converting Western Australian alumina into Victorian aluminium were high. Parbo liked to point out that Victoria's electricity was far from the cheapest in the world. In Canada, Venezuela and Brazil, where fast rivers could be dammed, new electricity was far cheaper than in Victoria. In fact the Aluminum Co. of America was about to expand in Brazil and shrink in the United States partly because hydro-electricity on the rivers near the Amazon was so cheap.

When the debate switched to the television news, Parbo seemed to know instinctively when to use emphasis—he used it often but was never discourteous. He stood in front of the camera rather like a typical Australian foreman: physically strong, head erect, feet firmly planted, eyes fixed on the questioner, with every word concrete and down to earth. He was skilled in financial arguments but the intricacies of producing aluminium were almost too complex to be explained in a long newspaper article, let alone on television with its one-minute time slots.

For some time Alcoa had wondered how to cope with the loose anti-American, anti-foreigner feeling. So long as the feeling was fairly widespread it reinforced the vague arguments that Alcoa was receiving cheap electricity, or was extracting from, rather than adding to, Victoria's economy. Joe Bates, who had been managing director a decade earlier and was still on the board—but busy in Pittsburgh when most board meetings were held—had given thought to the anti-American feeling. He wondered whether Alcoa of Australia Limited should change its name. The name, he said privately to Haymaker, was a giveaway: 'If you look around at the various corporations in Australia, I think you will agree that as soon as you see "of Australia", you automatically say to yourself that this is a company headquartered in England, USA or elsewhere'.

From Pittsburgh came Joe Bates' suggestion that the phrase 'of Australia' should be dropped from Alcoa's formal title. In Melbourne, however, several Alcoa executives thought that the word 'Australia' was a confident assertion that it was a local company. Indeed it was more Australian than any rival, with 49 per cent of the Alcoa shares being held in Australia compared to only 10 per cent of the rival aluminium company, Comalco. And yet somehow Comalco seemed, in Bates' view, to convey the more Australian image. John Ridley, in charge of public relations, agreed that the company's name should be changed. In the end the company's name was not changed but the internal debate extending over six months showed how sensitive the company was to the anti-American feeling.

Some of the criticism was based on the assumption that there were huge profits in aluminium. For Alcoa the year 1981 was very profitable, most of the profit coming from the sale of Western Australian alumina rather than Victorian ingots. But in the space of one year the return on shareholders' funds had slipped from 12.6 per cent to 10.1 per cent. The worry was next year's result, for the price of aluminium was falling and the cost of borrowing money—and Alcoa carried a growing debt—was rising. At Wagerup and Portland the company had two major projects in construction, both of them eating up capital but with little hope of earning a profit when they were opened.

Portland was the perturbing project. It was far from completion: perhaps work should be halted now. The low price of aluminium and the high cost of electricity made Portland more worrying. In September 1981, following a sudden jump of 25 per cent in the price of electricity, Alcoa thought of stopping all construction work at Portland. The government replied by speedily setting up one and then another independent inquiry into the cost of supplying electricity to Portland. Both inquiries concluded that the electricity was too expensive.

Two former managing directors, Joe Bates and Waldo Porter, arrived from Pittsburgh to attend the board meeting on 2 December 1981. Haymaker was now cautious on Portland's prospects. Phil Spry-Bailey, the chief financial executive, was even more cautious. Another board meeting, held two days later, resolved that work should continue at Portland. It was hoped that in the new year metal prices might improve, a kinder electricity deal might be signed, the raising of overseas capital might be easier, and the wages explosion in Australia might soon end. To hope for more than two of these four outcomes was to be optimistic.

Ironically, only a year earlier, in the financial pages of newspapers and in houses of parliament, there had been excited talk about the coming resources boom. Aluminium was to be a front rider of the boom. The federal government and the relevant state governments had been eager to encourage the smelting of alumina in Australia—it created jobs and it fostered exports. To export aluminium ingot instead of the white powdery alumina would provide four times the revenue from a given tonnage of alumina. Furthermore, to build massive smelters would erode the popular, though exaggerated, argument that Australia was a mere quarry. There was logic in this argument. But the incentive to build a smelter was vanishing, largely through world economic events but also because Australia was suffering from high inflation and weak industrial relations.

Alcoa continued to search for the capital which Portland and Wagerup needed. When the expansion was planned in 1979 it was cheerfully thought that one billion dollars would be sufficient and that half of it could be financed from within. The costs grew beyond predictions. There were Eurobond and Eurodollar loans, there were loans from Citibank, Mellon, the Chemical Bank, Chase and the Pittsburgh National. Major Australian and United Kingdom banks came together to lend more money. Additional capital came through promissory notes, commercial paper and underwriting facilities. Between 1980 and 1985 the company negotiated a total of 29 loans.

In March 1982 the board discussed the possibility of selling a minority holding in Alcoa, in return for precious cash. Perhaps an outside partner should be enticed into Alcoa, bringing new capital. That idea fell by the way. Then the director thought of cutting off the Portland smelter, that potential millstone, and selling an interest in it. They decided to seek 'Japanese customers and Australian investors' who might take 50 per cent of the shares in Portland. In that way the financial pinch could be eased.

Haymaker remained the optimist. He flew away in search of partners. In the following four weeks he spoke with four large Japanese metal firms and in Melbourne he spoke with National Mutual Life and BHP. He reported his lack of success to the board meeting called at the early time of 9.30 a.m. on 27 April 1982. That was virtually his last speech as managing director.

He already knew that he was to be recalled to Pittsburgh where he would be promoted to the post of vice-president (international) in Pittsburgh while retaining oversight of the Australian operations and keeping, for several years, his seat on Alcoa's board. Later he was to become world head of the old rival, Kaiser.

The successor to Haymaker was known for his willingness to say 'no'. John L. Diederich was born near Chicago and followed, in his education and in his promotions, almost the same career path as Haymaker. From engineering school he was recruited by the Aluminum Co. of America to sell aluminium castings and forgings in the Los Angeles district. Moving later to Seattle, he handled the Boeing contract—manufacturers of aircraft were heavy consumers of aluminium. He then spent eleven years in Pittsburgh where he was head of corporate planning when in 1982 he was selected to move to Australia as managing director of Alcoa. Most of his predecessors who crossed the Pacific had arrived in a tranquil business climate. 'Jack' Diederich landed in a gathering storm.

On his first visit to Portland he inspected the rising smelter, which was less than half built. Already $300 million had been spent, a sum that would be totally wasted if the smelter was not completed. On the other hand, if the smelter was completed, it would be working at a heavy loss—so long as the price of aluminium, now sinking, remained low. The Western world was in a recession, the worst since the war. In the Hunter Valley, the Canadian owners of Alcan's big Kurri Kurri smelter, buying electricity at a more favourable price than Portland's, made their own assessment. They halted all work on their new potline.

Diederich realised that the existing contract to buy Victorian electricity would be death to the smelter even if metal prices improved a little. As he stood on the exposed headland at Portland and felt the sea wind on his face he looked around at the concrete foundations, earthworks and works huts and thought they were all rather 'eerie'. At head office, Philip Spry-Bailey was to note in an internal memo that 'our customers are all in a difficult and depressed situation, while our Japanese customers are in a desperate situation'. Alcoa itself was likely to make a loss in the coming year. Assets would have to be sold and the workforce reduced. The danger of Alcoa collapsing through over-borrowing was glimpsed by a few realists at head office.

Attending his first meeting of the board in Melbourne on 28 May 1982, Diederich persuaded the directors to prepare to curtail further spending on the smelter. The decision was not announced at once. The government had to be consulted. The decision was made public on 19 July. It caused a commotion.

John Cain junior had been elected premier of Victoria just when Diederich came to Melbourne. The news that Portland was to be halted was a blow to Cain. He had promised, before his election three months previously, to give priority to Portland. He wished to show that his government was eager to attract foreign capital to Victoria, a state hit harder than most by the recession. He was first inclined to believe—his advisers told him so—that the electricity deal was fair and that therefore he should make no concessions.

At Portland there was confusion. A big workforce had assembled solely to build the smelter. Much of the concrete work, the structural steel, the underground gas and air pipes and many other items had been built or were well advanced. About three-tenths of the total cost had already been spent. Some contracts—including the foundations for the long conveyor belt that would carry alumina from the wharf to the smelter—had been let and there was no alternative but to honour them. In all, 115 houses were being built by Alcoa for skilled employees who would operate the smelter. Should work on them be halted?

On 2 August 1982 a confidential report to the directors passed on the simple news: 'The orderly shutdown of Portland has begun'. It was not quite that orderly, and on the following day a picket line of workers guarded the main gateway to ensure that no equipment was removed from the site. Nearly all work ceased for a time, the unions hoping that industrial action would somehow force the company to resume. On 26 August the unions voted to resume work but many of the construction workers had already left the town. Some who remained were out of work and in debt, having borrowed to buy or furnish houses in the town. A hardship fund was set up by the company, and the Victorian Trades Hall Council agreed to administer it. There was still work for some 250 people who were completing certain tasks, but just before Christmas the construction village was closed.

The company's revenue from the sale of alumina in Western Australia and from ingots and can-sheet in Geelong was falling. Imports were entering Australia: perhaps some were dumped. The introduction of the 38-hour week at Point Henry temporarily increased costs. The company had high debts, and they had to be met.

At the Melbourne office, Diederich called for the broom and began sweeping away what waste he saw. Money had to be saved. With heavy interest payments due each month on money borrowed, the company was short of money. Many major loans had been negotiated overseas on the strict condition that the company's total debts should not exceed one and half times the total of shareholders' funds. Now that danger sign was almost reached. On 3 November 1982 the board authorised an approach to major borrowers seeking permission for the ratio of debt to equity to rise, if necessary, to the risky maximum of two to one. The borrowers agreed.

Inside the company many activities had to be eliminated. Under Haymaker the head office in Bourke Street Melbourne had grown in anticipation of a steep rise in the output of aluminium. A doctor had been employed full-time solely to look after employees: his services were no longer needed. Publicity was one of the bigger departments with perhaps twenty employees, all busy explaining the company's case at a time when that case was not widely understood. Soon one public relations person was considered enough. The section of the office devoted to market research was closed. The staff specialising in industrial relations were dispersed to the industrial plants.

Would the price of aluminium rise, thus easing the strain? In 1982 the world's consumption of aluminium was the lowest for seven years. Ironically, one of the reasons for the slump was the success of the recycling schemes in many nations. Much aluminium that normally would have come out of the smelter gates now came from the small factories which remelted a total of billions of discarded cans. Alcoa's 'Cash-A-Can' depots were competing indirectly with its refineries and smelter.

In Pittsburgh there was even more financial strain. The parent company was hit more than Alcoa of Australia by the recession. In 1982 the salaries of its top 1800 American employees were frozen: in short the salaries slid in real terms, for the cost of living was rising. Another 1435 permanent members of the company's salaried, as distinct from the wages, staff were dismissed or retired. The profits or 'net income' of the Pittsburgh company fell to almost nothing. In 1979 profits had reached US$505 million but three years later they were less than US$11 million. There was only one consolation: in this slump the steel industry, almost everywhere in the world, was hit harder than aluminium.

Back in Australia, Jack Diederich worked quietly at the economic obstacles. Much more than his predecessor, he kept to himself. Often he said little but his demeanour made it clear that he thought Alcoa could be in a hazardous position. Portland, where hundreds of construction workers lost their jobs, and scores of offices and shops lost their new customers, hoped that he would back down or that the Victorian government would make a concession. Negotiations, they knew, were going on nearly every week in Melbourne. Perhaps the deadlock would suddenly be broken.

Krome George, head of the Aluminum Co. of America, came from Pittsburgh to see Portland for himself. He glimpsed its possible fate: he called it 'an aluminium Stonehenge'. In his private view it was better that the company lose the $300 million already invested than complete the smelter and thereafter face the risk of a total loss of more than $300 million because the price of electricity was just too high. As Krome George was emphatic that the era of 'Lights Out' was spreading around the world, and that the smelter with the dearest electricity would not survive, his conclusion fitted his logic. If necessary the Portland smelter would have to be abandoned, thus becoming a ruin.

'An aluminium Stonehenge': John L. Diederich (managing director), John Cain (premier of Victoria) and Sir Arvi Parbo (chairman) visit the partly constructed Portland smelter after the decision was made to halt all work.

The pruning caused fears in all of Alcoa's plants. In Geelong the anxiety was almost as intense as in Portland. The Point Henry smelter was one of the district's biggest employers. Depending on cheap electricity, it drew more than half of it from the State Electricity Commission under a secret long-term contract that expired in March 1983. It could also become unprofitable if electricity became too expensive. Month after month the rumours sped or skulked along the streets of Geelong. Point Henry, said the rumours, was about to put off hundreds of its 2000 employees. People who were paying instalments on their houses or cars wondered if their jobs were at risk.

No news came from Alcoa. Negotiations with the Victorian government were held in secret, and the government alone held the right to release news of the talks. Spring Street was silent: Bourke Street was silent. For twenty years, Geelong employees had been accustomed to prosperity and security. Understandably they resented the absence of news, as was made clear by Royce Bird, the plant steward for the Federated Ironworkers' Association. 'The blokes out here have had a dream run, no one can deny that,' he told the *Geelong Advertiser* on 8 April 1983. 'But when a man is worried about his job, the least they could do is tell us something and not just nothing.'

One year after the closure of the unfinished smelter the Portland town council tried to count its losses. How, reported the *Portland Observer* on 18 July 1983, will the town pay off its huge debts—borrowed to build arterial roads, municipal offices and water and sewerage mains—if the smelting works do not go ahead and the town reverts to peace and quiet?

The future of the half-built smelter was complicated by Aborigines who claimed a traditional interest in its site. Part was sacred ground, claimed several Aborigines. From the High Court they gained permission to approach the Supreme Court of Victoria. An awkward case at law, it virtually erected another fence around the smelter site.

Alcoa had commissioned surveys of the site, and a report of 1981 set out evidence showing that Aborigines had once occupied parts of it. Written by S. Simmons of the Victorian Archaeological Survey and by the consultant A. Djekic, it pointed to 'assemblages of chipped stone tools' on Aboriginal camp sites inhabited in the last 6000 years and also to large shell middens—the remains of Aboriginal meals of shellfish eaten long ago. The investigators found no site of 'high scientific significance' and identified no site that was sacred in Aboriginal eyes. Nonetheless it was agreed that Aborigines with an interest in the site should be entitled to advise and assist the archaeologists in further work. A few special sites, on heathland or farmland near the smelter site, were protected by simple fences of wire and later by stronger fences.

The price of electricity, not the existence of Aboriginal sites, was the main obstacle. In debates about what should be the price of electricity bought by the smelter, little headway was made for half a year. Many informal meetings were held, and sometimes Diederich met the premier, John Cain, and other ministers. There was no animosity on either side, just a reluctance to accept each other's assessment of the situation. 'A lot of brinkmanship went on,' Diederich recalls. Cain was later to write generously of Diederich: 'I liked him and I think he reciprocated'.

Some observers who closely followed the dispute were inclined to exaggerate the efficiency of the State Electricity Commission. They thought that it produced electricity at bargain prices and that Alcoa was already gaining the benefit of those bargains. In fact the electricity industry, partly because of poor industrial relations, was not as efficient as the public imagined. Alcoa had inside knowledge of the electricity industry of Victoria simply because at Anglesea it was itself a generator of electricity from brown coal. In the first half of the 1980s Anglesea was producing electricity at a capacity factor—or efficiency—of 91 per cent. But in the La Trobe Valley two of the government's power stations normally averaged closer to 60 per cent and in 1983, two power stations in the La Trobe Valley were actually working at less than 50 per cent of capacity. Part of Anglesea's higher efficiency came from the practice of closing for a brief period every two years and conducting all necessary repairs and maintenance rather than waiting for mishaps to happen. Part of its efficiency came from the fact that its brown coal was superior. But a large part of its efficiency came from the fact that it was free from the political and industrial handcuffs which retarded the State Electricity Commission. Anglesea proved every month that the government power stations were not producing at reasonable efficiency. Therefore the power they sold was unnecessarily dear.

John Cain, his treasurer, Rob Jolly, and his minister for minerals and energy, David White, argued that Alcoa had been given a favourable deal. They believed that electricity provided at the current price would enable Portland to make good profits in years when aluminium prices were at about average. Diederich did not agree for one moment. He thought Victorian electricity was far too expensive. The deadlock between the two sides was as rigid as ever.

15

Gold At Last

The dispute over the potential Stonehenge at Portland was eased early in 1983. One day Jack Diederich found himself, almost out of the blue, offering a new proposal to John Cain. Alcoa, he said, would accept the old price for electricity if the government of Victoria showed its faith by buying shares in the smelter. In short, he said to Cain: 'if the electricity deal is so good, and if the smelters' profits are assured, then your government should be happy to enter the Portland venture as a shareholder'.

Cain was inclined to accept the offer. Jobs would thereby be created during the continuing recession. Government ownership of part of the smelter, especially if it was interpreted as a mild form of 'nationalisation', would please the left wing of his party. That John Cain tentatively accepted the offer showed that he had not been bluffing. He believed that the original Haymaker electricity contract was a fair arrangement.

Under the formula proposed, Alcoa would take 55 per cent of the shares and the Victorian government 45 per cent, with Alcoa operating as manager of the venture. For the government to pay for 45 per cent was to incur a substantial liability. Its liability, however, would fall if a little later other financiers could be persuaded to take some of the shares. At first those new financiers seemed just around the corner. At the start of 1984, Diederich confidentially told his directors that Mitsubishi might take 5 per cent of the shares. He added that CSR, which had an interest in the alumina refinery at Gove in the Northern Territory, was 'very interested' in 15 per cent on condition that it could supply a proportion of the alumina used in the smelter. Then again the Commonwealth government's superannuation fund might take 10 or 15 per cent. One by one these partners withdrew. Hyundai of Korea remained the only prospective partner.

Cain and Diederich called on other overseas companies in the hope of selling 30 per cent of the smelter. Those who were approached were not enthusiastic. They thought the high price of electricity was one factor jeopardising the venture. Diederich had proved his point—that Victorian electricity was dear. For his part Cain continued to prove one of his points: that he was genuinely interested in finding a fair solution. 'I trusted Cain', said Diederich.

The hope of solving the Portland deadlock was increased by the revival of the world's aluminium industry and the rising prices for alumina and ingot. The slide of the Australian dollar was also good news, giving Alcoa a higher price in Australian currency for its exports. In July 1983 one of the six units of the Kwinana refinery, idle for six months, was reopened. The Pinjarra refinery also increased output. In times of expensive energy a refinery is less brittle than a smelter, for the refinery is not such a massive consumer of electricity.

Early in 1984 the new but unopened Wagerup refinery was taken out of mothballs. A stockpile of 150 000 tonnes of bauxite from the nearby Willowdale mine was waiting to be processed. In February 1984 the refinery was launched into that initial phase of mishaps and breakdowns that are almost inevitable in a new plant.

For Alcoa the economics of a refinery were usually more favourable than those of a smelter. The revival of alumina prices therefore did not necessarily solve the smelting problem. Meanwhile John Cain had to commit his government to providing 45 per cent of the capital if work on the smelter was to be resumed. Diederich suggested that John Cain and his wife, Nancy, should visit Pittsburgh at a convenient time to meet the heads of the Aluminum Co. of America, thereby helping the Victorian government to make up its mind. The visit was a success. The unsolved question was the price of electricity, for which Dr Peter Sheehan, a leading Victorian public servant, was encouraged to devise a flexible formula in place of the rigid formula normally preferred by aluminium companies. Under the Sheehan formula the price of electricity at Portland would vary, rising when world aluminium prices were rising, and falling when aluminium was harder to sell. At the same time the price would never be so low that the State Electricity Commission would be selling electricity at below its operating costs. Point Henry, it was agreed, would buy electricity on the same formula as Portland. The new electricity contract, it was hoped, would run for 30 years.

On 31 July 1984, two years after the closure of Portland, John Cain and Alcoa signed an agreement. At Portland almost everyone cheered when the construction workers began to return to Stonehenge and the windy headland. Soon 800 workers were building the smelter, and with plenty of overtime their pay was high. At the weekends several hotels were again alive with fist fights. One hotel was christened the Broken Face, another the Duck and Weave.

Alcoa and the Victorian government found a partner willing to join with them in financing the smelter and its planned extension. The First National Resource Trust, a new subsidiary of the National Australia Bank, took up 10 per cent of the shares in Portland, paying $100 million for the shares in January 1986. The search for an overseas partner was successful when the People's Republic of China resolved to buy an interest. At first—to Alcoa's dismay—it wanted a share in the new Wagerup alumina refinery but as second choice took up 10 per cent of

Directors visiting the smelter in 1986 (from left to right): Norman Stephen, Roger Vines, Sir Laurence Muir, Sir Arvi Parbo, Donald Morley and Hugh Morgan.

More directors at the smelter in 1986 (from left to right): John Pizzey,
Philip Spry-Bailey, John Darling and Jack Davenport.

the Portland smelter through its China International Trust and Investment Corporation. China would take its profits in the form of 10 per
cent of the ingots actually produced by the smelter.

Alcoa now held 45 per cent, the Victorian Government 35 per cent,
and the two other partners 20 per cent in the Portland venture. At times
it seemed likely that a Japanese steelmaker or a Vienna aluminium
company would take up another 10 per cent. It was not until 1992 that
the long-awaited third partner, the Marubeni Corporation, was found.

Having seen his idea of combined ownership take shape, Diederich
prepared to leave his position as managing director of Alcoa and return
to Pittsburgh as group vice-president of the metals & chemicals division.
His last day with Alcoa of Australia included a board meeting at which
Sir Arvi Parbo thanked him for his work on the Portland project and

his skill in making the whole company more efficient during his four and a half years at the helm. Diederich had virtually completed the first stage of the project. The first ship had unloaded its cargo of Western Australian alumina and in a fortnight, Diederich hoped, the first pots would produce molten aluminium at Portland.

Norman Stephen came from Pittsburgh as managing director in October 1986. Once a pilot in the United States Air Force, he had joined the Aluminum Co. of America in 1958, selling aluminium in big cities, and finally becoming general manager of the chemicals division which manufactured an increasing range of products based on alumina. Kwinana was now entering chemicals, and Stephen's experience was therefore very relevant. Visiting Portland for the first time, he was impressed by the quality of the equipment and the innovations. Technically it was perhaps the best smelter in the world but a skilled, reliable labour force was needed to make full use of it. By November 1986, 27 pots were working well and soon the entire potline was working. In the new year, on 9 February, John Cain formally opened the smelter which his government had done much to rescue.

Looking back, the directors of Alcoa were inclined to agree that because of unpredictable metal prices and electricity prices they had begun to build the Portland smelter at the wrong time. Between 1980 and 1986, when Portland was in the process of being built, Alcoa's total return on its assets fell from 6 per cent a year to 1.7 per cent. Whereas Alcoa's net profit was close to $100 million in each of the first two years, it was closer to $40 million in 1985 and 1986 and much of that profit was eroded by fast inflation. Alcoa's inability to finance a large part of Portland's construction from profits had led it to the moneylenders. Even after Portland was producing its first ingots, the outlook remained gloomy, for the world was flooded with aluminium. Even alumina—the company's strength—was hit by the output from new refineries in Latin America and India.

Portland's aches and bruises, suffered for at least six years, came about partly because Alcoa was a victim of a geographical shift which was occurring more quickly than perhaps it realised. In the early 1960s Alcoa had chosen Victoria as its smelting home because Western Australia was weak in energy; but 25 years later the discovery of natural gas in the northwest and massive coal in the southwest had removed some of those obstacles. Likewise Alcoa had decided not to smelt near the black-coal fields of New South Wales because their industrial relations were thorny and their costs, being underground mines, were high; but by the 1980s the industrial relations in New South Wales had improved and open cuts had mostly replaced the dearer underground coalmines of the Hunter Valley. Again, in the early 1960s Alcoa did not consider

Queensland because its main coalmines in the Bowen basin had not yet been explored adequately; but now Queensland was a low-cost producer of coal.

The original choice of Victoria as the smelting base had been based on valid reasons: the mining of brown coal and the generating of electricity in Victoria were becoming efficient, and there the industrial relations were superior to those in New South Wales. Moreover, as metal for Australian fabricators was then seen as potentially far more important than the export of aluminium to other nations, the smelter was sensibly placed near Melbourne, a large industrial consumer. By the early 1980s several of Victoria's special advantages were slipping away. Industrial relations on its brown-coal fields were poor, and the power stations were less efficient, though they would soon improve. In contrast, the relative advantage of at least three other states as smelting bases was improving.

In 1987 the gloom was dispersed. Aluminium prices rose. Within a few months the Portland smelter was profitable. A decision was even made to enlarge it in order to gain economies of scale by producing 300 000 tonnes of aluminium annually, compared to Point Henry's 180 000 tonnes. In October 1988 the board congratulated Norman Stephen on completing the second potline at Portland nearly six months ahead of time, at a cost well below that predicted. Here stood the biggest smelter in Australia—but not the huge smelter, almost twice as large again, that was initially envisaged. Portland later was to become some-what larger in output, not through the building of more pots but by winning more efficiency from each pot.

Portland did not venture into the fabricating of aluminium. It remained just a smelter. Even Point Henry, on Diederich's advice, was now retreating from some of the activities which, back in the 1960s, were almost seen as the ultimate purpose of the whole aluminium venture: the production of specific aluminium products or shapes for the expanding Australian market. At Point Henry in some years, more than half the smelter's output had gone straight into rolled products, which were often profitable in the very years when aluminium prices were low. Later the profit was marginal. With a lowering of protective tariffs, the imports of rolled products were pouring in; and in 1983 Point Henry ceased, after twenty years, to extrude aluminium and to produce flat sheet. In 1989 it was to cease producing the aluminium foil widely used in packaging and in the insulating of buildings. The production of rigid can-sheet for beverage cans remained the only fabricating activity at Point Henry—and it was on an increasing scale, especially after the opening in 1993 of the coil-coating plant which reflected the boom in providing aluminium cans for Australian and east Asian breweries and soft drink factories.

Gold At Last

The enlarged Portland was completed just in time to share in a short phase of profit. The price of aluminium leaped. The world glut of aluminium that had closed the construction site at Portland gave way to scarcity more quickly than expected. More important, Alcoa in Western Australia was making alumina on such a scale—output passed 4 million tonnes in 1985 and 5 million in 1988—that it was now the biggest producer in the world. In addition, the output of smelter ingots in 1989 was more than treble that of ten years previously. Portland produced 320 000 tonnes of aluminium in that year; Tomago (NSW), in which Pechiney of France was the largest partner, produced 240 000 tonnes; Gladstone 230 000; and Point Henry 180 000. They were followed by the smaller smelters of Alcan at Kurri Kurri (NSW) and Comalco at Bell Bay in Tasmania. In that same year Alcoa produced almost 50 per cent of the alumina and more than 40 per cent of the aluminium produced in Australia. With the prices so high, Alcoa became Australia's second biggest earner of export income, winning more than 5 per cent of the nation's export revenue.

After a run of disappointment, the two years 1989 and 1990 were highly rewarding. Profit before taxes leaped above $1 billion in each year, being about thirteen times the record profits of the early 1980s. The dividend in 1990 was $600 million, which was far more than the sum total of dividends paid in all the years to 1988. Even if earlier dividends were indexed for inflation, the two years 1989 and 1990 far exceeded all the dividends to the end of 1988. These bumper years and the sheer extent of the profits were unexpected.

There was another, surprising, contributor to Alcoa's success. For almost a century gold had been sought by nearly all the prospectors who crossed the Darling Range on foot, pushbike, horse and cart or car. The only treasure they found was bauxite. In the 1980s signs of gold came to light in, of all places, deposits of the same laterite rock that produced bauxite. It was found not in the main area of mining on the western and central slopes of the Darling Range but in what was considered worthless ground on the eastern slopes.

The Western Australian government's own geologists surveyed this territory in the late 1970s and, to the surprise of many, identified a belt of greenstone with similarities to Kalgoorlie. Further investigations revealed the presence of traces of gold and grains of arsenic in the soils and the stream sediments on the far eastern edge of the bauxite country, not far from the inland town of Boddington. The minerals showed promise but were seen as unpayable.

T. Jaap Langenberg was a geologist working for Shell Australia, one of Reynolds' partners in the Worsley alumina venture, and was fascinated by the information. Theorising that the rock which held the bauxite might also contain payable gold, he examined many of the cores of buried rock that had been kept after the early drills had tested the ground for bauxite. He found, sprinkled in the shallow rock and also in the surface clay, grains of gold that were invisible to the naked eye. Large-scale prospecting disclosed that the gold was low grade but, at the high prices which prevailed, it could be mined efficiently by Worsley in a big open cut. So was born the Boddington mine which began large-scale production of gold in August 1987, the year in which the Portland smelter was opened on the opposite side of Australia.

Next to the Boddington mine Alcoa held a smaller portion of the promising ground. Its drills soon revealed that there was gold beneath the state forest. In an area roughly 1500 metres long and 500 metres wide, payable gold was dispersed through the shallow laterite and the first zone of clay lying below: the basis of the Hedges goldmines. Knowing that the mine would need a large area in which to dump its tailings, Alcoa bought 130 hectares of private ground from an adjacent farmer, Walter Johnson, for what was then the enormous sum of $1 million. At the close of 1987 the Alcoa directors were informed that at least 460 000 ounces of gold could be recovered from Hedges, at a handsome profit; and that profit was to be increased when Alcoa arranged to sell most of its gold, in advance of production, at what turned out be a very favourable price.

Western Mining Corporation, itself a major producer of gold, designed the gold-treatment plant with a high level of automation, and the Alcoa engineer, Malcolm Wills, used his Kalgoorlie and Wagerup experiences to set up an operation that cut costs to the bone. For the sake of efficiency he used contractors wherever possible and he eliminated the bureaucracy: each senior member of staff had to type his own letters and reports, and that kept reports to the minimum. Meetings of the senior staff were few, being virtually confined to a small time slot on Thursday afternoon.

The cheapest way to operate the Hedges gold deposit was to extract it quickly on the large scale, exhausting it in, say, four years. Heavy trucks hauled the newly mined ore along a wide dirt road some five kilometres through the jarrah forest to the treatment plant. Water came from a dam built on private land. On 6 October 1988, just over a year after the mine was opened next door, Hedges produced its first molten gold. In 1989, with an output of 156 602 fine ounces of gold, Hedges was one of Australia's top six gold producers for that year. In its third year the mine earned the remarkable profit of $124 million. Deeper drilling found further ore in the underlying clay, poor but just payable, and thereby the 8 million tonnes of gold-bearing ore in the original plan

Gold At Last

Hedges processing plant where, since 1988, more than 1 million ounces of gold have been extracted.

was increased to 28 million tonnes. The goldmine, instead of ceasing production in 1992, was still busy four years later and its total output of gold was more than 1 250 000 ounces.

Next door the bigger Boddington mine won about three times as much gold. Boddington and Hedges, working at each end of what was really the same long ore body, together produced more gold in each year than any other goldfield in Australia—until the big superpit at Kalgoorlie captured the lead. Curiously, the shallower parts of the ore body carried alumina that was almost payable, but it was not extracted.

At Hedges the tailings dam now fills part of a large valley. To stand on the high wall of the dam and to look over the open country far below is to see a quiet pastoral scene. From the wall there is no town in sight, and indeed the mine gave rise to no town. In its short working life, the Hedges mine will have won as much gold as Walhalla, one of Victoria's famous Victorian goldfields, produced in its first century; and Hedges will have produced that gold after mining and treating far more ore than Walhalla's famous mines had to treat. It is a sign of the heavy mechanisation of today's mining, and the sparseness of the workforce, that whereas for at least half a century Walhalla supported a large town with its own brewery and its own member of parliament, the Hedges mine did not even spawn a village.

White Gold

In Western Australia the company's production of gold ran parallel with the launching of new mineral products based on alumina. In addition to the big tonnages of alumina for aluminium smelters, Alcoa began to manufacture hydrated alumina. Resembling alumina in its white colour and grainy composition, alumina hydrate was used to purify water and as an ingredient in the making of commodities as diverse as paper, pharmaceuticals and even nitrogenous fertilisers.

Kwinana had begun to produce considerable quantities of this alumina hydrate without intending to do so. The glut of hydrate resulted from bottlenecks that developed in the production line in the early 1980s. In small quantities the hydrate was ladled into bags and sold in Australia, but the potential market was overseas. The vital task was to prepare the hydrate to suit specific industrial needs. Initially it was like a plain-ice cream: the higher rewards were in the flavoured ice-creams.

Norman Stephen, who was in charge of hydrate for the Aluminum Co. of America before coming to Australia, could see the possibility of Australia exporting its surplus. In Tokyo, Mike Schreier, who was Pittsburgh's manager of industrial chemicals for Asia, had the same idea. At Kwinana the manager, John Sibly, was equally enthusiastic. At the same time Robert Slagle, who in Pittsburgh had succeeded Stephen in the control of the chemical plants and was later to become managing director of Alcoa of Australia, realised that when an alumina refinery became somewhat antiquated it did not have to die: it could be simply diverted to the making of alumina chemicals where the production runs were smaller, the value-added tasks of grinding and packaging were important, and the potential for overall profits was higher. The message was clear. If an outdated refinery could survive by making special aluminas, larger profits must be waiting for a relatively efficient refinery like Kwinana which decided to make these products.

The Kwinana refinery was not only close to the east Asian markets for alumina products but had an incentive to try something new, for its plant was older, and its costs were much higher than those of Pinjarra and Wagerup. If Kwinana turned partly to special industrial aluminas, it would be tapping the more profitable end of the alumina market. Here was a chance for Kwinana, the most vulnerable of the three refineries, to earn more profits.

In 1992 and 1993 the company began to make the calcined hydrate products KA 25 and KA 13. Much of the output was the filler in the making of products as diverse as toothpaste, tyres, ceramics and glass. By 1994 a total of 350 000 tonnes of combined hydrates was shipped from Kwinana and Fremantle to ports in Singapore, Indonesia, North Korea and other Asian nations. In 1993 Alcoa bought a one-third share in the new and nearby factory of Australian Fused Materials. Today its furnaces produce a product that is an ingredient of the windscreen glass used in Japanese automobiles.

Whereas the hydrates that went into fertilisers were worth less than orthodox alumina, each tonne of the premium hydrates was worth more. Alcoa set out to make these premium hydrates, and David Dabney came from the United States to manage the special company, ACAP Australia. A continuous plant was designed, combining the latest technology from America and new ideas from Western Australia.

In the alumina industry new plants are usually tricky; and the trials made in the small pilot plants do not always foretell what will happen in a big plant. Early in 1995 the new high-temperature plant began to operate. For the first six or eight weeks, while being slowly run in, it was expected to yield only the lower value A 30 hydrate. But after about three weeks it seemed to be on the verge of producing the first run of the expensive B 30.

On the afternoon of Easter Sunday 1995, David Dabney was at home with his family when the phone rang. At the other end was the voice of John Lochore, the engineer in charge. 'David,' he said, 'I want you to know that we're pulling the B 30 off the drier right now.' David's reaction was almost astonishment, especially after Lochore read aloud the results of the tests he had just made on the new product. The white powder conformed to all the required specifications. After he put down the phone he found himself celebrating: 'I was doing a small dance in my living room.' Two days later, when the office was reopened for business, that inaugural product was sold to Japan where almost certainly it helped to make those detergents that wash clothes without producing an effluent that pollutes streams.

By the second half of 1995 more than one-fifth of the alumina produced at Kwinana was in the form of industrial chemicals. The demand for them is growing at a more rapid pace than the demand for the alumina that is smelted into aluminium. The day could come when most of the output of Kwinana is in the form of special aluminas. Curiously, Kwinana had been originally set up to produce just one product—alumina for the smelters—whereas Point Henry had been set up to produce a multitude of products. But by the late 1990s the roles were reversed.

16

The End of the
Time-clock

Point Henry was the first Alcoa workplace to suffer from patchy industrial relations. The trouble began to simmer in the early 1970s when Gough Whitlam was prime minister, and public sector wages were leaping high and other wages were leaping in imitation. The increased wages officially awarded to one group bred dissatisfaction in the group working next door. Inflation ran high and that also made for wage claims. Point Henry's employees reacted strongly to the economic unpredictability. They knew that it was easy to dislocate a smelter by going on strike. The smelting process had to be continuous, going on for 168 hours a week; and if the potline was no longer attended and became cold, the cost of restarting was high.

In the winter of 1973 relations were turbulent at the smelter. The members of the Federated Ironworkers' Union would suddenly stop work in the middle of a shift and go on strike. Most of Alcoa's managers could not cope with this hostile climate, partly because the company was unduly centralised. The central view in head office was that the refineries in Western Australia and the mills and smelter at Point Henry should pay the same wages for broadly the same kind of work. Later that view was abandoned in the realisation that the economic activities, working conditions and the main trade unions in the two states were different.

At Point Henry the smelter employees, in making their sudden strikes, usually stayed out for several consecutive eight-hour shifts. As a stoppage did serious damage to the metal being treated, the bargaining position lay with the union. Its favourite time for suddenly calling a strike was the weekend. The risk of sudden strikes—and the possible closing of the potline—was so high that the company for some months held a permanent booking in a motel in nearby Geelong so that salaried staff from the office in Melbourne could be ready to assist salaried staff from Geelong in running the smelter at short notice. Clerks and engineers learned how hot, dirty and exhausting were some of the smelting tasks. Moreover they did not have the physique to do some of these tasks satisfactorily. Accordingly, when the smelter hands returned to work at the end of the sudden strike, they received the bonus of overtime pay so that they could do the backlog of tasks as well as their normal work. In effect they were rewarded for stopping work.

Several strikes were so carefully timed as to create the maximum dislocation. One strike began between eleven and twelve on the day of the grand final of the Victorian Football League. In a city that was crazy about football, that was high provocation. The months from June to November 1973 were tense. A new industrial award was in the offing, and both sides were determined to win the best terms. The company miscalculated its bargaining position and paid a high price. 'We had rolling strikes for about three months, and the smelter was reduced to a shambles,' recalled Geoff Hayward. 'It took years to recover.' Moreover, the unions won much of what they had claimed.

Relations slowly improved. One cause of the improvement was the Point Henry managers' custom of bringing together employees each year in groups of about 25 and explaining to them the company's plans and attempting to answer criticisms. This annual exercise in talking frankly usually occupied three weeks. The practice led to more respect and confidence and to fewer rumours.

Managers realised that many of the flaws, as well as misunderstandings, at Point Henry were their own fault. Thus several sections of the works were glaringly inefficient. In the 1970s hidden havens accommodated employees who could not cope: some were sent there in the hope that they would remain out of sight and be slightly useful. The 'Pack & Ship Department' was such a place. There the sick, old and the injured were filed away. All big factories nourish a poet or two, and several of those poems which people love to read aloud at retirement dinners and other occasions for hilarity made much of this notorious department. 'The Ode to the Pack and Ship Department' described how a visiting foreman in search of some scrap bins found an old shipping clerk lying behind the mill, sunbathing and 'completely stark'. Then came reforms, as the poem lamented:

No more can you go to old Pack and Ship,
Where once you could have seen them,
Showing less activity,
Than the stiffs in a mausoleum.

Many work tasks at Point Henry were physically demanding, and on the hotter summer days the heat was oppressive. One tiring job, which had to be performed daily, was the removal of some three hundred exhausted anodes from the potlines. Once a heavy anode was taken out, the metal crust and metal lumps left behind had to be broken up with a sledgehammer and removed before a new anode could be installed. The work was also unpleasant because the air was heavy with fumes from the smelting process. The fumes carried fluoride, and men working on those tasks usually showed, when tested medically, the highest level of fluoride in their urine. The work easily gave rise to disputes.

In May 1978 a new way of changing the anodes was tried. A jackhammer suspended from an arm above a tractor speedily broke away the crust of metal. The men were less exhausted at the end of the day and less exposed to the fumes. The only hitch was that the 'crustbreakers', as they were called, created such a din that further changes were called for. At a cost of $3 848 000 the noise was reduced. Later, big sums were to be spent in lowering the emission of fluoride, carbon monoxide and organic carbon at both the Point Henry and the Portland smelters. A decade in which threats to the natural environment were taken seriously by public opinion and parliament was, inevitably, also a time when the health of the employees in smelters was safeguarded more than before.

In the crisis of 1983–84, when the Portland smelter was in mothballs, employees at Point Henry feared that their smelter might also be closed. As the fear of loss of jobs ran high, the process of consultation was carried further. Seminars were held in a hotel at the sea resort of Lorne so that the financial troubles and debts of the company, and all the implications for the workforce, could be explained. Hundreds of people from the shop floor went to Lorne. 'Many of them', said Ken Mansfield, 'had never stayed in a hotel in their life'. The outing, and the passing on of information about the company's costs and operations, helped morale. The company realised that in the early 1970s it had allowed the distinction between 'them' and 'us' to become too wide.

In Western Australia the unions and industrial conditions differed from those in Victoria. Even the background of the workforce differed from site to site. The oldest mine, Jarrahdale, had a few come-out-fighting employees, but employees of the modernised mines further along the Darling Range tended to be more peaceful. Each refinery, too, had a workforce of more than a thousand which differed in background, from the workforces of the other refineries. The oldest, Kwinana, at one time employed mostly migrants from England, especially the northern counties, who had reached Australia in the 1940s and 1950s. Kwinana's unions, it was observed, 'were active but not destructive'.

Pinjarra refinery, the second oldest, attracted most of its workforce from nearby farms and country towns, and many of these rural workers did not even join a union. While this should have made for smoother industrial relations, the smoothness did not last. Over a long period, no manager remained at Pinjarra for more than a couple of years and that made for instability. Several of the short-term managers were not wholly successful.

Each refinery had its own pattern of industrial conflict which, in retrospect, was as clear as a tartan. In the first years of a refinery the relations between unions and management tended to be constructive. In that initial period of quick expansion, an excitement was in the air, and promotions were frequent as new units of the refinery came into operation. The challenge of a complicated process made the jobs interesting as well as demanding. Then expansion ceased, a more humdrum routine was in place, the chance of promotion came less frequently, and the refinery became more inward-looking. Tensions and disputes seemed to multiply. Pinjarra reached this stage in the late 1970s. Its jobs, compared to Kwinana's, seemed secure because its profitability was virtually assured by its modern equipment. Unions realised that their bargaining position was strong.

At the start of the 1980s the unions at the Pinjarra refinery pressed hard for a working week of 35 instead of 40 hours. They went on strike; and their victory—they won a working week of 36 hours—owed much to the big Australian Workers Union and to the determined members of the small Federated Engine-Drivers and Firemen's Association who worked in the company's power station. Several unions were willing to go to unusual lengths to defend their members. When a unionist was dismissed for stealing, some of the unions stood firm, refusing to allow their member, even if guilty, to be dismissed from his job.

Industrial relations at Pinjarra were to improve from 1983 when Geoff Hayward, an engineer reared in Broken Hill, began his nine years as manager. Hayward at first thought the workplace was a bit of 'a shambles' with the unions exerting more power than was consistent with efficient operations. Bit by bit the relations improved with the Australian Workers Union and there was more talking on both sides. On the other hand, the Amalgamated Metal Workers Union was wary of change: it opposed anybody who, not a member of their union, tried to use a spanner to do minor repairs. The sixty or so members of the Electrical Trades Union—highly skilled electricians who handled the latest instruments on the control panels—were radical but willing to talk. The improving industrial mood was reflected in a leap in Pinjarra's output from about 6500 to nearly 8000 tonnes a day.

In the mid 1980s the company began a campaign to reduce injuries.

It was calculated that in the Western Australian mines and refineries the total injuries were the equivalent of eleven people being absent through injury for the whole year. Many of these injuries could easily be prevented if both bosses and employees took care.

Jobs were analysed, and ways were found for making most of them safer. Traffic accidents were reduced in those parts of the refineries where road vehicles ran about. The causes of injuries as diverse as bad backs, loss of hearing and 'sprains and strains' were tackled. As a result, the frequency rate for serious injuries fell away. For each 200 000 working hours in Western Australian refineries and mines—and they employed about two-thirds of Alcoa's workforce—there were 12.8 serious injuries in 1984 but only 8.46 in 1986. Three years later the Western Australian employees celebrated the seventh successive year in which there was a fall in the frequency rate for serious injuries. Indeed the small team which operated the Hedges goldmine experienced no serious injury in the first couple of years.

At Point Henry a similar campaign reduced the injuries. At Portland ways were sought of improving safety at work and health at home. By the 1990s all the major workplaces accepted the principle that, if employees came to work nursing fewer worries about family and home, they were less likely to experience accidents. In 1994, Monash University began, at the company's request, a five-year study of the health of those working in the aluminium industry. Already the results of the safety campaign were heartening. Across Australia the injury rate in Alcoa fell in six years from 6.7 to 2.6 injuries for each 200 000 hours of work. In a big workforce this equalled less than three accidents a week.

Norman Stephen's monthly report as managing director now began with a section on safety, and directors could read—before each board meeting—what had been gained. There were still accidents. Thus in 1989 an employee at Point Henry slipped and immersed his foot and the lower part of the leg in a molten pot, entailing a brief stay in hospital and a skin graft.

The accidents and ailments were much less frequent than a decade earlier, though the improvements in safety varied from place to place. At Portland, David Judd had a special influence. An Englishman who had trained as a mechanical engineer, he moved from the South Australian Electricity Commission to Point Henry where in his fifteen years he developed his ideas about management. In the potroom he tried to temper the tradition of semi-militancy which he believed was as much the fault of management as of men. His radical ideas were not self-evident when he was promoted to Portland in 1986 to operate the new smelter.

The first thing that the Portland employees observed about Judd was his height—he was about 'six feet six inches with gangling arms that were like an orang-outang'. His manner was open, his grin was boyish, and a few strands of his straight hair hung untidily over his forehead. If after going to bed he did not sleep well he would dress himself, drive to the works and walk around in a leisurely way, talking to the night shift about any subject from photography to sport. His energy and self-motivation were captivating. He gave the impression that each employee had something special to offer. He believed, once the smelter was operating, that much more could be wrung from the equipment and much more could be enticed from the employees than was expected. People, he said, were the untapped source of power at Portland. From the United States he recruited a New Age evangelist to spread the message. Those who did not subscribe to the new ideology tended to leave: doubters were not welcome.

By the start of 1988, Judd was letting it be known that in his view the traditional way of managing the smelter was inefficient. Hitherto one group of people had run the smelter and another had done the maintenance work, a division which seemed unwise since the two tasks were intimately linked. Now the smelter was divided into four separate and almost competing operations, and each section had its own manager, accountant, personnel officer and maintenance staff. Judd thought smaller self-contained groups worked better than big anonymous groups, and he allowed each small group, within reason, to set up its own work practices. He disliked what he described as 'the plethora of inter-departmental relationships'. Normally his prose was more conversational than that.

Judd tried to lower the barrier between the salaried staff and wages employees, between work and leisure, between town and the smelter. In the end he dropped the use of the word 'employee' because it smacked of segregation. The wages people normally had to punch a clock when they arrived or departed from the site, but Judd removed the time-clocks at Portland. He also said that everyone, whether manager or cleaner, should dress alike; and so the managers ceased to wear collar and tie. The special spaces in the car park for the highest officials were abolished. In September 1991, members of the staff ceased to have luncheon together in their own room because the practice was seen as segregation and as inimical to teamwork and the sharing of ideas.

No specialist officer was entrusted with public relations; that was seen as the task of everyone. Amenities were provided, including a big gymnasium and creche. Television sets were mounted around the plant and they carried, in print, local news, workplace news and 24-hour AAP news. Not all these ideas originated in Portland. Some had come from other Alcoa plants where the same reform movement was at work in a less flamboyant way.

White Gold

Health and safety is fostered at all the company plants. These employees are training near the gymnasium at the Portland Smelter.

David Judd won a devoted following and, of course, he stirred up critics. When it became known that he had cancer and a tumour on the brain, a sadness settled on the works. For a time in 1993 he continued to come to the smelter but in his last weeks he had to be dissuaded almost forcibly from coming. His funeral, a blend of Church of England and New Orleans, is vividly remembered. His grave, in sight of the sea and the smelter, has a slabtop of black marble on which are depicted a pelican and a dolphin. In death he is no less a hero. While his grave was being shown to me, a former employee in a rattletrap of a car arrived to pay his respects, calling Judd 'the master'.

What he began, others extended. Near the smelter a large area—much of it was swamp—had been set aside as the site for a rubbish dump that was regularly covered with soil. By 1989 the wastes were being deposited there at such a rate that more land would soon be needed. In that year a total of 1083 cubic metres a month was dumped. After a year-long campaign against wastefulness the monthly waste was reduced to 39 cubic metres, or less than 4 per cent of the total of two years previously.

Dozens of ways of saving waste were adopted. Broken bricks from the potroom were used in making roads and agricultural drains. Carbon dust was saved and sent in bags to the cement works near Geelong. Oil was now bought in bulk; and so the thousands of large used oil drums ceased to accumulate. Packing material made of cardboard was no longer burned, but was turned into compost to fertilise the soil. Scraps of food went to a worm farm, from which were released the worms that slowly improved the soil.

Every aluminium smelter gives off fumes. Normally about 32 kilograms of fluoride are released during the production of each tonne of metal. If the smelter fumes are not 'scrubbed', the fluoride escapes into the atmosphere. When scrubbing is not practised at a smelter, the nearby vegetation slowly dies because fluoride in the sapstream of plants is toxic. In the vicinity of some smelters almost nothing grows where the wind-blown fumes travel.

Fumes from the Portland smelter also blew out to sea, and some local fishermen out in their boats said they could smell the smelter. They wondered whether the fumes would affect the fish and even harm their own health. As a result they were given instruments with which to monitor the air, for it was possible that the smelter's emissions were somehow being concentrated in the one area by winds and currents. Mussels, abalone and other seafood were regularly tested, for they would be quick to pick up industrial waste. Scientific evidence suggests that the fumes do not impair the health of shellfish or human beings.

On occasions the smelter was a visible polluter, and the failure of the 'carbon bake scrubbing system' sometime gave rise to billows of black smoke. While Portland was eventually successful in curbing fluoride emissions to perhaps the lowest level in the world, it was slower to succeed in tackling the emissions of sulphur dioxide. Those who worked in the potroom of the smelters were prone to asthma, and Portland was not very successful in reducing the asthma until a medical expert prescribed 'protective and respiratory equipment' for certain tasks. In the five months ending in July 1989 the Portland smelter reported not one case of 'occupational asthma'.

Accepting the challenge to 'green' the surroundings of the smelter, Judd set out to create what he called 'A Smelter in the Park'. While the catchy phrase came from another smelter, the initiative was his. The site was windy and much of it had been low heathland, and yet it was eventually made into a presentable kind of park. Plants were even grown with success beside the walls of the potrooms. As Judd proudly explained to a visiting American: 'If our emissions went up to high levels, then none of this would exist'. Near the smelter the company established a farm where sixty or seventy cattle grazed, and annual tests show that their meat is not affected by fluoride fumes. On 7 December 1992, the American magazine *Industry Week* suggested that Judd 'stands at the helm of what may be the most innovative smelting operation in the world'.

It was observed after Judd's death that his methods of managing the smelter offered rewards in personal satisfaction but did not increase output as much as he had expected. Portland was simply not as productive as it should have been. Curiously, its safety record was uneven, though care for the injured was first-rate. Many ingots varied in their grade of metal instead of being identical, and some ingots were cracked on the surface. Almost inward-looking, Portland was rightly proud of its human achievements but not fully alert to the need for technical efficiency.

The Portland smelter still did not fulfil the original financial hopes. When ingot prices were high it yielded good profits, but its total return on the huge sum invested was, at the time of writing, disappointing. For the government of Victoria the investment was slightly better, because it bought its holding from Alcoa at a discount and sold part of it at a very high price. In 1996, the Victorian government still owned 25 per cent of the smelter.

The recession of the early 1990s and the slump in aluminium prices promoted another step towards reforming the workplaces. Kwinana, the oldest and most vulnerable of the three refineries, led in this step. Its employees had the motivation to act because they knew that they could lose their jobs—if a refinery had to be closed, Kwinana would be the first to disappear. At Kwinana a radical solution was proposed. All overtime payments would be abolished: in return the workforce would receive an annual salary. The deal was accepted.

A new method of organising the work was adopted at Kwinana. In effect small teams of employees were placed in charge of each section of the refinery. Each team had to operate its part of the plant throughout the year. If a member of a team was absent his mates had to do the work, borrowing if necessary the labour of other groups and repaying it in kind. The members of each team had the right to determine who belonged to that team. When a vacancy occurred they themselves chose the newcomer, choosing with time-consuming care. If they made an error in their selection and the newcomer proved to be work-shy, every member of the team suffered. So each team became like a small business, fully responsible for the success of its area.

A miracle affected the now venerable practice of paying overtime for work performed outside normal hours. Under the new scheme there was little need for extra work on Saturday and Sunday. Maintenance work and other tasks were done during the week, even in advance of requirements. Jobs were no longer deliberately left undone so that at the weekend, employees could come in to do them at a special overtime rate of pay. Machines ceased to break down regularly on Friday afternoon. As employees were paid the same salary on Sunday as on Friday they had an incentive to do extra tasks on weekdays rather than lose the freedom of the weekend. The total overtime worked on weekends at Kwinana fell like a stone. The same scheme was introduced at Portland. There, in the very last pay period before the annual salary was introduced, about 1500 hours of overtime were worked. Under the new system, however, overtime was rare.

Teamwork became normal: demarcation disputes fell away; the man with many skills was welcomed in a work team. As each team looked for ways of making its work easier, innovations were welcomed, no matter how humble the source. In the new regime the salary was based on skills and performance, and so it was an incentive for employees to improve their qualifications. Training became a priority. Talent and ideas that were previously neglected or under-used began to blossom in many teams. It was not all plain sailing but for most the sailing was faster and more enjoyable.

While the Kwinana refinery led in many of the new ways of organising work and pay, other plants were moving at their own pace, in their own way, in a similar direction. New ways could not be tried unless the leaders of trade unions were sympathetic or, at least, not hostile. The union heads at the plant could see, more easily than those at the distant Trades Hall, the gains for their employees, and usually cooperated. Ted Hardcastle of Point Henry was one union leader who persuaded workmates to try the new formula. Once a French-polisher, then a taxi driver, and later the relief manager of Radio Rentals in Geelong, he realised in January 1969 that he was earning much less than a semi-skilled smelter hand at Point Henry. So he signed on at the smelter and did the hot and heavy labouring work, lifting up the heavy slabs of aluminium with big asbestos gloves. 'I thought I'd walked into Hades,' he recalled.

Ted Hardcastle, who eventually became the most influential trade unionist at the site, agreed there might be gains in a new approach. Most of his mates in the union were on his side. He initiated many of the changes at Point Henry when he realised that pay could be higher and jobs more secure under the new approach. Without him the annual salary for every employee—and the superannuation and other advantages—could not have been introduced in February 1993. Interestingly, he had no time for theory and little time for experts. He referred to 'these tertiary-educated gentlemen' with an air of derision and fun. He once said with pride: 'I've gone through eight industrial-relations managers here'.

Wasteful practices were more easily detected, once everyone agreed that they were running a business that had to stand on its own feet in hard times. At Point Henry some of the benefits which had been fought for in the 1970s were no longer seen as benefits. Thus the unions had once gone on strike in order to win an excellent canteen and cafe that was open day and night, seven days a week. It had a chef but in the course of the night shift maybe only a dozen employees would eat in it. The canteen's annual loss was about $400 000 a year—or closer to $750 000 at today's costs. When eventually, the canteen opened only for day shifts, five days a week, the saving was huge. As compensation, vending machines were installed to dispense warm food, and arrangements were made for pizzas to be delivered to the plant at night. Some employees disliked the new arrangement but most accepted it. 'The employees realise we have to run a business, and they understand the business,' said Wayne Osborn, who ran the rolling mill.

In 1991 the cost of producing one tonne of aluminium at Point Henry had been higher than at any of the Aluminum Co. of America's smelters around the world, but two years later its costs were lower than those of these rivals. Visitors came from factories and other industrial plants to see this transformation, and sometimes to copy it, just as they visited the refineries in Western Australia. Not everything, they noticed, was cut to the bone. Point Henry, for example, had a full-time chaplain—he conducted most of the marriages and funerals for employees and their families—and contract gardeners who grew flowers, tended shrubberies and mowed lawns at the site. In each lunchroom there was a television monitor that passed on messages and factory news, enabling employees to advertise that their car was for sale, informing incoming employees that a problem might arise on the next shift or that a baby had just been born to the wife of a workmate.

Across the company the paying of superannuation was transformed. There had long been superannuation, with the salaried staff and the wages employees in separate schemes, but the staff fund was much the wealthier in June 1984 with a market value of $55.6 million compared to $16.2 million in the 'wages employees' fund'. In January 1990 a superior superannuation fund was opened for wages employees, 94 per cent of whom had joined it by the end of the year. This paved the way for an unusual scheme to which all employees contributed the same proportion of their salary. On retiring, all were eligible for a superannuation payout that was based on their years of service and the level of their final salary. Sir Laurence Muir, a director of Alcoa who had served as senior partner in one of the country's biggest stockbrokers, became chairman of the superannuation fund in 1986. The elected representatives from nearly all sections of the workforce began to share responsibility for the fund's investment decisions. In ten years the funds in their charge more than doubled from $160 to $340 million. One of the side effects of this responsibility was that leaders within the workforce, beginning to see business partly from a shareholders' viewpoint,

The End of the Time-clock

Paul O'Neill (chairman and chief executive, Aluminum Company of America) visits Langford Park in 1993. He stands on a site mined in 1960s.

realised how much their own industry, their jobs and their social security depended on global economic forces that could not be held at bay.

Stimulus for efficiency came from a new attitude to industrial relations, low aluminium prices and the industry's swift move from boom to slump in the early 1990s, but it also came from Pittsburgh, where Paul O'Neill was the new chairman and chief executive. He appointed Thomas Carter as vice-president in charge of quality. One of Carter's bright ideas was to point out to Alcoa what the smartest Japanese companies were doing in their mechanised workplaces. More than forty of the senior managers from Alcoa went to Japan to observe.

At head office in Melbourne, as in all of Alcoa's offices, the processing of information was being transformed by the new wave of computers. 'Computer programs that were dazzlingly powerful and fast when they appeared two years ago are now regarded as clunkers,' wrote Andrew Lodge in 1995. One gain achieved by the swift computers and the new drive for efficiency was speed in producing the monthly accounts. In Melbourne the accounts were being speedily produced ten days after the end of the month, and then the lag was reduced to two days. Melbourne's tight deadlines were to be imitated in Pittsburgh where the Aluminum Co. of America was often the first company in the United States to calculate and report its quarterly earnings.

17

A Global Alliance

Western Mining Corporation, the real initiator of Alcoa, was swimming in deep water in the mid 1950s, with no shore clearly in sight. It was tied to gold, a metal which seemed to have a shrinking future. But for the special taxation concessions granted to gold companies in the hope of keeping them alive, Western Mining might have ended its days in the late 1950s. At that time the total assets held by Western Mining were much less valuable than those held by its Australian partners in Alcoa—Broken Hill South and North Broken Hill. Just at the time when it became interested in the bauxite of the Darling Range, a sensible forecaster could have reasonably said that of the top 100 companies on the Australian stock exchanges, Western Mining was one of the most fragile.

It explored its way out of trouble, though its road to success was painful. Its decision to search for other minerals led to the development of the bauxite in the Darling Range in the late 1950s, major finds of nickel in Western Australia in the mid 1960s, the huge Olympic Dam base metals and uranium ore body in an arid region of South Australia a decade later, and a variety of gold discoveries as the price of that metal at last revived. During these years it remained the largest Australian shareholder in Alcoa, and members of its board provided the three successive chairmen of Alcoa—Clark, Forrest and Parbo. If by chance the other Australian shareholders of Alcoa decided to sell out, Western Mining was the likely purchaser.

The Alcoa project, huge as it was, did not yield the profit expected during its first two decades, but the other Australian shareholders showed no sign of selling their shares in Alcoa. As late as 1978, when the decision was made to commence the building of the Portland smelter, they still held just over one-quarter of the shares in Alcoa. Then Broken Hill South began to think of selling shares.

A holder of valuable assets, Broken Hill South was also a roving company in search of new mines. Having sold for virtually nothing its famous but almost exhausted silver–lead–zinc mine at Broken Hill, it then spent a fortune in trying to develop a big phosphate deposit in northwest Queensland. It still retained interests in copper mines at Cobar (NSW) and Kanmantoo (SA), and the old Electrolytic Refining and Smelting Co. at Port Kembla; and it held an impressive portfolio of shares in which Alcoa was the most valuable. But it experienced four lean years in the late 1970s. In order to reduce its debts it virtually decided late in 1978 to sell a portion of its Alcoa shareholding.

While Alcoa shares were not listed on stock exchanges, they were a prize for any alert investors. Broken Hill South sounded out potential buyers and then formally asked the board of Alcoa, as was legally required, for permission to sell some of its Alcoa shares. On 5 February 1979 the board of Alcoa accepted 'for admission to membership of the Company' the T & G Mutual Life Society which was buying 1 250 000 of the Alcoa shares held by South. On 30 April 1979 another Melbourne life office, Colonial Mutual Life, bought 2 million shares from South. Other shares were sold to a third Melbourne life office, National Mutual Life, and to the trustees of the BHP superannuation fund. None of the new owners sought a seat on the Alcoa board. In September 1979 Broken Hill South announced that its remaining Alcoa shares formed 'a substantial portion' of its total assets and were well worth retaining. In fact the shares it held in Alcoa were two-edged. The shares seemed likely to ensure South's survival but they also attracted raiders.

North Broken Hill was the company most likely to buy out South. Relations between the two boards had been close for much of their history. North Broken Hill had prospered in the 1970s, its shares rising more than most mining shares, and it could easily have made an attractive share offer, or even cash offer, for Broken Hill South. Indeed North already owned almost one-fifth of the shares in South. The two boards even met to discuss a merger, but South rejected the idea.

North could have forced the issue. Lawrence Baillieu, the managing director of North, had sat on the board of Alcoa for the last ten years as North's representative and he could see that South's holding of Alcoa shares was of enormous potential value. He concluded in a private note in September 1979 that 'Alcoa had a chance to become second only to BHP' in earnings and assets. But North's chairman, M.L. Baillieu, now in his late seventies, did not think as highly of South and its assets, including its remaining holding in Alcoa. So North missed its chance.

In 1980 it made a spectacular bid for a bigger company, Dunlop Olympic (the predecessor of Pacific Dunlop), rather than for Broken Hill South.

Broken Hill South, with its rich portfolio of shares, remained an obvious target for a takeover. At last it became a target for National Mutual Life. The Bond Corporation, then rising fast, tried to outbid the life insurance office. Alcoa did not wish the Bond Corporation to be one of its major shareholders. And so Western Mining Corporation, as the largest of the Australian shareholders in Alcoa, joined in the race. It won control of Broken Hill South and so acquired a further interest in Alcoa.

North Broken Hill retained its 12 per cent of Alcoa and at first showed no signs of selling it. North expanded strongly in the first half of the 1980s, acquiring two of Tasmania's largest ventures, Electrolytic Zinc and Australian Pulp & Paper Manufactures. As a result its debts were high. To lower those debts it decided in June 1986 to sell its 12 per cent interest in Alcoa to Western Mining. The price was $125 million.

The purchase price seems low today but in the context of the time it was realistic. Alcoa had not yet become highly profitable. In the space of 25 years (1961–86) Alcoa had paid to federal, state and local governments far more in taxes and royalties than it had paid to its shareholders in dividends. It had paid a total of $820 million to governments but only $264 million in dividends to shareholders. The ratio was about to alter. Western Mining, in buying the Alcoa shares from North, acquired a bargain, for the shares would multiply four times in value in the space of four years.

With the purchase of these shares, Western Mining's interest in Alcoa climbed almost to 45 per cent. Its interest continued to creep higher. It bought, whenever a chance arose, those relatively small percentages of Alcoa shares which Colonial Mutual and National Mutual and other superannuation funds and life offices had acquired from Broken Hill South. Western Mining's last major purchase of Alcoa shares was in September 1990 when it bought from C.T.B. Nominees a packet of 14 226 699 shares. The price was just over $128 million dollars. By 1993 the only shareholders in Alcoa were the Aluminum Co. of America (operating through Alcoa International Holdings Co.) with 51 per cent, Western Mining Corporation with 48.24 per cent, and two Australian funds, QBE Securities and QBE Nominees, with a total of 0.75 per cent. QBE was a large insurance office, founded in 1886 as the North Queensland Insurance Co. Its interest in Alcoa represented a small part of the shares which Broken Hill South had sold.

So by the early 1990s Alcoa of Australia Limited was essentially a partnership between a Pittsburgh industrial company and a Melbourne mining company. Most of the directors represented these two owners but there were also outside Australian directors, the oldest of whom had originally been appointed to look after Pittsburgh's interests. The fierce disputes that sometimes broke out in the earlier period were no more. Decisions made at the board meetings in Melbourne were unanimous: when there was a division the decision was deferred. Relations between the two main shareholders were harmonious and even cordial, being strengthened by the fact that Sir Arvi Parbo, who was chairman both of Western Mining and of Alcoa, sat on the board of the Aluminum Co. of America which met in Pittsburgh. Alcoa and its fortunes were more important to Pittsburgh than ever before. In several years, from the late 1980s onwards, the profits from Alcoa supplied more than half of the total profits earned by the Aluminum Co. of America.

The board of Alcoa now consisted of three distinct groups of directors—four executive directors from Alcoa; three directors, including the chairman, from Western Mining Corporation; and four outside part-time directors. The tradition persisted of an Australian (Sir Arvi Parbo) serving as chairman and an American (Robert F. Slagle) as managing director.

Three of the four executive directors—Phil Spry-Bailey, G.J. Pizzey and R.A.G. Vines—were Australians who had begun work with Alcoa as young engineers, while the fourth executive director, Robert Slagle, was now the only American on the board. The three Western Mining representatives—Sir Arvi Parbo, Hugh Morgan and Don Morley—were senior executives of that company: Hugh Morgan, a son of Bill Morgan, was managing director and Morley was finance director of Western Mining.

Of the four outside directors, John Darling had been sitting on the board since 1964 and was therefore the longest serving director in the company's history. Sir Laurence Muir, a director since 1982, had been a partner in the leading sharebrokers Ian Potter & Co. before joining the board of some of the major banking, insurance, newspaper and manufacturing companies as well as the Canberra Development Board, of which he was chairman. There were two recent appointees: John Phillips who had been deputy governor of the Reserve Bank of Australia, and Professor Adrienne Clarke who was chairman of the Commonwealth Scientific and Industrial Research Organisation and the first woman to hold an influential position in Alcoa. Of the eleven directors, Phillips and Darling lived in New South Wales and Vines lived in Perth, but the other eight lived in Melbourne.

The company had become one of the most successful companies in Australia's long mining history and by normal standards its future seemed assured. Sir Arvi Parbo, looking far ahead, was not so sure: he was not certain partly because he looked so far ahead. Addressing about two dozen of his executives in a private hotel at the Victorian seaside resort of Portsea in October 1992, he wondered about Alcoa's opportunities for expansion in the long term.

Thinking aloud in the presence of his senior executives, he said that the bauxite in the Darling Range, while it remained a magnificent asset, was being extracted on such a huge scale that it could no longer expect the long life which was predicted in the early 1960s. In support of his argument he offered a few calculations. If the Wagerup refinery were to reach its government-approved capacity of 2 million tonnes a year—an increase that soon took place—then Alcoa's three refineries would be capable of producing 6.6 million tonnes of alumina a year. At that rate the company could mine for another 95 years. On the other hand if environmental warnings, especially the fears of increased salinity in the water catchment, forced the company to abandon the eastern half of the Darling Range, then the bauxite at the present rate of production would last for only another 46 years.

Parbo wondered whether Alcoa should continue to expand its mines and refineries. If it expanded, it might run out of bauxite too quickly. Could the company expand by mining the bauxite it held in the Kimberley, in the tropical northwest of the continent? These deposits were not yet payable, though their day might come. Could the company expand by building new smelters? Parbo thought only small additions were likely to be made to the Point Henry and Portland smelters. Coal-fired power stations were falling from favour because of the surge of greenhouse arguments. In all, Parbo was far from pessimistic. After all, the Darling Range was a giant, often supplying more than 15 per cent of the metallic content of the world's second most important metal. In few of the world's major minerals was one supply region so crucial.

Alcoa now stood amongst the top ten profit-makers in Australia in a normal year, but where should it spend that slice of the profits which it set aside for financing expansion? The opportunities in aluminium, said Parbo, seemed fewer than in the last two decades. The 'natural response will be to look outside' Australia for expansion opportunities, he said. He recalled that fourteen years ago Alcoa had been invited by the Aluminum Co. of America to take part in developing the aluminium industry in Brazil. To that proposal the board of Alcoa had finally said a firm 'no', mainly because it was flat out in financing Portland. But the next time another Brazil became available, Alcoa might be strongly tempted to say 'yes'.

Parbo, without specifically saying so, foreshadowed the possibility of new joint ventures between Melbourne and Pittsburgh. Two years later those arrangements began to take shape, partly under the influence of Robert F. Slagle. A Cornell graduate in engineering, Slagle became head of the chemicals division based in Pittsburgh before succeeding Norman Stephen as managing director of Alcoa in 1991. An admirer of Krome George—he had been recruited from Cornell University by George—he was as interested as his mentor in long-term business strategy. After several years in Australia he could see that the rise of Alcoa as virtually the world's leading producer of alumina had altered the foundations on which the original Pittsburgh–Melbourne alliance was built.

In the early 1990s the two companies were still very different. The company based on Pittsburgh with at least 55 000 shareholders was much larger and wealthier, being one of the big industrial companies of the world, though the disparity between its size and that of Alcoa was no longer so wide. In some years from the late 1980s onwards Pittsburgh depended heavily on the profits coming from Australia.

In their activities the American and Australian companies were far apart. Whereas Alcoa of Australia was primarily a specialist in producing alumina, and less important as a smelter and a fabricator, the Pittsburgh company was more than ever before a manufacturer of aluminium products. In annual revenue the Pittsburgh company earned some US$10 billion, of which only about 30 per cent came from aluminium ingots, alumina and chemicals. The bulk of its revenue came from aluminium can-sheet and foil and other packaging products, from aluminium items used in building and construction, and from hundreds of other aluminium products—ranging from wheels for Boeing 747s to the aluminium spaceframe bodies for motor vehicles, which were first made in Germany in 1992.

Not all the products of the Pittsburgh-based company were aluminium. About one-sixth of the total revenue came from such items as fibre optic cable, electronic components, packaging machinery, vinyl windows and the plastic closures that were replacing aluminium closures on cans. By most definitions the Aluminum Co. of America was primarily a manufacturing company, though its mining and smelting activities were still large and global.

Beginning life as a small spoke in a big American aluminium wheel, Alcoa as a profit earner had become almost half the wheel in some years. Beginning as a learner, it had become a teacher. The Western Australians were so experienced in making alumina that they had skills and expertise not always available in the Aluminum Co. of America. Accordingly, when Pittsburgh saw a chance to build a new refinery somewhere else in the world—and India was to the fore—it called on the expertise from Western Australia and was tempted also to call on Alcoa for capital.

There was another reason why Pittsburgh and Melbourne should cooperate rather than compete in mining bauxite and in refining and smelting aluminium for world markets. Their industry was cyclical, and the times were tough again. The yield on Alcoa's financial assets fell from about 24 per cent in the late 1980s to 8 per cent in 1994. Profits slumped, though there was still a profit. For the international aluminium industry the recession of the early 1990s and the slump in metal prices was deepened by the fall of communism in the Soviet Union. With a lower military and domestic demand in Russia, cheap Russian aluminium was exported, almost flooding markets. In 1993 the export from the new Commonwealth of Independent States probably equalled 1.5 million tonnes, or three times the combined output of the Portland and Point Henry smelters.

Around the world the unsold or unused piles of ingots grew high. Between 1989 and 1993 the world price of aluminium fell by about three-quarters. Its price in real terms had probably never been as low. The governments of the six countries that dominated the world's aluminium industry agreed to cut output by about one million tonnes of ingot; and Portland and Point Henry shared in the cut. As competing nations could agree, there was every reason why Alcoa and the Aluminum Co. of America could agree to dovetail their activities.

If Pittsburgh and Melbourne were to cooperate in ventures outside Australia, were their existing structures suitable? Bob Slagle, as managing director of Alcoa, raised this question and outlined his case for a regrouped alliance between the Americans and the Australians. Richard Fischer, who had been the top legal officer in Pittsburgh and was now the chairman's counsel, wondered how a concerted plan could be implemented. He mentioned it almost casually to Sir Arvi Parbo, chairman both of Alcoa and of Western Mining, when he was in Pittsburgh to attend a meeting of the board of the Aluminum Co. of America, of which he had long been a director.

The central plan was that Pittsburgh and Melbourne should merge and then coordinate their bauxite, alumina and chemicals activities: for Melbourne this was the core of its business but for Pittsburgh it was the minor though important part of the business. Under the plan they would jointly own and operate one global business in bauxite, alumina and alumina chemicals. In contrast, Pittsburgh and Melbourne would each retain its existing smelters and fabricating and can-sheet plants.

Parbo could see merits in a combined and coordinated global business in alumina and chemicals. The idea fitted in with the thoughts he had privately expressed at the Portsea conference less than two years before. A joint venture would provide more opportunities for Alcoa, its assets, its staff, and its expanding profits. Moreover, Alcoa would no longer be confined to Australia. For a company with big assets and expertise in the aluminium industry, Australia was no longer quite so enticing. Here was a chance to operate in the whole world.

Parbo's initial view was that the idea would meet obstacles. Feeling that he faced a conflict of interest as chairman of two of the companies and a director of all three relevant companies, he took no part in the detailed investigations which Hugh Morgan conducted as managing director of Western Mining. Morgan's conclusions were favourable: the likely gains outweighed the likely losses.

The crucial question was how to place a monetary value on the various assets that both Pittsburgh and Melbourne would contribute to the new organisation. The Aluminum Co. of America, in view of its major mines and refineries in South and North America and the Caribbean and its huge business in chemicals, would be contributing more global assets than Western Mining with its bauxite mines and refineries. It brought to the alliance the bauxite mines in Jamaica, Brazil, and Suriname; the refineries in Brazil, Jamaica, Suriname and Texas; the alumina chemicals plants in lands as diverse as Singapore, Japan, Holland, Germany and the United States; and the Alcoa steamship company that carried raw materials.

In Alcoa the shareholders now consisted of the Aluminum Co. of America with 60 per cent, Western Mining Corporation with 39.25 per cent, and the Australian insurance company QBE with the remaining fraction. In the new global company, QBE did not participate. A new organisation called Alcoa World Alumina now formally operated the alumina and chemical business. Western Mining owned 40 per cent and the Aluminum Co. of America 60 per cent of its shares.

Alcoa World Alumina was supervised by a strategic council of five representatives—two from Western Mining and three from the Aluminum Co. of America. Richard Fischer of Pittsburgh, who was succeeded by Alain Belda, acted as first chairman, with Hugh Morgan of Western Mining as deputy chairman. The strategic council was not in charge of daily operations: it took a global view when it held its first meeting in Perth.

Australian executives who began their career in Australian refineries and smelters now had their first chance to win high managerial positions in the United States. At the end of 1994, G. John Pizzey was living in Knoxville, Tennessee, as president of the primary metals division of the Aluminum Co. of America, and Roger Vines was president of the same company's bauxite and alumina division. Early in 1996 Vines returned to Melbourne the first Australian to be chief executive of Alcoa.

The main phase of the alliance was formally launched on 1 January 1995. It involved three major changes: firstly, Western Mining Corporation became a part owner of world-wide interests in alumina and chemicals; secondly, the Aluminum Co. of America became a larger shareholder in Alcoa than before; and thirdly, the global operations of the two companies in alumina and chemicals were coordinated far more than previously.

Alcoa World Alumina now controlled these various activities around the world, and as part of that control it made the main decisions affecting the mines, refineries and smelters of Alcoa of Australia. The Melbourne board with its wide-ranging membership was now seen as unnecessary, and even the traditional siting of the head office in Melbourne was seen as inappropriate, because Perth was the hub of the alumina industry. Soon the board of Alcoa of Australia would consist solely of full-time executives, with Roger Vines as chairman and managing director—the first time the two roles had been combined. On the board of six, two of the executives came from Western Mining, which from 1996 was known simply as WMC.

On 5 June 1996, at a dinner in the Australian Club in Melbourne, the five departing directors—Sir Arvi Parbo, Professor Adrienne Clark, Sir Laurence Muir, John Phillips and Jose Rodolfo Lopes, a Brazilian new to the board—were farewelled. Sir Arvi Parbo, who had been chairman since 1978, thus spanning half of the company's history, made his observations and expressed his thanks, as did his colleagues. He had on another occasion put on paper the lessons he had gleaned from the history of the company from which he was now stepping down. He offered four simple lessons:

1 'The mineral resource on which a successful major mineral operation can be founded does not have to be high grade if other factors are favourable.'
2 'A project can grow much faster and become much larger than anyone can imagine at the beginning. While projections and assessments must be made, our limitations in being able to see the future must be kept in mind.'
3 'If the parties in a project are to have differing benefits from it, these should be settled up front. When operations start, the interests of all participants should be the same.'
4 'The real value of mineral operation can be a long time in emerging. Alcoa of Australia's present major significance to its shareholders did not become evident until 1987, twenty-six years after the formation of the company.'

As an afterthought, Parbo observed what many distinguished mining engineers must have said to themselves after a long career: 'I have come to the conclusion that my ability to predict the future is minimal, and that nothing is impossible'.

In retrospect, the decision to mine in the Darling Range had had far-reaching effects. It helped Western Australia become one of the two fastest growing Australian states. It spurred one of the fiercest clashes that the continent had experienced on environmental concerns. It helped to lift Western Mining from a struggling company to one of the ten or twelve top companies on the Australian stock exchange. It boosted Australia's export revenue, and as a result Alcoa, which now contributed about 5 per cent of exports in a normal year, was one of the nation's leading exporters.

In the world-wide aluminium industry the Darling Range is also vital. Few mining fields of any kind in Australia, indeed few in the world, have been so important on a global scale, for today aluminium is one of the world's five most important minerals.

Around the world, whenever people drink from an aluminium can, or travel in a jet airliner constructed largely of aluminium, the chances are maybe one in seven that the aluminium comes from bauxite mined in the Darling Range.

Sources and Acknowledgements

This history of Alcoa of Australia was written largely from the company's internal records and the recollections of those who played a part in its first forty years. It traces the company's story from the finding of large deposits of bauxite in the Darling Range in Western Australia in 1957 to the reshaping of the American–Australian partnership in the mid 1990s.

Recollections

While writing this book I spoke with Americans who were prominent in the company's early history. They included W.H. Krome George, a former chairman and chief executive of the Aluminum Co. of America, and five former managing directors of Alcoa of Australia: Allen C. Sheldon, Joe C. Bates, Waldo Porter, J.L. Diederich and Norman Stephen. In the United States I also talked with Charles Parry, C.E. 'Ned' Pfeifer, R. Banks Smith, Harry W. Fawcett and G.C. McBride who had taken part in important episodes in the growth of Alcoa. F. Worth Hobbs kindly arranged these interviews while I was in Pittsburgh.

In Melbourne I gained much from Sir Arvi Parbo, Hugh Morgan, John Darling, Sir Wilfred Brookes, Sir Archie Glenn, R. Lawrence Baillieu. H. McE. Scambler and R.L. Bowlby, all of whom sat on the board of Alcoa and some of whom sat on the boards of the Australian mining companies which helped to set up Alcoa. I am also grateful to Robert Slagle, Roger Vines, G.J. Pizzey, and Phil Spry-Bailey, who were executive directors of Alcoa while I was investigating its history. Phil has taken a special interest in this project: a lot of the history of Alcoa he carries in his head. Gilbert Ralph, the historian of Western Mining

Corporation, guided me to vital sources, especially from the period when that company was nursing the infant project. Don Campbell, who did more than anybody to 'discover' the bauxite in the Darling Range, gave me information and ran his eye over my version of the early exploration of the bauxite.

I was especially helped by employees at the company's sites: Les Davey, Ken Mansfield, Wayne Osborn and Ted Hardcastle at Point Henry; Geoff Hayward, Wade Hughes, Murray Allen, George James, John Hill and Ken O'Connor at Portland; Greg Davis, Gerrard Waller, Chris Rolland and Tony Cust at the Anglesea power station; John Hannagan, David Parker, Eleanor O'Reilly, Sheralyn Derrick, Chris Welberry, at head office as well as Chris Eves and other ex-employees; John Sibly, S. Rex Baker, Hamish Petrie, David Dabney, Pat Hicks, John Lochera, Brian Wills-Johnson, Errol Kirke, and Colleen Aspher at Kwinana and Perth; Malcolm Wills and Neil Bennett, the successive managers of Hedges gold mine; Russell Williams at the Huntly mine; and Graham Slessar, John Gardner, John Day, and Gordon Baird who discussed the major environmental problems encountered in Western Australia. I gained much from notes written by Des Hay (Anglesea) and J.N. Langford (early mining) and especially Keith Bower who supplied answers to my queries on the early laboratory at Kalamunda and early Kwinana.

I am indebted to Sir Charles Court who played the crucial political role in the development of the alumina industry in Western Australia, to Roy Woodall (early exploration), Alan Lobban (law and finance), Richard M. Griffin (raising finance in London), Sir Laurence Brodie-Hall (a director with a strong interest in ecology) and his wife Jean Verschuer (landscaping at Carcoola), and Douglas Stewart (conveyor belt to Pinjarra refinery).

Company Records

The board minutes of Western Aluminium No Liability, incorporated in August 1958, are vital for the years 1958 to 1961. The board minutes of Alcoa of Australia become central from 1961. The agenda papers usually give the background to the decisions which are reported rather sparsely in the minutes. The annual printed reports of Alcoa of Australia were lean in the first years but by the mid 1970s they were comprehensive. The 1982 annual report of the Aluminum Co. of America is crucial to Australian operations. It carries a survey of the world's aluminium industry, signed by W.H. Krome George. For many of the later years, speeches made by the chairman of Alcoa of Australia at annual general meetings published are informative. Especially important is Sir Arvi Parbo's statement of 2 March 1981.

Of strong interest to an historian are the two typewritten volumes prepared in Pittsburgh in 1978 on 'Alcoa of Australia: Its History and Development'. I have not located most of the early correspondence quoted in detail in the report. Also vital are a 22-page address given by Sir Arvi Parbo to his senior executives at Portsea on 14 October 1992; the transcript of a discussion of history by Sir Arvi Parbo, J.C. Bates and G.M. Ralph on 13 October 1989; a 1993 paper by J.D. Campbell on 'The Birth of Alcoa in Australia', and a 1992 letter by J.C. Bates recalling the origin of the environmental policy.

In the company's records are numerous internal reports on specific issues ranging from finance to 'forest dieback', collections of news clippings, which are intermittent rather than continuous, cassettes of radio and television interviews especially in the 1980s, brochures and speeches written for the opening of plants, and the company's own newsletters including *Corroboree*, *Imagineer*, *Insight*, *Points and Angles*, and *Landcare*.

The historical collection of what is now called the WMC Group (Western Mining Corporation) includes reports and letters written between 1957 and 1961 when WMC largely guided the development of the aluminium project. There are also letters by Lindesay Clark, W.D Brookes, W.M. Morgan, Fred. R Morgan, J.N. Langford, C.M. Kleeman, A.D. Marris, Sir Harold Raggatt; letters and geological reports by J.D. Campbell on Anglesea coal and Western Australian bauxite and coal, and his visit to Pittsburgh in August 1960; the key reports by Ralph Derr on Australia and William Morgan on his attempt to find buyers in Japan.

Parliamentary Debates

See the Western Australian *Hansard* for debates in the Assembly and Council in September 1961 when the initial Alcoa project was approved by parliament, and in October 1969 and April 1978 when Alcoa's expansion was debated. See also the Victorian Hansard for debates in the Assembly and Council on the Mines (Aluminium) Agreement Bill in November and December 1961, and in the Assembly on 8 October and 6 November 1963 when S.E.C. electricity prices were examined, and 25 March 1980 when the Portland project was outlined.

Books and Bulletins

The following list includes only books and articles which provided material that appears in the narrative:
John Cain, *John Cain's Years: Power, Parties and Politics*, Melbourne University Press, Melbourne, 1995. Part IV of this book describes Cain's relations with Alcoa and the stalemate over the Portland

smelter. My parallel chapter was largely written before his book appeared, and I have incorporated little of his interesting information, for it is more relevant to a history of Victorian politics than to the history of Alcoa. His interpretation and mine, when they are boiled down, are not far apart in highlighting the points of disagreement and the essence of the conflict between the Cain government and Alcoa. Incidentally Cain suggests (p.132) that Alcoa had decided—but not announced it 'because of the political implications'—to halt construction of the smelter some months before he won his election in April 1982. The company's papers and board minutes do not support this suggestion.

Duncan C. Campbell, *Global Mission: the Story of Alcan*, vol. 1, Ontario Publishing Co., 1985.

J.D. Campbell, *Hidden Gold: the Central Norseman Story*, 2 vols, Australasian Institute of Mining and Metallurgy, Parkville, 1990.

G. Lindesay Clark, *Built on Gold: Recollections of Western Mining*, Hill of Content, Melbourne, 1983, especially chapter 17.

Wilfred K. Grummer, 'Bauxite' in *Encyclopaedia Britannica*, vol. 3, 1962.

D.P. Mellor, *The Role of Science and Industry*, Australian War Memorial, Canberra, 1958. Vol. 5 of the civil series of the official war history, 'Australia in the War of 1939–1945', especially useful for aluminium in the war and the creation of Bell Bay.

A.M. Murray, 'Bauxite' in R. T. Prider ed., *Mining in Western Australia*, University of Western Australia Press, Perth, 1979.

H.B. Owen, *Bauxite in Australia*, Bulletin 24, Bureau of Mineral Resources, Canberra, 1954.

Arvi Parbo, *Down Under: Mineral Heritage in Australasia*, Australasian Institute of Mining and Metallurgy, Melbourne, 1992.

H.G. Raggatt, 'The Mineral Resources of Australia', in A. B. Edwards ed., *Geology of Australian Ore Deposits*, Australasian Institute of Mining and Metallurgy, Melbourne, 1953.

Edward S. Simpson, *Minerals of Economic Value*, Bulletin 19, Geological Survey of Western Australia, Perth, 1905.

Edward S. Simpson and Chas. G. Gibson, *The Distribution and Occurrence of the Baser Metals of Western Australia*, Bulletin 30, Geological Survey of Western Australia, Perth, 1907.

George David Smith, *From Monopoly to Competition: The Transformations of Alcoa, 1888–1986*, Cambridge University Press, Cambridge, 1988. This is a perceptive history of the parent company, with brief sections on Australia.

Alan Trengrove, *Discovery: Stories of Modern Mineral Exploration*, Stockwell Press, 1979.

Articles on the Environment

Among many articles in technical journals are discussions of environmental problems in the Darling Range, including S.R. Shea in *Forest Focus*, April 1975, articles on jarrah 'Dieback' by Michael Tooby and Peter Akerman in *Landscape Australia* in November 1980 and February 1981, and on salinity by S.R. Shea and Eugene Herbert in *Forest Focus*, November 1977. A critique of Alcoa by Friends of the Earth was written by Jane Hutchinson and Bill Hare in *Chain Reaction*, November 1981.

Papers by company staff include Roger A.G. Vines, 'Successful Rehabilitation: the Key to Land Access?', delivered at Canberra on 2 February 1993; and S.R. Baker, J.H. Gardner and S.C. Ward, 'Bauxite Mining Enviromental Management and Rehabilitation Practices in Western Australia', Australasian Institute of Mining and Metallurgy, Melbourne, 1995. The company has a useful, unpublished undergraduate thesis by Kathryn White of Edith Cowan University, 'Historical Overview of Bauxite Mine Rehabilitation Techniques used by Alcoa in Western Australia'.

Directors Since 1961

CHAIRMEN

G.L. Clark	1961–1970
J. Forrest	1970–1978
A.H. Parbo	1978–1996
R.A.G. Vines	1996–

MANAGING DIRECTORS

J.C. Smith	1961–1965
A.C. Sheldon	1965–1968
J.C. Bates	1968–1971
W. Porter Jr	1971–1978
G.T. Haymaker	1978–1982
J.L. Diederich	1982–1986
N.F. Stephen	1986–1991
R. F. Slagle	1991–1996
R.A.G. Vines	1996–

DIRECTORS

M.M. Anderson	1961–1963
H.C. Erskine	1961–1961
L.E. Hickman	1961–1963
J.M. Mitchell	1961–1963; 1967–1972
O.V. Peterson	1961–1963
G.L. Clark	1961–1972
F.F. Espie	1961–1962
J.C. Guest	1961–1970
W.D. Brookes	1961–1983

DIRECTORS cont.

J.C. Smith	1961–1965	
W.M. Morgan	1962–1971	
R.C. Blasingame	1963–1966	
J.R. Burt	1963–1973	
C.W. Parry	1963–1966;	1977–1982
P.L. Hartsock	1963–1964	
J. Darling	1964–1996	
A.C. Sheldon	1965–1968	
J.K. Sliger	1966–1967	
F.E. Tyrrell	1966–1968	
R.L. Bowlby	1967–1974	
W.H.K. George	1967–1971	
C.E. Pfeifer	1967–1975	
J.C. Bates	1968–1971;	1977–1982
R.L. Baillieu	1970–1986	
W. Porter Jr	1971–1978	
R. Banks Smith	1971–1977	
L.C. Brodie-Hall	1971–1983	
H.O. Clark	1972–1977	
A. Glenn	1973–1986	
H. McE. Scambler	1973–1986	
E.W. Lussky	1975–1978	
H.L. Johnson	1975–1977	
H.M. Morgan	1977–	
G.T. Haymaker	1978–1984	
R.L. Fischer	1978–1984	
L. Muir	1982–1996	
J.L. Diederich	1982–1986;	1989–1992
K.F. Parry	1983–1986	
P. Spry-Bailey	1983–	
H.S. Evans	1984–1989	
R.A.G. Vines	1984–1995;	1996–
J.N. Davenport	1986–1993	
N.F. Stephen	1986–1991	
D.M. Morley	1986–	
G.J. Pizzey	1988–1994	
R.F. Slagle	1991–1996	
M.J. Phillips	1992–1996	
A. Clarke	1993–1996	
J.R. Lopes	1994–1996	
J.M. Sibly	1995–	

Works Managers Since 1961

KWINANA

A.B. Kaltwasser	1961–1964
E.L. Wahlsten	1964–1968
R.E. Whitson	1968–1971
E.W. Lussky	1971–1974
R.A.G. Vines	1974–1974
L.N. Buckett	1974–1977
S.R. Baker	1977–1986
J.M. Sibly	1986–1993
A.H. Petrie	1993–

PINJARRA

P.H. Kimpel	1970–1974
R.A.G. Vines	1974–1975
M.J. Webb	1975–1979
L.B. Davey	1979–1981
C.J. Agnew	1981–1984
G.C. Hayward	1984–1993
J.M. Sibly	1993–1995
L.H. Jones	1995–

WAGERUP

M.F. Wills	1984–1987
P.J. Bailey	1988–1993

| M.F. Wills | 1993–1994 |
| W.G. Osborn | 1994– |

MANAGER OF MINES

J.N. Langford	1961–1972
S.R. Baker	1972–1977
C.J. Agnew	1977–1979
M.J. Webb	1979–1980
G.H.C. White	1980–1983
G.C. Hayward	1983–1984
L.G. Opie	1984–1986
S.R. Baker	1986–1996
R. Williams	1996–

POINT HENRY

R.C. Blasingame	1961–1966
F.E. Tyrrell	1966–1967
F.O. Shepherd	1967–1971
J.A. Lang	1971–1976
R.E. Ray	1976–1980
C.P. Fletcher	1980–1982
D.L. Schaffer	1982–1986
L.G. Opie	1986–1988
L.B. Davey	1988–1995
W.G. Osborn (rolled products)	1992–1994
D. Willett	1995–
C.J. Lynch (rolled products)	1994–1996

PORTLAND

M.J. Webb	1984–1986
D.J. Judd	1987–1993
G.C. Hayward	1993–1995
D.J. Carney	1995–

Financial Chronicle
Since 1961

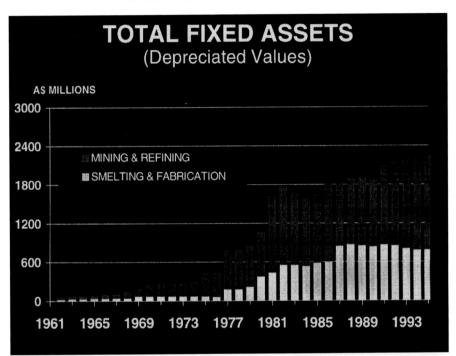

TOTAL FIXED ASSETS
(Depreciated Values)

A$ MILLIONS

MINING & REFINING
SMELTING & FABRICATION

3000
2400
1800
1200
600
0

1961 1965 1969 1973 1977 1981 1985 1989 1993

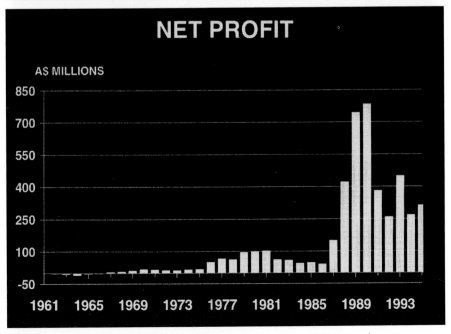

NET PROFIT

A$ MILLIONS

850
700
550
400
250
100
-50

1961 1965 1969 1973 1977 1981 1985 1989 1993

Index

Anglesea, *cont.*
105–6, 115, 121, 179–81 (illus.);
power station, 61, 88, 90–1, 105–7,
105 (illus.), 134, 180–1, 181
(illus.), 206, Pl. 8
Anglesea Surf Life Saving Club, 105
Anthony, Doug, 175
anti-trust laws (USA), 50–1, 149
antimony, 13
Armstrong, A.N., 27
asbestos, 13
Aspher, Colleen, 79
Associated Pulp and Paper Mills
Limited, 44
asthma, occupational, 225
Australian Consolidated Industries, 121
Australian Fused Materials, 216–17
Australian Labor Party (ALP), 125,
131, 173, 175, 197
Australian Mineral Development
Laboratories, 40
Australian National Line, 82, 191; *see
also* shipping
Australian Pulp & Paper
Manufacturers, 232
Australian Resources Development
Bank, 117
Australian Workers Union (AWU),
93, 107, 221
aviation industry, 6,7, 201; *see also*
aerial surveys

Bailey, P.J., 247
Baillieu, John M., 65
Baillieu, M.L., 231
Baillieu, R. Lawrence, 120 (illus.),
231, 246
Baker, S.R., 247, 248
Ballarat mineral field, 21
Bank of New South Wales, 115
Banks Smith, R., 119, 130, 146, 246
Bartholomaeus, Neil, 175
Bates, J.C. (Joe), 114, 120 (illus.),
122, 126–7, 134, 138, 144–5, 162,
164–5, 165 (illus.), 198–9, 245, 246
bauxite, autogenous grinding process,
128, 130; Darling Range
exploration and survey for, 14, 16,
17, 18–24, 27, 28–33, 36, 47; lower
grade use, 118–19, 123; silica
impurities and aluminium refining,

bauxite, *cont.*
18, 19–20; specimens, 4–6, *see also*
bauxite laboratories; Darling Range
bauxite
bauxite deposits, 7–8; Africa, 33, 38,
87; Australia, 9, 15, 33, 86–7, 234,
see also Darling Range; Brazil, 237;
British Guiana *see* Guyana;
Caribbean, 7; Costa Rica, 52;
Darling Range *see* Darling Range
bauxite deposits; Dutch Guiana *see*
Suriname; East Asia, 40; France,
87; Gove, 85; Greece, 87; Gulf of
Carpentaria, 15; Guyana, 7, 87;
Hungary, 87; Jamaica, 86–7, 237;
Kimberley, 234; Latin America, 52;
Malaysia, 9, 18, 87; North America,
19; Northern Australia, 33, 234, *see
also* Weipa; Northern Ireland, 7;
Panama, 52; South America, 87;
Soviet Union, 87; Suriname (Dutch
Guiana), 7, 52, 57, 87, 135, 237;
United States of America, 48, 87;
Weipa, 15–17, 19, 23, 27, 57, 63,
191; West Africa, 30–3, 38, 44,
52–3, 57; West Indies, 7, 86–7;
Yugoslavia, 87
bauxite laboratory, East St Louis
(USA), 78; Kalamunda, 28–30, 28
(illus.), 32–4, 47
bauxite leases, 111–12, 144–5
bauxite mines, Australian, 130, 137,
see also Del Park, Dwellingup,
Huntley, Jarrahdale, Mount
Saddleback, Willowdale; mobile
crushing plant, 130; rehabilitation
of, 165–6, 165 (illus.), 171, 175–81,
Pl. 4, Pl. 5
bauxite refining, 'liquor poisoning',
38–40, 46, 182–3; wastes, 77–8,
125, 182–4; white dust, 124–5
bauxite refining *see* alumina refining
Baxter, Norman, 163
Bayer, Karl, 80
Bayer process, 19, 80–1; 'liquor
poisoning', 182–3, *see also* 'liquor
poisoning'
Begg, Ken, 53
Belda, Alain, 237
Bell Bay refinery and smelter, 8, 9, 15,

goldfields, *cont.*
    Norseman, 12, 14–15, 26; Walhalla
        goldfield, 215; Wiluna, 29
goldmines, 12; Bendigo, 12;
    Boddington, 213–15; Bullfinch, 13,
    15, 26–7, 62, 84, 118, 188; Central
    Norseman, 12, 14–15, 26; Darling
    Range, 4, 213–14; Great Western,
    13, 15, 26–7, 62; Hedges, 214–5,
    215 (illus.), 222, Pl. 13; Kalgoorlie,
    29, 45, 55, 215, *see also* Kalgoorlie;
    Nevoria, 13, 188; Southern Cross,
    13, 26; The Granites, 11; Western
    Australian, 3–4; Western Mining, 66
goldrush, The Granites, 11
Gormanston 10
Gove, bauxite deposits, 85; refinery,
    124, 137, 207
Granites, The, 11
Great Western Consolidated N.L., 13
Greece, 87
green movement, vii, 166, 190, 193;
    Wagerup refinery protest, 173, 174,
    175; *see also* Dark Green
    Movement; Friends of the Earth;
    conservation
Greenbushes, tinfield, 5, 163
greenhouse gases, 234
Greenland, 96
Griffin, Richard, 117
Griffin Company, 43
Griffith, Arthur, 80
Grummer, Wilfred K., 19
Guam, 161
Guest, J. Chester, 21, 32, 62, 65, 120,
    246
Guiana, British *see* Guyana
Guiana, Dutch *see* Suriname
Gulf of Carpentaria bauxite deposits, 15
Guyana, 7, 87

Hall, Charles Martin, 48
Hall, N.R., 158
Hall–Héroult electrolytic process,
    48–9, 96; *see also* Bayer Process
Hamer, Sir Rupert, 194, 195–6
Hardcastle, Ted, 227
Harper, John D., 105 (illus.), 112,
    119–20, 130–1, 156
Harrison, Ed, 75, 118
Harrison, James, 90

Hartsock, Perry L. (Red), 116, 246
Hawke, A.R.G., 22, 68
Haymaker, George T., Jr, 174, 189–91,
    193, 195–6, 199–202, 245, 246
Hayward, G.C. (Geoff), 219, 221, 247,
    248
Hedderwick Fookes & Alston, 121
Hedges goldmines, 214–15, 215
    (illus.), Pl. 13; injury reduction
    campaign, 222
Héroult, Paul, 48, 96; *see also*
    Hall–Héroult electrolytic process
Hickman, L.E., 245
Holland, 196, 237; *see also* Dutch
Hong Kong, 155
Hoover, Herbert, 50
Hornbeck, Bob, 173
housing, aluminium, use in, 104
    (illus.), 154, 154 (illus.), 155;
    Carcoola, 127–8, 154 (illus.);
    company provision of, 100–1,
    127–8, 135; *see also* building industry
Housing Commission, 100
Howard, Peter, 21
Howarth, Arthur, 104
Hungary, 87
Hunter Valley smelter, 191
Huntley mine, 137; wash-down
    stations, 178
hydrates, alumina, 216–17
hydro-electricity, 8, 42–3, 88, 97, 190,
    193, 198
Hyundai, 208

Ian Potter & Co., 233
ICI *see* Imperial Chemical Industries
Imperial Chemical Industries
    (England), 53
Imperial Chemical Industries of
    Australia and New Zealand, 53,
    134–6
India, 211, 235
Indonesia, 58, 161, 168
industrial chemical production, 211,
    216–7
industrial relations, 218–29; 35 hour
    week, 221; workplace reform, 221,
    223, 226–9
Infant Welfare Centre (Newcomb), 104
Iron Knob mineral field, 21
iron ore, Koolanooka Hills, 66; Mount

Western Australian government, *cont.*
Jarrahdale to Kwinana railway, 80;
Kwinana Refinery, 77; Pinjarrra
refinery bill, 164; Wagerup refinery
bill (WA, 1978), 173
Western Mining Corporation, 12–17,
20–23, 25–6, 31, 53, 55–67,
109–10, 118–21, 128–9, 165, 168,
188–9, 214, 233, 237–8; Alcoa
shareholder, 230, 232, 237; Alcoa
World Alumina, 237–8; aluminium
Industry and, 42–5, 53–8; bauxite
cargo to Tasmania, 38; Darling
Ranges bauxite exploration, 27–33;
Dwellingup bauxite pit, 22 (illus.);
foreign partner proposals, 34–7, 46;
prospecting rights, 22–3; raiders
and, 34–5, 46; Victoria Agreement,
112; Western Aluminium N.L. and,
30–2; WMC, 238
White, David, 206
White, George H.C., 166, 168, 171,
248
Whitlam, E. Gough, 218
Whitlam government, 136
Whitson, R.E., 247
Wildlife Habitat Enhancement
Council (USA), 185

Willett, D., 248
Williams, R., 248
Willowdale mine, 208
Wills, Horatio, 90
Wills, Malcolm F., 214, 247, 248
Wilson, I.W. (Chief), 52, 59–60
Wiluna goldfield, 29
WMC, 238; *see also* Western Mining
Corporation
Wongan Hills, 4
Woodall, Roy, 17–18, 20
woodchip industry, 143
workplace reform, 221, 223, 226–9; *see
also* industrial relations;
occupational health and safety
World Environment Day, 185
worm farms, 225
Worsley refinery, 145, 149, 213–14
Wran, Neville, 197
Wright, Orville, 6
Wright, Wilbur, 6
Wunderlich Limited, 97

Yallourn power station, 196
Yugoslavia, bauxite producer, 87

zinc, 30, 66
Zinc Corporation, 17
zinc mine (Broken Hill), 231